The Magical Animal

ADOPTION AGENCY

1 CLOVER'S LUCK

The Magical Animal
ADOPTION AGENCY
1 CLOVER'S LUCK

BY **Kallie George**

ILLUSTRATED BY
Alexandra Boiger

Harper*Trophy*Canada™
An imprint of HarperCollins*PublishersLtd*

Clover's Luck
Text copyright © 2015 by Kallie George.
Illustrations copyright © 2015 by Alexandra Boiger.
All rights reserved.

Published by Harper*Trophy*Canada™, an imprint of HarperCollins Publishers Ltd

First published in Canada by HarperCollins Publishers Ltd in a hardcover edition: 2015
This Harper*Trophy*Canada™ trade paperback edition: 2015

HarperCollins books may be purchased for educational, business,
or sales promotional use through our Special Markets Department.

HarperCollins Publishers Ltd
2 Bloor Street East, 20th Floor
Toronto, Ontario, Canada
M4W 1A8

www.harpercollins.ca

Library and Archives Canada Cataloguing in Publication
information is available upon request

ISBN 978-1-44341-981-9

Printed and bound in the United States
RRD 9 8 7 6 5 4 3

To my Nono, who knew I would be a writer
way before I did
—K.G.

To Vanessa and Andrea,
with love, always
—A.B.

Contents

ONE	Clover	1
TWO	The Agency	9
THREE	The Small Animals	20
FOUR	The Stables	32
FIVE	The Note	45
SIX	Moondrop's Mishap	56
SEVEN	Snort's Sneeze	70
EIGHT	Esmeralda's Enchantment	92
NINE	A Wicked Plan	107
TEN	Serendipity	119

1
Clover

Luck is like magic. It's mysterious and exciting and impossible to explain. It can't be described by equations or logic or even by books. You just have to believe.

Clover believed. She believed luck existed—and that all of hers was bad. From the time she was born under a moon as thin as a cat's whisker—a bad omen, she'd decided—her life had been filled with one misfortune after another, from burst bike tires to burnt toast. Not to mention problems with pets.

She tried everything to change her luck. She painted her room bright green, the color of lucky clover, her namesake, and pasted shooting stars on her ceiling that she could wish on every night. She hung a horseshoe over her bed and collected shiny pennies in a jar that she kept on her windowsill. She even carried a lucky charm with her at all times. This morning she had tucked a wishbone in her pocket. But nothing seemed to work.

The wishbone certainly wasn't helping her now. It was only the first day of vacation and already her whole summer had been ruined. Her best friend, Emma, had just called to tell her that she was going to Pony Camp after all. Both Emma and Clover had wanted to go, but the camp was full. This morning, though, someone had canceled, and Emma's name was first on the waiting list.

"Cheer up," Emma said when she gave Clover the news. "Maybe someone else will cancel, and you can come too."

But Clover knew that would never happen.

The camp lasted till school started. So much for sleepovers and sharing ice cream. So much for adventures and excitement. So much for spending the summer with her best friend.

"At least I have you," she said to Penny, her new pet

canary. "I can train you to sing and, well, do all sorts of things. It'll be fun."

Clover checked to make sure her bedroom window and door were tightly shut before taking Penny out of her cage. She was stroking the bird's yellow feathers when . . . *Smash!* A baseball broke through the window, narrowly missing the jar of pennies and a jade tortoise paperweight, and landed on her bed with a thump.

"Oh no!" Clover cried.

Quick as a wink, with just one tweet, Penny left Clover's finger and flew out through the hole left by the baseball.

"OH NO!" Clover cried even louder.

She ran out of her room, down the stairs, and out the front door. "Penny!" she shouted, racing after her bird, her shoes pounding the pavement. "Penny, come back!"

The street was empty. Whoever had thrown the ball was gone. Penny soared over the lawn and headed down the street. Clover chased after her.

At the end of the block, Penny perched on a picket fence. Clover tried to sneak up on the bird, but the moment she was within arm's reach, Penny took off, flying down the next block. Penny landed a few more times, but Clover still couldn't catch her.

Soon they reached the edge of the village. Penny kept on going. Clover had a stitch in her side, but she didn't stop either.

She ran through farmers' fields, over rolling hills, and along a twisty path that grew ever more rough and overgrown. She had never gone so far from the village. The stitch in her side grew into a knot.

The path took a turn, and she lost sight of Penny for a moment. When she rounded the bend, she froze. There before her was a line of trees and bushes, blocking her way like a great green wall. The Woods.

Her canary was perched atop a small, twisted tree, like a tiny star.

"Come to me, Penny! Good little bird," Clover called, holding out her finger. But as she crept closer, Penny gave a cheeky tweet and flew off, disappearing into the Woods.

Keep away, keep away, the Woods are where wee beasties play. The rhyme sung at school echoed in Clover's

head. People from her village stayed far away from the Woods. They were a strange place, and even stranger lands lay beyond them—or so the rumors rang.

The trees ahead creaked and groaned, and shadows flickered. An eerie breeze whistled through the branches as if in tune to the rhyme.

Clover gulped and reached for the wishbone in her pocket. So far it hadn't proved lucky, but she would give it one more chance.

She took a deep breath and looked for a path. There was a tiny trail so overgrown it was hard to see, but when she pushed past the first few bushes, it opened up.

The trees cast dark shadows, but were also lush and green. Rotting logs covered the forest floor, yet so did feathery moss, dotted with white flowers. The air smelled clean and fresh.

The Woods were beautiful, and only slightly ominous. They weren't strange at all. But Penny was nowhere to be seen. She was gone. Really gone.

"Stupid bad luck!" Clover said, blinking back tears. She reached into her pocket again and pulled out the wishbone. "This is the worst charm yet!" She threw it away as hard as she could.

The wishbone glanced off a stump, bounced back, and almost hit her in the face.

But Clover didn't notice. She was staring at a large sheet of thick yellow paper nailed to the trunk of a nearby tree. The paper was curled and faded, the hand-written message streaked from rain.

Clover stepped closer to read it.

DO YOU LOVE ANIMALS?
DO YOU WANT TO HELP THEM
FIND HAPPY HOMES?
OUR AGENCY NEEDS YOU!
VOLUNTEER AT THE M.A.A.A.

At the bottom were little slips of paper with directions. Not one had been torn off.

Clover read the notice again. And then a third time. She desperately wanted a pet of her own. But Penny's escape made it clear—once and for all—that she was just too unlucky.

If I worked at an animal adoption agency, she thought, *I could be with animals without actually owning a pet. I could help them. I could set things right.*

Carefully, she tore off the first slip and read it.

"The M.A.A.A.—#1 Dragon's Tail Lane. Down the path. Just around the bend. Follow the signs."

She hesitated for a moment. Going into the Woods to chase her bird was one thing. Going to apply for a volunteer position was quite another. Who would run an animal adoption agency in the Woods? Weren't beasties supposed to be the only creatures that lived here?

Clover looked around again. The treetops bobbed in the wind. A squirrel chattered to its friend. Already there were creatures other than beasties.

Just around the bend, thought Clover. *That's not too far to go. I can at least check it out.*

Folding the slip in two, she stuck it deep in her pocket and set off down the path, in search of the first sign. Despite her unluckiness, Clover always kept a hopeful heart.

2

The
Agency

Signs were scarce, and it took Clover much longer than she expected to wind her way through the Woods.

At one point she reached a place where the path branched in many directions. Nailed onto a huge tree in the center were several signs shaped like arrows. SHOPPES made sense. Though she was surprised to find there were shops in the Woods. What kinds of shops would they be? Not ordinary ones that sold shoes or sweets, surely. But if there was an adoption agency, who knew?

MEADOWS and OUT also made sense. The OUT sign pointed to the path that she was standing on, so it must mean out of the Woods and to her village.

But HEART and BEYOND were a little more puzzling.
The HEART sign pointed down a dark, twisty path. *Maybe
it leads into the heart of the Woods*, thought Clover. So,
did BEYOND mean there were villages and towns on the
other side of the Woods? She looked to see what kind of
path it pointed to and nearly tripped on an arrow lying
flat on the ground.

She picked it up. M.A.A.A. was etched into the wood
in black letters.

"Oh no," Clover moaned. "Now how will I find it?"

She looked again at the other arrows. All the paths
except the one to the far left were clearly marked.

Was that the path to the Agency? It had to be.

Leaning the arrow against the tree, she started down the path to the left. It wasn't long before she came to a clearing, and she could see what appeared to be a charming cottage in the distance, with smoke curling out from a chimney. Where the path narrowed, there was a sign that read DRAGON'S TAIL LANE. There wasn't really a lane to speak of, not like at home, but there were no other buildings in sight, so that had to be it. A sense of well-being filled her. She felt almost . . . lucky.

But that feeling lasted only a moment. Dark clouds had filled the sky, and it began to rain. Hard. Soon raindrops dripped from her nose.

To top it off, a lady clutching a white kitten bustled by and bumped into her. Clover stepped out of the way and right into a mud puddle.

Dressed in a billowing black raincoat, her face hidden by the floppy brim of her hat, the lady looked like a thundercloud. The kitten, unprotected and dripping, mewed as they passed.

"Mind your way," snapped the lady, as though it were Clover's fault.

Mind your kitten, Clover wanted to reply, but the words caught in her throat as the lady hurried away.

11

Clover thought things couldn't get worse.

But, of course, they could. And they did.

The Agency was tucked away at the end of the path, which curved like a giant tail. Whether it was like a dragon's tail, as the sign said, Clover wasn't sure. The only dragons she had seen were those in storybooks.

This Agency too seemed like it had popped out of the pages of a storybook.

Number 1 Dragon's Tail Lane was a large, low-lying wooden building with a thatched roof covered in moss as thick as fur. Vines snaked up its sides, and a thin tendril of smoke rose out of a chimney at the back. Protruding from the right was a rickety tower. An old wooden fence circled the building like a toothy grin. At the front gate stood a small, sleepy-looking garden gnome. Over the gate a sign read:

WELCOME TO THE M.A.A.A

The bottom of the last letter *A* was partly missing, and ragged, as though something had bitten it off. Something big.

It didn't scare her exactly, but it *was* startling. Clover felt in her pocket, forgetting for a moment that she

had thrown her wishbone away, and touched the slip of paper she had torn off the sign instead. Her heart took courage.

Feet squishing in her shoes, she trudged through the gate, up the path, and up the steps. An ENTER sign hung on the doorknob, but underneath, in tiny letters, were the words AT YOUR OWN RISK. This sign looked eaten too—nibbled around the edges. The doorknob was made from wood, carved in the shape of a beak.

Slowly, she pushed open the door.

The room smelled faintly of smoke and looked as if it hadn't been cleaned in years; everything was dusty and old. There was a tilting bookshelf brimming with books and a desk piled high with papers. A red quill pen stuck out of a bottle of ink. A small silver bell perched on a stack of papers on the desk with a sign reading RING FOR SERVICE.

Beside the desk, on a thick rug, were two chairs and a couch around a small coffee table. On the table were pamphlets titled *From Spark to Flame: How to Encourage Friendly Fires*; *Proper Care of Unusual Eggs*; and *Troublesome Toads: When Warts Turn Weird*.

An enormous golden book rested on a stand, in a corner by itself.

Although the room was cluttered, there were no pictures or posters of cute little animals on the walls like Clover was used to seeing at every pet shop and vet's office she had ever been in, only a slogan on a hook behind the desk: NO ANIMAL IS TOO UNUSUAL TO ADOPT. Clover liked that. Perhaps this agency dealt with pets like parrots and hedgehogs.

She rang the bell, being careful not to knock over the papers.

She waited for a long time, but there was no response.

She was about to leave when a door behind the desk burst open and out came an old man.

"Wait a minute. Don't be so impatient," he called, as though he was annoyed at being disturbed.

He was only a tad taller than Clover, with a short, pointed white beard. His shirt was streaked with soot.

He examined Clover with raised eyebrows, from her mud-splattered stockings and dress to the water dripping off her freckled nose.

"May I help you?" he asked.

"Excuse me, is this the Animal Adoption Agency? This is my first time in the Woods. I lost my bird and found you instead."

The old man's bushy eyebrows rose higher. "I'm

15

sorry," he said after a pause, "but we can't help you here. Lost birds are a lost cause; but if it is in the Woods, it will surely make friends."

"Oh," said Clover. "I hope you're right. But that's not why I'm here. I came to volunteer."

The man looked her up and down again intently, then shook his head. "You're out of luck."

"I always am."

"I didn't mean—" the man began, seeing how upset she was, but Clover kept talking.

"I'm especially unlucky with pets. My fish jumped out of his cup and went down the drain when I was cleaning his bowl. My mom was allergic to my puppy, and we had to give her away. My kitten decided he liked our neighbor's house better than ours and stayed there. And now my bird . . ." Clover gulped.

"I highly doubt—" The man tried to jump in again, but Clover still didn't stop.

"My parents like me to have a pet, because they're so busy working and don't want me to be lonely. Plus they know I love animals. But I'm too unlucky to keep a pet myself. Maybe I can help out here instead. I saw your notice on a tree." Clover showed him the slip of paper.

The man tugged at his beard with one hand and tapped on the desk with his other.

Clover slumped. "I'll . . . I'll go now."

"Wait," he said. "What animals are you afraid of?"

She gave him a puzzled look. "None. Not even big ones. I went to the zoo once in the city, and I saw an enormous elephant and two huge lions. I wasn't scared at all. In fact, I felt sorry for them. They looked so unhappy."

"Can you help every day?"

"Yes, I can."

17

"But what about school?"

"It's summer. There's no school."

He nodded. "Ah, of course. Good." He leaned closer, resting his elbows on the desk and looking straight into Clover's eyes. "Now for the most important question. You must answer honestly. Can you keep a secret?"

"Yes," she replied, slowly but without hesitation. "I don't really have many people to tell things to anyway." This was especially true now that Emma was gone.

The man nodded. "Then I've changed my mind. You may have bad luck with regular pets, but you might fit in perfectly here."

"What do you mean?"

"My name is Mr. Jams, and this"—the old man paused and gestured to the room—"this is the M.A.A.A.: the Magical Animal Adoption Agency."

"Magical animals?" Clover's eyes grew wide.

Mr. Jams pulled out his pocket watch. "Oh, cripes and clawscratch! I don't have time to explain right now. I have a lot to do today. Be back here at seven o'clock sharp tomorrow, and I'll begin your training."

"Tomorrow morning?"

"Of course, and don't be late," said Mr. Jams sternly. With that, he turned, pulled open the door behind the desk, and disappeared.

The small sign on the wall shook as the door slammed shut. Clover reread the words on it:

NO ANIMAL IS TOO UNUSUAL TO ADOPT.

This time, they made her tingle.

3

The Small Animals

By the time Clover got home, it was already late afternoon. Her parents were still at work at the mayor's office, as usual. Clover didn't really mind. She was used to it. She had everything she needed, including a number for emergencies, and her parents always checked in to make sure she was okay.

Besides, being alone meant that it was easy to keep secrets. It also gave her plenty of time to ponder things, like what Mr. Jams meant about the magical animals.

She thought about it as she cleaned up her room and taped cardboard over her broken window. She thought about it as she warmed up the supper her parents had left for her in the fridge. (It was her favorite, macaroni and cheese.)

She was so distracted thinking about magical animals that she dropped and broke not just her glass but also her plate when she was doing the dishes. And at bedtime, her toothbrush slipped into the soap dish, and no matter how much she rinsed it, it still tasted like soap.

Even so, she couldn't stop wondering what Mr. Jams had meant.

They must be pets for magicians, she finally decided. She liked that. Maybe magicians' pets had their own built-in luck.

When Clover's mom called just before bedtime, Clover told her about Penny but not about the Agency. Her mom listened sympathetically and afterward, encouraged by the conversation, Clover sketched a picture of her lost bird. It took a mix of her gold and orange colored pencils to get the color right. When she was done, she pinned it onto her Memory Wall, next to the pictures of her fish and her puppy.

From the time she was tiny, Clover had loved animals. Her first word hadn't been "Mama" or "Papa";

it had been "meow." And when she was three, she had painted whiskers on her cheeks every day for a month. All she wanted to do was be with animals. She hoped the Agency was her answer.

She curled up in her covers, patterned with ladybugs, and went to sleep, dreaming of Penny flying happily through a forest filled with magicians' pets—doves and rabbits and small white mice.

♣

The next morning, ten minutes early, with the sun still low in the east, Clover opened the Agency's door.

Mr. Jams greeted her at the front desk. "You came back. Wasn't certain you would."

He was wearing the same shirt with black smudges down the front. The room still smelled like smoke, but now also of cinnamon toast. Mr. Jams was holding a big slice.

"Right, let's get started. You may have already heard about some of the animals here. After all, most of them have been written about in tales of luck and love, wonder and wishes. Fairy tales . . ." He said this with a grimace. "Not that I don't like fairy tales," he added quickly. "I do. It is just that our animals' true tales are not so enchanting."

He took a big bite of his toast before continuing. "In this room, you can read their real stories." He gestured to an antique-looking cabinet behind the desk. "All the files on each animal are kept in here." Then he pointed to the enormous golden book on the stand. "That is the Wish Book. All those who come in and are looking for an animal that we don't have can make their request in it. That way we can call them when the animal they desire arrives.

"But," he added sternly, "you must examine every customer who comes in with a careful eye—even those who have been here and made a request before. Is he or she suitable? Has the person come to the right place?"

"What do you mean 'suitable'? Do you mean whether or not they are magicians?" asked Clover.

"No. Suitable, meaning right for the particular animals here," said Mr. Jams. "Who are, by the way, anxious to meet you. I told them all about you." Mr. Jams strode through the door behind the desk, turned, and, with a wave of his hand, beckoned Clover to follow. "This way."

Mr. Jams kept munching his toast as they passed a storage room filled with boxes. A rope ladder hung down from the ceiling like a swing. There were cages too—some with bent bars, and one that looked like it had been melted. *I wonder if there was a fire here*, Clover thought. Before she could take a closer look, Mr. Jams continued down the hall.

They passed more rooms: a laundry room, a washing room with tubs of various sizes that hung from the ceiling like strange decorations, and a kitchen that contained the biggest refrigerator she had ever seen, with three separate doors. In one corner sat a giant black cauldron. She didn't know cauldrons like that really existed.

Halfway down the hall, Mr. Jams pointed to the right. "This way leads to my quarters." He pointed to the left. "That way leads to the room where we keep the smaller animals. Straight ahead leads to the stables, where the bigger pens and stalls are."

A muffled roar came from that direction. Clover jumped. So did Mr. Jams.

"Cripes and clawscratch! Snort must be in trouble again. Acquaint yourself with our smaller pets. I'll be back momentarily."

Mr. Jams hurried out, gulping down the last bit of his toast as he went.

With a knot in her stomach, Clover opened the door and stepped into a big room lined with small cages and tanks. It was warm and smelled like the forest.

In the first tank was a tiny pool of water surrounded by moss. Nestled in the moss was a glass ball, and sitting on top of the ball was what Clover thought at first was another lump of moss. But the card on the bottom corner of the tank said it was a toad named Esmeralda.

Clover was disappointed. She had been expecting magicians' pets like cute white bunnies, not a warty green toad.

But then she read the rest of the card and gasped.

HISTORY: This toad was discovered long ago
in a well, abandoned and under a curse.
Unfortunately we could not lift the curse,
but its effects appear to be benign. Our oldest
resident, Esmeralda would make the perfect
companion for a patient, color-loving client.

A curse? What does that mean? Clover looked back into the tank and, to her amazement, Esmeralda's warts had changed color. Instead of green they were now a startling orange!

"Oh!" Clover pressed her face against the glass. Suddenly, Esmeralda snapped out her tongue, hitting the glass right above Clover's eyes.

She jumped back in surprise. The toad seemed to glare at her.

"I'm sorry," said Clover. "I didn't mean to upset you." The toad let out a loud croak, then hopped into the water with a splash.

Cautiously, Clover turned to the tank that came next.

It was quite a bit larger than the toad's tank, and decorated like a miniature forest, with ferns and moss and sticks and a few lumps of what seemed to be white sugar. Clover looked closely, but she couldn't see anything else. Then out from the ferns paraded five tiny horses—the smallest, prettiest horses she had ever seen. They were all shades of gray and white with tails no longer than her little finger, and hooves no bigger than her fingernails. Two jumped over the sticks, which to them were as big as logs, while the others settled in to lick the sugar cubes.

28

"Miniature horses!" she cried. "They're so cute!"
She read the card.

NAMES: Acorn, Hickory, Tansy, Butternut &
Buttercup
SPECIES: Fairy Horses
AGE: 200 years
HISTORY: These gentle horses were rescued from
a cave where they were being held captive and
mistreated by ogres. They are workhorses by

nature, and with consistent good treatment
would happily plow a fairy's field or pull a
small wagon filled with peas or flowers.

A shiver of excitement ran through Clover's body.
What else might she find? She turned quickly to see the
next animals.

In a large tank, a big black rock rose up to form
a peak like a small volcano. Lounging on one side of
the rock, like thin sticks of red licorice, were two salamanders. They were unlike any salamanders Clover
had ever seen. Steam rose from their nostrils. Clover
touched her fingertips lightly to the glass. It was hot.

The card said:

NAMES: Ash and Flame
SPECIES: Elemental Salamanders, commonly
known as Fire Salamanders
AGE: Indeterminate, considered immortal
HISTORY: The previous owner gave these
salamanders up because she feared the long-
term commitment of an immortal pet. They
are perfect adoptees for a family with a
constantly heated hearth.

Clover turned to the next cage. It was empty. She took a deep breath. She was trembling. *These aren't magicians' pets at all. They must be the pets of the strange people that live in the Woods and Beyond.* She had always imagined that the creatures that lived in the Woods were scary—after all, they *were* called "beasties." But so far this hadn't been the case. *These* animals certainly weren't scary beasties. They were *magical.* Really, truly magical.

Although she believed in luck and charms, she had never believed *this* kind of magic existed. She wished her best friend were around. Emma would love this. She was always talking about the magic creatures found in her storybooks as if they were real.

And now it turned out that they were.

4

The
Stables

"That used to house a grimalkin, a witch's kitten." Mr. Jams's voice startled Clover. He was standing beside her now, pointing to the empty cage.

"Witches' cats are usually black, but that fellow was white. I found him in a ditch in the Woods. Some cranky witch must have culled him out of a black cat's litter, or maybe the mother herself abandoned him. Anyway, he was adopted right before you arrived yesterday, and the witch who adopted him seemed particularly pleased that he was white. A bit of an unusual case. But enough of that," he said. "It's time for you to meet the other animals. Come on. Don't just stand there tongue-tied like a troll." He chuckled.

Clover followed Mr. Jams out of the room for small animals and down the hall that he had told her led to the stables.

He pointed to a closed door on the right. "In there we have an aviary for phoenixes and other magical birds, but we haven't had any of those for a long time. And through that door," he said, gesturing to the one beside it, "are large tanks, in case we get abandoned sea serpents or hippocampi."

He noticed Clover's puzzled expression and explained, "Hippocampi are sea horses. Not the tiny sea horses you may be familiar with, but actual sea *horses*. Horse from the waist up and fish from the waist down. They eat only sea foam. It takes hours to froth up salty water, so be thankful we don't have one right now."

They passed several other rooms with closed doors and soon reached the end of the hall. "Through here are our stables, where we keep our unicorns. You know what those are, I assume?"

Clover nodded promptly, and held her breath as they walked into the stables. Soft whinnies and the sound of swishing tails greeted her, along with the smell of hay and, strangely, smoke. It was a giant barn with large stalls in two rows facing each other.

The stalls on the left housed unicorns more beautiful than any picture in Emma's books. They poked their heads up over the gates, their long horns raised toward her. Their manes and horns were as white as milk. A few looked directly at her with their blue eyes. The unicorns were much smaller than Clover imagined unicorns would be—hardly as tall as she. The smallest one, closest to the door, came up to her shoulder.

Clover could barely believe that only a day ago she had been jealous of Emma going to Pony Camp, and now here she was, face-to-face with honest-to-goodness unicorns.

"We always have a lot of unicorns," said Mr. Jams. "At the moment there are half a dozen. That is a manageable herd. But at times we have had as many as a dozen. Unicorns are popular gifts for young princesses, and, well, spoiled princesses

34

get a unicorn whenever they demand one. All too often they become bored with their new pet and abandon it or give it to us. But unicorns are easy to look after. Water and mush is all they need. They're shy, and the ones we get here often feel unloved. They need a gentle touch. That little one came to us only a few days ago," said Mr. Jams. "But he is very sweet. Hold out your hand. And mind his horn."

Clover did. Gingerly the little creature nuzzled her fingers. His nose was soft, dry, and cool.

She could see how thin he was. Every rib was visible. His tail was so long it dusted the ground, and his forelock fell over his eyes. But saddest-looking of all was his horn, which was rounded and short, as though it had never properly grown.

"Poor thing," murmured Clover, picking up a handful of hay from a barrel beside the stall and holding it out. The unicorn quickly ate it up. Clover glanced at the card on the stall gate.

"Mistypoo Moondrop," she read aloud. "Mistypoo? Is that really his name?"

"That's a princess for you," Mr. Jams said with a grunt. "Less sense than a sprite. This fellow's history is especially unfortunate. The princess not only gave him that name, she didn't care for him at all and didn't feed him properly. She filed down his horn because she thought a rounded horn was more stylish. I call him Moondrop and never use his first name. Unlike most unicorns, he wasn't abandoned. Another princess told me about the situation and I investigated, and then I seized him."

"But if princesses abandon unicorns, who adopts them?"

"Usually other princesses," said Mr. Jams with a sigh. "Hopefully they are good, compassionate princesses, ones who really *want* unicorns."

"That's a lot of princesses!" exclaimed Clover.

"Well, there are a lot of little kingdoms beyond the Woods. Too bad most of the kings and queens aren't better parents. I have a drawer full of special paperwork for princesses. I'll show you later. At least these creatures are better off than Snort. Who knows *who* will adopt him. . . ."

"Who is Snort?"

"Stay close and I'll show you."

Clover left Moondrop to follow Mr. Jams. On the left, they passed more unicorns, with cards pinned to their stall gates. There wasn't time to read them now, but she wondered what their names were and planned to go back and check as soon as she could. On the right, after the tack room, which Mr. Jams mumbled was for "saddles and such," and a room for storing straw and hay, there were giant pens, much bigger and completely enclosed. Each had a square window to let in light. All were empty. "For a while a griffin lived in this one," Mr. Jams said. He pointed to another pen. "And a winged horse lived in that one."

"A winged horse?" Clover repeated, in amazement.

"Similar to a unicorn, but bigger, and with wings instead of a horn," explained Mr. Jams.

"I know. I mean, I didn't *know* know, but . . . Oh!" exclaimed Clover as she looked up. They had finally reached the very back corner, where the biggest pen stood. It was three times larger than any of the others and was made entirely of bricks. Buckets filled with water surrounded it, and they had to climb over them to get to the metal door.

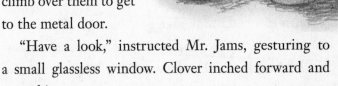

"Have a look," instructed Mr. Jams, gesturing to a small glassless window. Clover inched forward and peered in.

No hay was strewn on the floor of this pen. The only thing inside was the creature living there.

"A dragon!" she gasped.

Indeed it was a small, but not tiny, dragon. He lay curled up in a ball in the middle of the floor, looking somewhat like the remains of a campfire, an ashy black heap. His tail ended in a heart-shaped point, and his wings, pressed to his sides, looked like black paper fans. From large nostrils, wisps of smoke curled up toward the ceiling. The dragon raised his head briefly, and, seeing Clover and Mr. Jams were there, jumped up, stood on his hind feet, and thumped his tail on the ground.

"There, there, Snort," said Mr. Jams through the window. "Calm down, you fiery fellow."

Snort stopped thumping his tail and dropped down to all fours. His eyes were green like emeralds, and his nostrils were as big as Clover's fist.

"Snort's just a baby. Every time he sneezes or coughs, or simply becomes overly excited, he snorts flames. I am not sure who abandoned him here. I found him tied to a post by the gate one morning. I assume that his fire problem is why. Even though there's nothing in his pen to catch on fire, I keep the buckets of water close by, just in case. And there's a chimney in the ceiling to let out the smoke. Several knights have come by wanting to adopt him, but I turned them away." Mr. Jams sighed. "Now, that's not to say I don't want a good home for Snort. But

38

knights, as you probably know, like to slay dragons. No prize is greater to a knight than a dragon-head trophy."

A dark and far-off look came over Mr. Jams. He turned to Clover. "Many people want magical animals, but not all of them for the right reasons. Our creatures are meant for those who truly deserve them, those with good hearts. The animals at our Agency aren't possessions to be shown off, but companions, pets to be loved and cared for. This is something that even residents of the Woods and lands Beyond have trouble understanding, so we can't expect people unfamiliar with magic to understand either, which is why word of the Agency cannot spread outside the Woods. You must keep the Agency secret from everyone, even your parents and friends, and you must carefully check each customer who comes in."

Clover knew it would be tough, especially not to tell Emma when she returned, but she knew how important it was. She looked Mr. Jams straight in the eye. "I will. I promise," she said.

"But take heart," said Mr. Jams. "In general, you will find the people of the Woods are a good sort."

"What about the beasties?" Clover couldn't help but burst out.

"Beasties?"

"You know, like in the rhyme: *Keep away, keep away, the Woods are where wee beasties play.*"

Mr. Jams chuckled. "Ah, yes. I think it was Lester the leprechaun who made that up. Non-magic folk are quick to believe in rumors. Although we have our share of bad princesses and knights and even wicked witches, there are no beasties," Mr. Jams assured her. "And, in fact, there were no Woods either until we put them here. The Woods were created long ago as a boundary between your world and the magic one. The magic folk prefer to keep to themselves and perpetuate the myth of beasties and other scary things to keep humans out. Humans are curious, but very few are willing to risk crossing the boundary. Over time the Woods have been populated by a few people and creatures who don't quite fit in anywhere else."

"What about me?" Clover asked. "I don't really belong here."

Mr. Jams simply winked.

Clover was about to ask him again, unsure if he had heard her, when he gestured to Snort.

"The trick is to make sure he's nice and calm before you feed him. He looks calm now," said Mr. Jams. "Why don't you introduce yourself?" He opened the door.

Clover took tentative steps into the pen, with Mr.

Jams behind her. Snort didn't budge. She reached out her hand.

"Can you see how his tail is thumping? He likes you," said Mr. Jams.

"He does?" whispered Clover. "I like him too."

"Ah, a gentle heart you have, my dear. But beware. Although I have mentioned the many characters I refuse to let adopt our animals, there are far more for whom I've arranged adoptions. Adoption is our Agency's purpose. It can be hard to part ways with our animals, but the Agency isn't a home for them. You will need to guard your heart, even as you keep it open."

Clover understood. At least, she thought she did.

"I do hope someone adopts Snort soon," added Mr. Jams. "Although his wings are small now, they are growing quickly. Then we'll have new problems to deal with."

"Will he start flying?" asked Clover, looking at his delicate wings. They seemed so thin and frail, all folded up on his back. It was hard to imagine them lifting him into the air.

"Yes, though pet dragons don't fly much. Their wings never grow too big. *Wild* dragons are a different matter. Their wings can grow to the length of these stables when spread out fully. Go ahead," continued Mr. Jams. "Give his scales a scratch. He likes it."

She was just about to when . . .

Just her luck. A piece of hay from feeding Moondrop had stuck to her sleeve and now it came loose—right as Snort took in a deep breath. He inhaled it.

His nostrils flared.

"Oh no!" cried Clover. "Duck!"

She and Mr. Jams threw themselves onto the ground.

A giant flame burst out of Snort's nostrils and whizzed over their heads, scorching the brick wall above the door.

"Holy buckets, that was close," Mr. Jams said as they cautiously stood up and backed out. Mr. Jams closed the door and latched it.

"I told you I was unlucky," said Clover apologetically.

"It has nothing to do with you. Snort is a fire hazard. That's all there is to it. You were as quick as a pixie. That's just the kind of instincts a good volunteer needs."

But Clover wasn't so sure.

"Now, let's get to work," said Mr. Jams. "I have a lot more to show you."

Clover nodded. Before following Mr. Jams, she glanced back at Snort through the window.

He was curled up in a ball again, with his tail covering his snout. Clover understood how he felt.

It wasn't fun to be unable to control what you did. Not one bit.

5

The Note

At the end of the first day, Mr. Jams swore her to secrecy *again*. When she got home, she was surprised to find both her parents there, and she was immediately tempted to break the promise. After all, so much had happened. But she didn't. Instead, at supper, when they asked about her day, she told them she was volunteering at an animal adoption agency and it was fun, and nothing more. Not a lie, but not the full truth either.

"Oh, Clover, that's wonderful. We're so proud of you," her mom said. "See, if you're plucky, you'll be lucky. Good things *do* happen to you. Clover *is* a lucky name."

"But what about . . ." started Clover, but then paused. There were so many things she could list.

"I know," said her mom softly. "Penny, right? Poor Penny. Are you okay?"

"Yes. I have the Agency's pets to play with now," said Clover, thinking, *Dragons and unicorns and fairy horses*, but she didn't say this aloud. She doubted they would believe her even if she did.

"So you do," said her dad. "Why, I remember my first job. My sister and I had a lemonade stand—I was in charge of all our signs and posters."

"I had to design a poster today at work," said her mom, "and pamphlets too. . . ."

And so began another supper talking about work. Clover was grateful that her parents didn't ask any other questions about the Agency. It was one good thing about having parents obsessed with their work. And now she wondered if maybe she had inherited their trait, since all she could think about was work too. Although the Agency wasn't really work. It was too much fun.

That night, instead of magicians' pets, Clover dreamed of the amazing animals she had seen at the Agency—the toad and the fairy horses, the salamanders and the unicorns, and the dragon. She even dreamed of the little white kitten.

She dreamed of all the things she had done with Mr. Jams—feeding and cleaning, and sorting the papers.

And in her dream, everyone, even the animals, ate cinnamon toast.

♣

The next morning, Clover woke up right as the sun was rising. With a sandwich in one pocket and a bunch of fresh carrots for Moondrop in the other, she headed to the Agency. She soon realized she was walking with a bounce in her step. Immediately she corrected this. There was no point getting too happy. Something was bound to go wrong.

And indeed, when she reached the Agency door, it was locked. The ENTER sign was turned to CLOSED (EVEN FOR ROYALTY!). The garden gnome, which she'd previously seen by the gate, was now standing beside the door. Under his foot was an envelope.

She pulled it out. On the front, in swirly handwriting, was her name:

Clover

Quickly, she tore it open.

Dear Clover,

I have been called away on an extremely important rescue mission. I would usually have my cousin look after the Agency, but he's unavailable. Luckily, there's you. I hate to leave you on your own so soon, but I have every confidence that you will be able to look after the Agency in my absence.

I will return the day after tomorrow. There are plenty of supplies.

I forgot to mention to you that Esmeralda the toad needs a vitamin pill every day. Curses can be very draining. The pills are kept in a large purple bottle on the shelf under her tank. Also, Coco the unicorn is allergic to sugar beets. Make sure she doesn't come in contact with the sugar beet biscuits.

In all other matters, simply do as I showed you yesterday. There is a copy of the feeding schedule in the kitchen cupboard beside the cauldron. I've cleaned all the cages and stables, but you will need to change the hay in the unicorns' stables every day. Snort burns up all his messes. The adoption papers are in the third drawer. They should be easy to understand. Just make sure that all the boxes are filled in. You can help yourself to tea and cinnamon toast.

Please find the key inside this envelope.

Lock up when it is time for you to go home. The gnome will guard the Agency at night. He sleeps during the day.

The animals are counting on you.

—Mr. Jams

P.S.—Remember: be wary of princesses, knights, and witches; they can be both good and bad.
P.P.S.—If an animal falls ill, phone Dr. Nurtch. She's a magical-animal vet. The number is in the jam jar on the desk.

Clover's heart sank. She shook her head. *I can't look after the Agency all by myself.*

She looked down at the garden gnome. His eyes, open before, were now closed. If Clover hadn't just seen it, she would never have thought he was alive. He looked just like one of the clay gnomes in her neighbor's yard. She wondered briefly if they were alive too.

There was no one else around.

"The animals are probably hungry for their breakfasts, right?" she asked him.

He didn't answer.

"Why can't you just look after them?"

At this the gnome's eyes blinked open. He stared at her hard.

She gulped. "I guess you would be too tired, looking after the Agency all night and then all day too?"

The gnome said nothing.

"But I only just came here. I barely know anything. And plus, Mr. Jams knows I'm unlucky! I told him."

The gnome seemed to stare at her harder.

She thought of all the animals inside. Skinny Moondrop, Snort with his fire problem, Esmeralda and her curse. Being unlucky was something she shared with them. They were worse off, really, because they needed looking after. And she was the only one there, the only one who could.

She took a deep breath. "Well, it *is* only for two days," she said. "Maybe everything will be okay."

The gnome's clay mustache rose up in a smile.

It made Clover feel good. "Two days. I can do it."

She looked back at the gnome. But his eyes were shut again, and when she leaned close to him she thought she heard a faint grunting, like snoring. He was already asleep.

Clover took the key from the envelope. It was really fancy with sharp, pointy teeth and, upon closer examination, looked as if it had been carved from an animal's tooth. Probably a magical animal's, thought Clover, though it looked too small to be a dragon's. After opening the front door and letting herself in, she used the string from the bunch of carrots to tie the key around her wrist. After all, it would be just her luck to lose it.

Then she hurried to the back to greet the animals and begin the day.

Of course, it wasn't easy.

Even though she had paid close attention yesterday,

there was lots to remember. Thank goodness Mr. Jams was well organized.

Each of the doors of the refrigerator was labeled. The biggest door read LARGE MEALS, the medium-sized door SNACKS, and the smallest door MISCELLANEOUS. She opened the biggest door to find the dragon's food, already portioned out in bags. Behind the snacks door were big bags of rosy apples and small ones of baby bean sprouts. There was a jar of squashed flies in there too, for Esmeralda, with a pair of tweezers inside and a note that said, *Maximum fourteen a day.*

Behind the miscellaneous door was food Mr. Jams hadn't explained to her. A bag that said "Slew Guts," a jar of "Friggles," and a box of "Panadalls." *I wonder what kinds of animals eat these,* thought Clover.

In the big cupboard were the special oats to make mush to feed the unicorns and the fairy horses. There was a label on each colorful bin saying how many scoops to mix together with water. The fairy horses only took one pellet of each, dry, and there was a tin of sugar cubes for them too. The small cupboard was full of jars of jam and honey, cinnamon and sugar, a loaf of bread, and a box of tea. These were clearly for Mr. Jams.

Of course, the one food Clover couldn't find was the salamanders'. And of all the foods to forget, this was the worst, because Mr. Jams said they absolutely HAD to eat first thing in the morning because they burned up a lot of energy.

Just my luck, she thought. Then she took a deep breath and tried to think logically. They were fire salamanders, so maybe they needed spicy food, like hot sauce or hot peppers. Her mom kept their hot peppers hanging up in their pantry, where it was cool and dark. Clover checked the back of the kitchen. There, on a shelf, was a row of jars of crushed peppers, with gloves hanging from a peg. *Fire Salamander food—one pepper each. Extra spicy. Use the gloves.*

She was right! Relieved, she got to work.

It took Clover much longer to get the food for the animals ready without Mr. Jams, especially since she accidentally dumped a pail of oats all over the floor. She couldn't find a dustpan to clean up the grain, so she had to do it with her hands. But she made sure to get every bit. Feeding the animals took her almost until lunchtime because she stopped to read the cards on all the unicorns' stalls. Most of their names made her cringe. Sugar-plumsy-Wumsy, Cuddly-Wuddly Coco, Tootsie-Wootsie Wugums . . . Mr. Jams had written simpler ones underneath (*Plum*, *Coco*, and *Tootsie*), which Clover used as she filled their buckets with the mush and rubbed their noses.

She had just finished washing the feeding bowls when the bell in the front room rang.

Clover froze.

"Hello? Hellooo!? Anyone there?" demanded a high-pitched voice.

6
Moondrop's Mishap

Clover hurried out to the front room. There, tapping her fingers on the front desk, stood a princess. Or, at least, Clover thought she must be a princess because of the way she was dressed.

The woman wore a bright pink dress that reminded Clover of a giant bell. It was cinched around her plump waist with a thin silver belt. Her hands were covered by long pink leather gloves that stretched up above her elbows. In one hand she clutched a purse made of the same pink leather. A tall, pointed hat perched on her head, and a veil of sheer fabric hid her face.

"Hellooo!" said the princess again upon seeing Clover, and added, with a note of surprise in her voice, "Who are *you*? Where's that dotty old man?"

"I'm new here," said Clover, not wanting to tell her that she had just started the day before. "What can I help you with?"

"Well, my dear, first of all, you can help me by addressing me as 'Your Highness.' I am a royal princess, as you can well see." She took a step closer to the desk, and Clover swore she smelled like onions and garlic.

Strange. I imagined princesses would smell like roses and strawberries. Of course, Clover didn't say this out loud.

"And then you shall serve me, my dear, by showing me the unicorns you have for adoption. I am looking for a sweet, darling unicorn to love and look after, forever and always. I am just dyyyying for one. I've been waiting a loooong time. I am shy, just like unicorns are, and it has taken me aaaages to get up the courage to come here and get one. So, my dear, be a good little servant and show them to me."

Clover remembered Mr. Jams's warning about princesses. "One moment, please," she said, and searched through the cabinet's drawers until she found the form titled Precautions for Princess Adoptions Regarding Unicorns.

The three starred items on the list, the requirements all princesses must meet, caught her eye.

★1 Determine the reason the princess wants a pet: a long-term companion or a birthday surprise? Unicorns are not to be adopted as gifts.

★2 Determine the princess's age. Older princesses are usually more reliable than young ones.

★3 Observe the princess with a unicorn. She MUST be kind and gentle when petting it.

Well, this princess met two of the requirements. She was certainly old, and she said she wanted a unicorn not for a birthday present, but to love forever. She was definitely bossy, but Clover had never met a princess before. Likely they all acted that way.

"We do have unicorns," Clover said at last, adding quickly, "Your Highness. We have lots of them. Follow me."

Clover led the princess through the door and down the hall. The princess had to duck to keep her hat from hitting the doorway. Her dress was so wide, it brushed against the walls.

When they reached the door that led into the stables, Clover said, "Here are our unicorns. Are you looking for a particular type?"

"How about that one!" the princess said, pointing to Moondrop's stall.

"Oh, I don't think I should adopt Moondrop out yet. He just came in and is quite, um, weak."

"Weak? Oh, my dear, I have plenty of food in my castle perfect for making unicorns strong."

She is plump, thought Clover. *If she adopted Moondrop, maybe she'd feed him lots.*

The princess pulled out a twisted carrot from her purse and thrust it toward the unicorn. Moondrop snorted softly and backed away.

"A yummy, nummy carrot, darling unicorn."

"His name is Moondrop," said Clover.

"He has such a beautiful mane and tail. I just loooove gorgeous hair. I want to get to know him better," said the princess. "Leave. I'll summon you when I need you."

"Um . . . I don't think that's how we do things here. I have to stay with you. Why don't I show you some of the other unicorns too?" said Clover, biting her lip.

Then, all of a sudden, the bell in the front room rang again.

"Another customer," said Clover. "I can't believe it."

"It's your lucky day," said the princess.

"But I'm usually unlucky," said Clover.

The princess tilted her head. "You are?"

"I can't help it. I was born under a whisker-thin moon," said Clover. "My parents tell me it isn't a bad omen, but why else would they name me Clover?"

The bell rang again. "Oh, go ahead. I won't move. You can trust me, dear."

Clover wasn't sure about that, but she said, "I'll be back in a moment," and hurried down the hall, with a brief backward glance at the princess, who was gently stroking Moondrop. *It*

would *be lucky if a nice princess adopted Moondrop*, thought Clover. But she wasn't sure this princess was nice.

In the front room a very different set of customers stood waiting at the desk. The man was tall with a grizzled beard. He was wearing an oversized shirt and patched overalls. Clover thought he must be a woodsman. A little girl stood beside him, holding his hand. She was much younger than Clover. Like the woodsman, she was wearing an oversized shirt and overalls. Her hair fell over her eyes in tangles.

"Hi, Miss, this is the Animal Adoption Agency, isn't it?" asked the woodsman. "My daughter and I weren't sure."

"Yes, it is. I'm Clover."

"Oh, good," said the woodsman, relieved. "I'm Olaf, and this is my daughter. I've been promising Susie, here, a pet for a long time, and today is finally the day."

"I love animals," piped up the little girl excitedly. "We have a donkey, and chickens too."

Do they know it is a magical animal adoption agency? wondered Clover. They looked about as magical as she was.

Just as she was debating what she should do, the princess came rushing out, nearly knocking Clover over.

"Your unicorns are not for me," said the princess.

"B-but . . ." Clover stammered.

The princess didn't utter another word as she swept past Clover. She no longer wore the pink gloves and was obviously trying to hide her hands as she hurried out, but Clover got a glimpse of them. Instead of being smooth and lovely like Clover imagined a princess's hands would be, they were wrinkly, with long, bony fingers and cracked, yellowed nails.

The princess clutched her purse tightly. From one corner of it hung something that made Clover's blood turn cold.

Hair.

But not just any hair—long and silvery and shiny hair.

Unicorn hair!

"Stop! Stop!" cried Clover.

The princess did not. She ran past the woodsman and his daughter, who looked stunned.

"STOP!" Clover yelled again, running after her.

The princess bolted out the door. Her pointy hat hit the top of the door frame and tumbled off her head.

She stooped to pick it up. Clover saw her face without its veil.

Her lips were pale and thin, and her eyes were cold and black. She was wearing earrings that looked like slivers of a broken mirror. Three thin white scars ran down her left cheek. Despite the scars, she was beautiful . . . in a terrifying way.

"Surprised, my dear?" she cackled. "I'd go check on your animals, if I were you." And with that, she grabbed her hat, turned, and was gone.

Clover's heart pounded. *Moondrop!* She spun around and ran across the entry room and through the door in a desperate dash to reach the unicorn. She sprinted down the hall to the stables.

Moondrop was neighing and rearing up on his hind legs in his stall, slashing his small rounded horn through the air. He kicked again and again at the stall door with his front hooves until finally it broke and fell to the side.

He ran out, his mane flying about his head like a flag in a storm. But his beautiful long tail . . .

It was ruined! Just half remained, all ragged, as though it had been hacked off with a dull knife.

"Moondrop! Stop! Stop!" The unicorn pushed past Clover and reared up. Clover shouted again. But her shouting further agitated the creature, and he continued to rear. One of his hooves glanced off Clover's foot.

She cried and fell back, her foot throbbing.

"Hush, hush," a voice whispered beside her. "Good horsey. Easy, there." Susie had followed Clover.

The little girl's tone was calm and steady. "Easy, easy. You're okay." She approached Moondrop cautiously. Moondrop froze.

When Susie reached Moondrop, she began to pet his neck in slow strokes, and then his forehead. His head fell gradually below his knees. Clover barely felt the pain in her foot, she was so amazed at the girl's effect on the injured unicorn. Within moments, Moondrop lay down, with the tiny girl crouching beside him, singing softly, *"Dreamy dust for you, sleepy dust for me, in this magic world, happy we shall be."*

"Wow," whispered Clover. "Thank you so much. How did you know how to do that?"

"Our donkey gets spooked easily too," she said,

continuing to stroke Moondrop's neck. "All you've got to do is keep your voice calm." She looked down at Moondrop's tail. "Did that mean woman do that?"

"She must have," said Clover. "I don't know why. She said she was a princess wanting to adopt a unicorn, but she seemed more like a witch or something like that."

"These unicorns are for adoption?" gasped Susie in awe.

Clover nodded just as Olaf entered the stables.

His hair was wild and he was huffing heavily. "I couldn't catch her," he said. "Tried to, but she got away through the Woods. What did she do?"

Clover and his daughter showed him the stub of Moondrop's tail.

"What would a witch want with a unicorn's tail?"

"I don't know. So she *is* a witch?" asked Clover.

"Looked like that to me," answered Olaf. "And a bad one at that. Only bad ones would take unicorn tails."

"Poor Moondrop. He's already been through a lot. The last princess who owned him treated him horribly."

"He likes my Susie, though," said the woodsman with a smile.

Indeed, Moondrop's head was now in Susie's lap.

"You were looking for a new pet. What do you think

about a unicorn, Susie?" asked her father.

"I can't have him. Unicorns are only princesses' pets, aren't they?" said Susie. "I'm not a princess." She brushed her matted bangs away from her face as if to prove the point.

But her father responded at once, "You are a princess. To me."

Clover nodded. She didn't care if Susie wasn't a princess. And she didn't think Mr. Jams would either. Mr. Jams had said just that a customer had to be "right"—he never said anything about unicorns needing to go to princesses only. In fact, he'd probably prefer that they didn't. But Moondrop was recovering. . . . Should she really let him go?

Susie was still stroking Moondrop's mane. A soft rumbling came from Moondrop's nostrils, the sound a cat might make when it's happy, and Clover knew. Susie was the right match. Her heart told her that with Susie, Moondrop would soon grow healthy and strong.

"You are perfect for Moondrop," she said aloud.

"Really?" said Susie.

"Really."

♣

Clover found the adoption papers in the third drawer, just like Mr. Jams's note had said. She filled out the sections she needed to, including the date and the animal's name and description, and copied the special feeding instructions from the file. The only thing to write with was the fancy feather pen, but when she tried to use it, she splattered ink on her dress twice, to her embarrassment. So she took a regular pen from her pocket instead. *This is the sort of thing that Mom and Dad do all day long*, she thought. *Thank goodness it's only a small part of my job.*

While the woodsman and Susie filled out the rest of the papers, Clover went back to the stables and trimmed Moondrop's tail so at least it was even. In time it would grow out.

Her foot still throbbed, but only mildly now.

She looked at the stall gate. It was badly broken. Moondrop looked up and blinked.

"It's okay," said Clover. "It isn't your fault. It's mine. I let that witch into your stall." She hugged his neck. "It's my bad luck that brought that horrid witch who cut off your tail. I hope I never see her again."

Already Clover had encountered two witches, this one and the one who had pushed her into the puddle on her first day in the Woods. *Mr. Jams never should have left me in charge. At least he'll be back soon. The day after tomorrow. That's what his note said. Then everything will be fine.*

She felt a bit happier as she waved good-bye to Moondrop, Susie, and Olaf. Moondrop's tail, though very short, still swished nicely back and forth as he walked down the front path with Susie riding on his back.

7

Snort's Sneeze

That night Clover's parents noticed the key around her wrist. "It's for the Agency," she explained.

"Such responsibility already," said her mom.

"Well done, Clover," said her dad.

If only they knew the full truth of it! But Clover wasn't sure her parents would like to know that she was looking after the place all by herself, so she just nodded and smiled when her mom gave her a second helping of strawberries and ice cream. Ice cream, she decided, was good for melting away memories of mean witches.

But the memories returned in the morning, especially when a boy and his parents, a witch and a wizard, came into the Agency looking for a pet for the boy. At first, Clover didn't know what to think of the witch and wizard—were they bad or good? But they didn't seem too different from normal parents, except for their pointy hats and long black robes. They left empty-handed, debating between the toad and a salamander. They promised to return when they had made a decision.

Afterward, Clover took a postcard out of her bag. Her mom had given it to her before she left. It was from Emma.

On the front was a picture of a pony standing in a windswept field. On the back, Emma had written:

Hi Clover,

My pony's name is Gracie, and she's chestnut-colored. She's so cute! We have to sleep in bunk beds, and my bunkmate snores louder than a dragon! I wish you were here. Miss you!

-XOXO, Emma

Clover smiled. Little did Emma know that Clover knew exactly how loudly a dragon snored now! Or, at least, a small dragon like Snort.

She took out a piece of blank paper from the desk. She wanted to tell Emma everything, but she couldn't tell her *anything*. Instead she wrote:

Hi Emma,

    Guess what? I got a job volunteering with animals. So far only a few unlucky things have happened to me. I miss you too!

                      -XOXO, Clover

Then Clover decided to add something special to it. There was still lots of room at the bottom of the page. In the stables, she stood by Coco's pen and sketched a picture of the unicorn. Coco was especially pretty. Close up, Clover saw there was a slight cinnamon tinge to Coco's horn and mane, which she hadn't noticed before. She tried to get Coco just right, with the sparkle in her eye and the exact length of horn. Emma would love it, and never imagine that Clover had sketched it from a REAL unicorn. Underneath she wrote, *I thought you might like this. I've been dreaming of unicorns lately. Send me a drawing of Gracie.*

After finishing her letter and tucking it in her bag to

mail, Clover had time to do a few things she had been longing to try.

During lunch, she cut up a bit of her apple and fed it to the fairy horses. They gathered around it, munching and swishing their paintbrush-sized tails. Then she brushed the coats of the unicorns until their hair shone like silver.

Later, after giving Esmeralda her vitamin pill—which took three attempts and involved lots of slimy toad spit—she played with the big toad. She placed Esmeralda on different-colored slips of paper to see if her warts would change color depending on her surroundings. They didn't. All Esmeralda did was snap her tongue and blink her bulging eyes.

Just as she was putting Esmeralda back in her tank,

the toad, with a grumpy croak, bounded out of her hands and hopped through the door and down the hall, into the front room. It took a long time to capture her from under one of the chairs. When Clover finally did, the toad's warts were flashing all the colors of the rainbow, and Clover's heart was pounding too.

Just my luck to almost lose her, thought Clover. *What would I have told Mr. Jams? I'd better not play anymore.*

As soon as Clover placed Esmeralda back in her tank, the toad hopped to her favorite spot on the glass ball. Her warts stopped flashing and turned a pale green. *Hmm, I wonder if she changes color depending on her mood,* mused Clover. But she didn't want to take out the toad again and test her theory.

So she sank into the couch and read the Wish Book to see what other sorts of magical animals people longed for.

Each page was divided into three columns. On the far left was a column for the name, address, and phone number of the person who was requesting the animal; the middle column was for the animal; and the far-right

column was to check off if the
wish had been fulfilled.

The book was fascinating.

There was a woman who was looking
for a griffin to guard her chickens (check
mark). A mermaid princess looking for her lost hippocampus (sadly, no check mark). And below that, a dwarf
looking for a hippogriff (no check mark again). *I wonder what a hippogriff is*, thought Clover. Mr. Jams had
explained a hippocampus but not a hippogriff. *I'd better start a list of questions for Mr. Jams to ask him when
he returns.* Clover didn't have time to read through the
whole book and planned to continue the next day.

She closed the Agency with relief, knowing Mr. Jams
would be back tomorrow. And that night at home, she
slept as soundly as a salamander, without any dreams
at all.

♣

The next day, earlier than ever before, she hurried to
the Agency, hoping Mr. Jams was already there. She
imagined the lights on and the smell of cinnamon toast
and coffee filling the rooms.

But it was not to be. The Agency was dark and quiet.

Clover was jumpy all morning, expecting Mr. Jams to arrive at any moment. She spilled some of the unicorns' breakfast mush while she was pouring it into the buckets, but it wasn't as bad as spilling the oats, and it only took half the time to clean up.

She had just finished lunch, a cheese-and-mustard sandwich that her mom had packed for her, when the bell rang. She hurried to the entry, hoping it was Mr. Jams. But it wasn't.

Four people stood in the front room.

Three she recognized from the day before—the mother and father and their son, who today was dressed in red overalls and a red hat.

A fourth man, also a wizard (she could tell from his hat and robe), but much older, accompanied them. A wild red beard grew down past his stomach, and his spectacles made his eyes as large as an owl's. His cloak was decorated in red flames.

"We want to look at the salamander one more time," said the mother in a no-nonsense tone. "Isn't that right, Henry? They like fire just like you."

"I don't *like* fire, I like to fight—" started Henry.

"The toad is nice too," interrupted the boy's father.

"But, Dad, I don't want—"

"Toad or salamander, son. We already talked about this."

To break up the argument, Clover said, "And you brought another member of the family?"

The mother, father, and boy stared at the older wizard and shook their heads.

"We don't know him," said the boy.

"And I most certainly do not know them," replied the older wizard, whose voice was gruff and grumpy. "I am here for me dragon."

That declaration got everyone's attention.

"Your dragon?" quizzed Clover.

"Me dragon. He's black and ashy and not too old. Had 'im since he was an egg, and I want 'im back. I heard from a friend that you have 'im."

"Mr. Jams told me the dragon was abandoned here."

"More 'n likely he just wandered by," claimed the old wizard. "And you took 'im in. I don't know how he escaped, but I miss 'im. Miss his fire. Miss his claws. Miss his company."

Clover could hardly believe it. Snort hadn't been abandoned after all. This wizard looked like a dragon-keeping sort, with his wild red beard and the flames on his cloak.

"See, son?" said the boy's father. "That's what having

a pet is all about. It is about companionship. It's more than just training to be a good wizard, it's training to be a good person too."

"But I don't want to be a good wizard. I want to be a good firefighter. And I want a Dalmatian, not a toad or a salamander," cried the boy, stomping his foot.

"Hush!" said his mother.

They argued just like an ordinary family. "If you don't mind waiting, while I help Mr. . . . ?" Clover began.

"Sir Wickity," said the wizard.

"Sir Wickity," repeated Clover.

"Very well," said the boy's mother.

"Congratulations," the boy's father said to Sir Wickity. "It must be a fine feeling to have found a lost pet."

Clover couldn't help but think of Penny, flying somewhere in the Woods. She hoped her bird was safe and happy.

"Indeed," said Sir Wickity.

Clover got out Snort's paperwork. "This is Snort's file."

"Snort?" The wizard looked confused.

"Oh, you probably don't know him by that name. That's what we call the dragon. What's his real name?"

"Why . . . Ruffles, of course."

"Ruffles?"

"Named 'im after me pet owl, long gone now, poor thing."

Clover didn't think Ruffles was an appropriate name for Snort at all, or an owl either, for that matter, but she was too polite to say so. Sir Wickity sat down and she gave him the paperwork.

"Even though he was yours before, I need you to fill out these forms," said Clover. "I'll go get Snort. I just fed him, so he might be sleeping."

She went to the stables, stopping in the tack room for Snort's leash. The tack room was filled with weirdly shaped saddles and bridles of different sizes, from as tiny as an acorn, to larger than Clover's body. There was a whole wall of unicorn bridles, each on a separately labeled peg. There was a wall of leashes too. One leash had three giant collars attached to a single rope, which Clover deduced—somewhat alarmed—was probably for a creature with three heads. But she couldn't figure out what the bottles might be for. Several bottles were stacked in a dark corner, and whatever was in them twinkled brightly. When she peered closer, she read on a tag: *Stardust. Real* stardust? She added it to the list in her head of things to ask Mr. Jams.

She found Snort's leash, a thick chain one, on a peg with his name. It was heavy, with a clip at the end to attach to his collar.

As she guessed, Snort was asleep in his pen. Two thin tendrils of smoke spiraled up from his nostrils. He didn't look like a Ruffles at all. *What strange names magical people give to their pets*, thought Clover, remembering Mistypoo.

"Ruffles!" she called out, opening his door. "Ruffles!"

Snort didn't twitch, not even his tail.

"Snort!"

He woke up at once.

This made Clover a bit suspicious. *Maybe he is just more used to Snort now*, she thought. "Come on," she said. "Your owner, Sir Wickity, is here for you." Snort gave her a blank stare. He thumped his tail hard on the ground, and his nostrils flared.

Clover gulped. He didn't look very calm.

Nervously, she stepped into the pen, with the chain leash in one hand and a bucket of water in the other. Although she had fed him a few times now, each time she had made sure he was sleeping before she entered his pen and filled his bowl. She hadn't come too close, afraid he might snort fire.

Make sure he's nice and calm, Mr. Jams had said.

Clover remembered Susie and how she had calmed Moondrop. "Hush, hush," Clover whispered like Susie had. "Good Snort. Easy, Snort."

Snort's tail slowly stopped thumping. His snout twitched. Clover drew closer and closer. Finally she reached the little black dragon. His snout was resting on his front legs. Clover put down the pail and reached out a tentative hand. The dragon sniffled and her heart leapt, but he didn't breathe fire. Slowly Clover touched his back. His scales were smooth and slick, like ice. She began to quietly sing the song that Susie had sung, *"Dreamy dust for you, sleepy dust for me, in this magic world, happy we shall be."*

Snort's tail twitched in time to the tune. When Clover was done, he gazed up at her with his emerald eyes: they were big and hopeful, but worried-looking. They reminded Clover of her own. Her heart filled with ache for the dragon. He knew that he was trouble.

"Sweet dragon," Clover said. "We all have problems, you know. You shouldn't feel bad. You can't help it that you breathe fire."

Snort sniffled again, and although Clover's heart jumped, she didn't move her hand from his back.

She clipped the chain onto his metal collar. Snort stayed still and patient.

Clover led Snort out of his pen and down the hall, still wondering why he hadn't responded to "Ruffles." Before letting him go, she decided she would double-check to make sure that Snort really was Ruffles. How exactly she would do this, she wasn't sure.

Back in the front room, Henry and his family were waiting in the corner (still arguing), and Sir Wickity was sitting on the couch, writing. He stopped when Clover and Snort entered, and stood up.

"Aha! Me dragon," he said. "You have grown so big. You barely fit through the door. Look at your wings, your claws! They are so long."

Snort took a few steps toward the wizard, thumping his tail on the floor, breathing heavily. It seemed as if Snort did know Sir Wickity after all. Clover breathed a sigh of relief.

"Good draggie. That's me draggie," said Sir Wickity.

But Snort's breathing grew heavier and heavier as Sir Wickity spoke. His wings raised, as though he were afraid, and then . . .

Roar!

Snort let out a big flame.

It whooshed across the table covered in the adoption papers.

The papers burst into flames.

"Oh!" cried Clover, dropping the leash.

Sir Wickity jumped away from the burning papers and table, toward Snort.

"Fire!" cried Henry's mother.

"Stay back," commanded Henry's father.

Henry didn't listen. He stepped forward and pulled a wand from his pocket. He muttered under his breath and waved his wand in circles.

"I've got to get a bucket of water!" Clover exclaimed, mad at herself for not bringing one to begin with. She turned to go, when suddenly a bucket thumped down right in front of Henry.

"WOW!" Henry looked delighted. "It worked!"

He didn't waste any time. Dropping his wand, he grabbed the bucket with both hands and tossed the water over the table.

The water splashed in a wave over the papers, putting out the blaze.

Clover glanced over at Sir Wickity just in time to see him pull out *his* wand! Sir Wickity waved the wand across Snort's snout and said, "*Sleep, sleep, fall into a heap!*" Snort closed his eyes and sank to the floor. In a flash, Sir Wickity pulled out a pair of curved scissors from his cloak. With them, he clipped off Snort's longest talon. *Snap!* The talon made the sound of a stick breaking. Snort grunted, but he did not wake up. Sir Wickity stuffed the clippers, claw, and wand into his cloak pocket.

"What are you doing?" Clover cried. She noticed something else too. "Your beard is smoking!"

"FIRE!" yelled Sir Wickity in a much higher voice than before.

Then he did something very odd. He didn't try to smother the flames. Instead, he ripped the beard completely off his face, revealing three thin white scars.

He was no wizard. . . .

It was that witch again!

"YOU!" exclaimed Clover.

Henry's parents drew their wands.

"So long, unlucky little girl," the witch crowed as she fled out the door and disappeared, before Henry's parents had time to do anything.

Henry stomped on the beard, putting out the flame. When the fire was completely out, he ordered, "Open the windows and the doors," and started to do so himself.

As soon as the windows were open, cool air rushed into the room. The smoke cleared. Water dripped off the burnt table and trickled across the floor in a tiny stream.

Snort lay perfectly still beside the rug. His left foot was stretched outward, his third talon clipped close to his toe. While Henry's parents used magic to dry the table and rug, Clover hurried to his side, her shoes squishing with water. Thin tendrils of smoke rose from Snort's nostrils. At least he was breathing.

"He was put under a sleep spell," said Henry's father,

gently prodding one of Snort's wings. "He'll wake up soon enough. Sleep spells always wear off. But, tell us, what is this all about?"

Clover explained, as best she could, "That same witch tricked me yesterday and stole the hair from a unicorn's tail. And now she's tricked me again and stolen Snort's claw. I don't understand either. Why would a witch want a claw from a dragon?"

"I don't know," said Henry's father. "I don't know of any good spells that call for dragon claws. Dragon spit, yes, but dragon claws . . ."

"Will it grow back?"

"Dragons' claws always do, but very slowly," said Henry's father. "Much slower than our toenails."

Henry was crouching near Snort, watching the smoke spiral from his nostrils. "I never realized dragons were so amazing," he said, lightly touching Snort's scales.

"Careful, son. We don't know exactly how long that witch's sleep spell will last."

"If the witch can cast sleep spells, why doesn't she cast a spell on all of us and just come and get what she wants?" asked Clover.

"It is strange," said Henry's mother. "Usually wicked witches swoop in from far away, do something dreadful, then speed away in the dead of night. I wonder what she's up to."

"Well, at least the fire's out," said Clover. "Thanks to you, Henry."

"Yes, well done, son," said his father. "Water spells are extremely tricky. Your mother's water spells cause floods, and mine tend to end with lightning."

"Thanks. I made it up myself," said Henry, looking proud. "I have other water spells too—depending on the type of fire. Firefighters must be on guard at all times."

"You'd be the perfect owner for Snort," said Clover. "He's always lighting things on fire."

The boy's eyes went big. "I never thought about it like that, but you're right. He needs someone like me."

"A dragon?" His mother shook her head. "That's a much bigger pet than we talked about."

"Wizards don't have dragons as pets, son. Toads, salamanders, owls . . ." said his father.

"Please can I adopt him? You said it wasn't just about learning to be a wizard. It was also about learning to be a good person."

"You did say that," his mother said to his father.

"I did, didn't I?" said his father with a sigh.

By the time new paperwork was made up and filled out, and Clover had found the pamphlets on dragon care for Henry, including one titled *Your Dragon's First Flight and Beyond*, Snort had awoken. He rose and walked toward Clover with a bit of a hobble, his tail dragging on the floor. Suddenly, Clover's heart felt like it was dragging too. Snort was tricky to deal with, but he was also the first dragon she had known. Mr. Jams cared about him a lot too. Would Mr. Jams mind that she had let him go? Then she remembered Mr. Jams's words—*Adoption is our Agency's purpose*—and felt better.

Henry would take care of Snort. Snort would finally have a family, a friend—a home.

"Good Snort," said Clover, clipping his leash back on. "Look, you have a new owner."

Snort thumped his tail on the ground and looked from her to Henry.

"Don't worry, Snort. What happened with that bad witch won't happen again. This is a nice wizard. He will make sure you're happy."

Henry smiled. "That's right," he said. He pulled out gloves from his pockets. "Firefighter's fireproof gloves," he explained. "I have a lot of stuff that'll be good for taking care of Snort."

"You're going to keep his name the same?"

"Yeah, of course." Henry put on the gloves and rubbed Snort's nose gently. Snort let out a yawn.

Soon Snort, a very happy Henry, and his rather skeptical parents were on their way. It was the end of the day. And Mr. Jams still wasn't back.

Clover frowned. *Where can he be?*

After feeding the animals, but before locking up, Clover dried her shoes by putting them on top of the salamander tank. While she waited, she played with the fairy horses, letting them gallop around her palms. Their tiny hooves made Clover's skin tingle. Tansy seemed to like her the best, and Clover had to use a sugar cube to coax the little horse to leave her hand. Secretly, Clover hoped she wouldn't get adopted soon.

When she put on her shoes they were toasty warm.

I won't let that witch trick me again, thought Clover, turning off the lights.

But she was worried that her bad luck had other plans.

8

Esmeralda's Enchantment

Clover got up early again, skipping breakfast this time but promising her parents she'd eat at the Agency. She had a present to give to the gnome and she hoped he'd like it. But more than that, she was anxious to find out if Mr. Jams was back.

But the moment she started up the curved path, her heart sank. All the lights at the Agency were off. The garden gnome stood awake and alert at the front gate.

After finishing the morning feeding and grooming, Clover took the rug outside and beat it to get rid of ashes. She put it back, then went to check on the gnome, who was now fast asleep in the sun.

"Hi," she said, trying to strike up a conversation.

He opened one eye a sliver.

"I wish Mr. Jams had left a number for me to call or something. Do you think he's okay?"

The gnome said nothing. But his forehead creased.

"Sorry. I didn't mean to upset you," said Clover. "It's just that he said he would be back yesterday."

The lines on the gnome's forehead grew deeper.

"You're doing a great job," added Clover quickly. "Nothing's gone wrong at night. In fact . . ." She took her tortoise paperweight out of her pocket. "I brought this for you. I thought you might like it. It's made of jade. Jade's supposed to be lucky, you know."

The gnome's forehead relaxed and he closed his eye. The tips of his white mustache rose up a bit. Clover placed the gift beside the gnome's boots. The tortoise, the same shade of dark green as the grass, became almost invisible.

With a brief glance past the gate into the mysterious Woods, Clover went back inside. Her heart was heavy like the paperweight. "I need a distraction," she said out loud.

She remembered Mr. Jams had told her to help herself to cinnamon toast. And all this worrying had made her hungry, and she *had* skipped breakfast, after all. She opened Mr. Jams's special cupboard full of sugar and cinnamon, butter and bread. Even after three days, the bread seemed remarkably fresh. The first slice burned in the toaster. But she popped the next slice up early and got it right. As she buttered the golden toast and sprinkled on the cinnamon and sugar, Clover remembered the Wish Book.

I'll finish reading it, she thought. Then she had an idea. Maybe the witch had put in a request for animals before and it was recorded in the Wish Book. Maybe she could find out something more about her. Of course, she knew it was unlikely, especially since it seemed the witch just came in and stole what she wanted, but it was worth looking into.

With her snack in one hand and the book in the other, Clover curled up on the couch and opened the pages to where she had left off.

A tooth fairy looking for a toothless night-light bug (check mark). A troll looking for a hippogriff (no check mark). A fairy godmother seeking a coach mouse (no check mark). A prince looking for a peryton (no check mark).

There sure were a lot of animals she had never heard of before. She added them to her list of things to ask

Mr. Jams. There were many more entries that weren't checked off. But no witches.

She flipped the page, munching the last bit of her toast, scanning only for the entries that hadn't been checked and for witches. A jockey looking for a winged horse. A professor looking for a sphinx. A giant looking for a three-headed dog. "Oh, that's what the leash with the three collars is for!" exclaimed Clover.

She flipped to the next page. A wizard looking for a phoenix. A pixie looking for a starbird. Still no witches.

And then she noticed a wish that made her pause.

It was written very neatly at the bottom of a page: *Miss Opal, fortune-teller, 22 Sibyl Lane, 222-222-SEER / Looking for a mood creature, firefly preferred, but any type will do.*

There was no check mark in the right-hand column.

"Mood creature?" wondered Clover. Although she had never heard of a mood creature, she immediately thought of Esmeralda, and how the toad's colors changed when she was excited. Esmeralda was cursed, Mr. Jams had said. But even so, it looked like the curse was there to stay. So maybe the toad was a mood creature now!

A toad wasn't exactly a firefly, but still . . .

What should she do? Should she call Miss Opal? But where was the phone?

In all her time at the Agency, she had never heard the phone ring.

She got up and searched the room.

At last she spied it, perched on top of the bookshelf. It was an ancient thing, with a dial and a single receiver at the end of a twisty cord. She had to stand on a chair to reach it.

She could feel something else on top of the bookshelf, too. She stood on her tiptoes and could just see, lying behind the phone, a big sword in a leather sheath. The initials *T.J.* were inscribed on the handle.

I wonder where Mr. Jams got that, thought Clover, remembering the dark look he had given her when he spoke about knights. Careful to avoid the dusty sword, she picked up the phone and carried it to the desk. The twisty cord stretched out like a noodle.

She dialed Miss Opal's number. The phone rang on the other end a few times, and then a voice answered.

"Miss Opal, your friendly fortune-teller, here. What can I see for you?"

"Well, I'm calling from the M.A.A.A.—" Clover started.

Miss Opal interrupted, "Oh, you must be Clover."

Clover jumped. *Wow, she must be a good fortune-teller!*

"Go on. . . ." said Miss Opal.

"Well, I was phoning because . . . because I was reading through the Wish Book, and I noticed your wish. I think we have a pet here that might be a fit for you."

"A mood creature? A firefly?"

"Yes, possibly a mood creature, but she's not a firefly. She's a toad."

"A toad?" Miss Opal seemed puzzled. Then, as though she had realized something suddenly, she exclaimed, "A TOAD!"

There was a sharp click as Miss Opal hung up.

Clover put down the receiver with a sigh. *I guess she*

didn't want a toad. It had been a silly idea to call. But she *had* distracted herself from thinking of what had happened to Mr. Jams—at least for a few moments.

She put away the Wish Book, cleaned up her plate, and fed the animals their lunches. She had just finished feeding Esmeralda, this time hiding the vitamin pill in a squashed fly, when the bell at the front rang. She hurried to see who it was.

An ordinary-looking lady in a pretty, yet plain, sweater and jeans and flats stood at the front desk. A thin golden chain hung around her neck. Her white hair was swept back in a ponytail. She looked a little like Clover's mom, but might be as old as her grandma. It was impossible to tell.

"How may I help you?" asked Clover hesitantly. She didn't want to be tricked by that witch again. But unless the witch had shape-shifted, there was no way this lady was her. Clover could tell she wasn't wearing makeup and, although there were a few wrinkles around her eyes, her skin was rosy and free of any blemishes, much less scars.

"I'm Miss Opal," the lady said.

"Miss Opal?" Clover blanched. *This lady* was the fortune-teller?

This was NOT at all how Clover pictured the fortune-teller. Fortune-tellers, at least the ones that she had read about, wore ropes of beads and rainbow-colored dresses and smelled of exotic perfumes.

"You must be Clover. I'm friends with Olaf, the woodsman. He and Susie live near me. They told me about you and how you helped them with Susie's unicorn."

"Oh, *that's* how you knew my name," said Clover.

Miss Opal laughed. "Of course. Now, please, I would like to see the toad you mentioned."

"Yes," said Clover, with a smile. "I know it's not quite the same as a firefly, but I hope you like Esmeralda."

She led Miss Opal down the hall and into the first room. But when they reached Esmeralda's tank, it was empty!

"Oh no!" cried Clover. The lid of the tank was partially open. "I just finished feeding her. But I thought I put the lid back on. In fact, I checked it. I'm sure."

"Maybe she jumped and pushed it off?" suggested Miss Opal.

Clover puzzled. "Maybe. Perhaps the vitamin pills are making her stronger."

"Vitamin pills?" said Miss Opal. "Do toads need vitamin pills?"

"Esmeralda does," said Clover. "She was put under a curse that makes her change color. But I discovered that she changes color based on her mood. That's why I thought you would like her. But now she's lost! It's just my luck. . . ."

Clover bent down, searching for Esmeralda under the tables. "Esmeralda!" she called out. "Esmeralda!"

There was no movement, no sound. Not even one croak. "ESMERALDA!" She felt tears sting her eyes.

"Oh my dear," said Miss Opal, crouching beside Clover and patting her shoulder, "Not to worry. Here, let me."

Miss Opal took a breath and called, "FLIT! FLIT! Come here, Flit!"

"Flit?" said Clover, confused. "Why . . ."

But she didn't have a chance to finish. With a chorus of happy croaks, the toad appeared in the doorway, hopping straight toward Miss Opal. She was jumping very high (the vitamin pills, perhaps), and each time she hopped her warts changed from violet to blue and back again. She leapt into Miss Opal's hands.

"It IS you, Flit! Oh, Flit, I thought I'd never see you again!"

With that, the toad's warts turned as pink as bubble gum.

Miss Opal looked at Clover, whose mouth was hanging open. "I guess you are wondering what's going on?"

"Yes," said Clover, nodding vigorously.

"It's a long story. Perhaps we should get comfy."

♣

Clover made herself and Miss Opal slices of cinnamon toast as Miss Opal filled out the paperwork. After Clover checked it, they sat on the couch and Miss Opal told her story. Esmeralda—Flit—settled on Miss Opal's lap. Her warts were now a calm sea green.

Miss Opal closed her eyes. "Long, long ago now, when I was much younger—"

"You don't look *that* old," interrupted Clover.

Miss Opal blushed. "Well, I do have a few wrinkles now. We fortune-tellers are lucky to live long lives. But this story happens when I had just finished my training as a fortune-teller. My teacher gave me a mood creature to congratulate me. It was a pet firefly. Like you, many people think they change color depending on their own emotions. But actually mood creatures change based on the moods of people around them. And they can even predict a person's feelings in the future. Fortune-tellers are able to tell which colors are foretelling a person's future feelings. That's why mood creatures are a great help to us."

Clover remembered how frantic she had felt when the toad had escaped, and how her warts had been flashing all the colors of the rainbow. It made sense.

"My firefly and I got along at once. I named her Flit. I didn't even need to keep Flit in a cage, she was that attached to me.

"Then, one day, something terrible happened. A witch and her wizard husband came to have their baby's fortune told. Instantly I saw that their child would bring great luck to others when she grew up. I thought they would be thrilled with the prophecy, but they were outraged. I didn't realize this witch and wizard were evil—they had hidden that well when they first arrived—and they wanted their child to carry on the wicked tradition of their families. They tried to curse me, but I dodged their spell. It hit Flit instead. I ran away to escape them, and when I came back, Flit was gone. I assumed she flew out one of the open doors or windows. I was heartbroken. I searched everywhere for my little firefly. I even checked here for her, but I didn't realize she had been turned into a toad. So many years have passed; I thought I would never see her again. Until you called today. It suddenly struck me that the witch's curse must have been to change me into a toad, but it hit Flit instead, and transformed her. Thanks to you, we've been reunited at last."

"Wow!" said Clover. "So she *is* cursed, but the curse doesn't make her change color. The curse made her a toad! How will you change her back?"

Miss Opal smiled at the warty lump on her lap. "I don't think I can. At least because she is bigger, it is easier to see her colors." Miss Opal turned her smile to Clover. "As part of my thanks, I'd like to offer you a free fortune."

Clover shook her head forcefully. "No thanks. I'd rather not know. Things don't usually work out well for me."

"Well, the offer stands, if you ever want to come by. I live in the Woods near Olaf and Susie. I must be on my way, then."

Clover gave Esmeralda—Flit—a kiss good-bye. Instantly Flit's warts shone in a mix of cinnamon and gold, just like the toast. "It looks like Flit gave you a fortune anyway," said Miss Opal.

"What do you mean?" asked Clover.

Miss Opal winked. "I thought you didn't want to know."

"You're right. I don't," said Clover, resolute.

"Few fortunes are bad, Clover," said Miss Opal. "Some, in fact, are good. Very good." With that, she gave Clover another wink. Holding her pet close to her chest, she headed out the door.

Clover shook her head, but secretly hoped Miss Opal's words were true.

She watched out the window as Miss Opal walked down the path. Miss Opal and the toad were perfect together. She felt a twinge of longing. And of missing. She knew she would miss Esmeralda. (She just couldn't get herself to say Flit.) She already missed Moondrop and Snort, even though she was happy for them too. It was a funny feeling—half happy, half sad. *I guess that comes with working at an adoption agency. That's what Mr. Jams meant about keeping an open but guarded heart.*

As she did her chores, she couldn't help but gaze at the empty pens in the stables and empty cages in the small animals' room. She hoped all the animals that had once lived there were doing well—the griffin and the winged horse, and the witch's little white kitten. She stood a long time in front of Snort's pen, the sad part of her heart growing bigger.

But later, as Clover put a check mark in the far-right column in the Wish Book, beside Miss Opal's entry, she felt more happy than sad. The day was ending, and that nasty witch hadn't turned up. Clover had made a successful match without anything going wrong. Even though Mr. Jams wasn't back, it felt like things were finally looking up.

9

A Wicked Plan

The next morning, as Clover walked up the path, she heard a ringing coming from inside the Agency. It sounded like the phone!

It must *be Mr. Jams*, she thought, hurrying to unlock the front door. She rushed into the room.

"Hello?" she said, picking up the receiver. "Mr. Jams?"

"Mr. Jams?" a faint voice on the other end said at the same time.

"No. I'm not Mr. Jams," said Clover. "I'm a volunteer helping at the Agency. What can I do for you?"

"Oh, thank goodness!" croaked a woman's voice on the other end. The voice sounded desperate. "I . . . I was hoping to catch Mr. Jams, but if you are helping there, you will do. I was taking my morning stroll in the Woods when . . . oh goodness me . . . lo and behold, I saw a little white kitten stuck in a tree. She's still there. She looks very scared. I would climb the tree myself, but I am too old and weak. I hobbled home as fast as I could to phone Mr. Jams. Will you come and rescue her?"

"Well . . ." Clover hesitated. Mr. Jams hadn't told her what to do in this situation.

"Please hurry!" the lady continued. "I think I saw a witch!"

Clover shuddered. *A little white cat*, she thought. *It might be the one that was adopted from the Agency. It might be in danger from that witch.*

"Where is the tree?" she asked.

"Follow the path, past the Agency, into the Heart of the Woods. It's the old oak in the middle of the forest. You can't miss it. Oh goodness me, please hurry. I will meet you there."

"I'll come right away," said Clover. She hung up the phone, grabbed her coat and the rope ladder from the storage room, and rushed out the door, making sure to lock it behind her. She turned the ENTER sign to CLOSED (EVEN FOR ROYALTY!). She stopped for a few moments at the front gate to shake awake the gnome. He blinked at her groggily.

"I've got to go and rescue a cat," said Clover. "Protect the Agency while I'm gone, okay? I'll be back soon."

She hurried to the signposts and found the one that read HEART. She had yet to venture anywhere in the Woods except to the Agency. And now here she was, going into the very middle of it. Clover knew Mr. Jams said there were no beasties in the Woods, but the Heart of the Woods sounded like the sort of place scary creatures might live. Still, with a deep breath, she ran on.

The trees in this part of the Woods, crooked and bare, looked lifeless. No birds chattered. No squirrels scurried. She could understand why most people from her village stayed away from the Woods, at least this section. It *was* spooky. She sang the song that Susie had sung to Moondrop and she had sung to Snort, to keep herself calm: *"Dreamy dust for you, sleepy dust for me, in this magic world, happy we shall be."*

She had just noticed a ring of moon-colored mushrooms when a faint voice interrupted her thoughts. "Here—over here!"

It was the same feeble voice she had heard on the phone.

Clover looked up. There stood a giant tree. The leaves were broad and the bark thick and rough like a toad's skin.

She was sure it was the right oak tree.

But the old woman who had called out to her was nowhere to be seen. She peered up at the tree. She couldn't see anything at first except green leaves and brown branches, but then there was a flash of white. Clover rose up on her tiptoes, trying to spy more white. "Kitty? Is that you?"

Suddenly, a woman's face loomed down out of the leaves. A face with three scars!

"Sleep, sleep, fall into a heap!"

As soon as the spell was cast, everything went dark.

♣

When Clover awoke she was tied to a hard chair in a large room that smelled like onions and smoke. A squat pot hung over burning coals in the fireplace near her. On the mantel perched a stuffed crow. Spilled salt and pepper speckled the floor. A few open umbrellas lay in dusty corners. Pointed black-heeled shoes sat on a wooden table in the center of the room.

The table was also covered in a strange assortment of objects including a saltshaker, a broken horseshoe, a pile of two-leaf clovers, and, most awful of all . . . dead ladybugs, spiders, and bees. Beside the table, on a small, high stool, was a birdcage with a little white kitten, just a bit larger than a ball of yarn, locked inside. Clover was sure he was the same kitten she had seen days ago, when she'd gone to the Agency for the first time—but he looked much scruffier and thinner and sadder. His green eyes were dull and his tail limp.

"Well, well, our unlucky child has finally awoken," crowed a voice. The witch entered from a back room. She wasn't wearing a princess's veil this time, or a wizard's cloak, just a simple black dress. Her long dark hair fell in waves to her waist. She was wearing her broken-mirror earrings. "At last we properly meet. I am Ms. Wickity."

"Let me go!" cried Clover, struggling against the rope around her wrists that held her tight to the chair.

"And lose my final ingredient? Sorry, but you, my child, are too important. I have been searching for someone like you for a very long time. Now I can finish my potion." She strode over to Clover and stood so close Clover could smell her vile onion-and-garlic breath. "You know, my child, we share a common problem— luck. You are unlucky and I am supposed to be the opposite. When I was baby a fortune-teller prophesied that one day I would bring great luck to others, spreading good wherever I went."

Clover jolted, remembering the fortune-teller's story. "It was Miss Opal! Your parents turned her fire-fly into a toad."

"Miss Opal indeed!" spat Ms. Wickity. "That loath-some fortune-teller cursed me forever. When my potion is complete, she will be the first one I get."

"B-but . . . everyone wants luck," stammered Clover.

"Luck!" spat Ms. Wickity. "I come from a long line of wicked witches. Wicked witches cast bad luck upon people—not good luck. I grew up afraid to wave my own wand, in case I might make the prophecy come true. Eventually I realized there was only one thing to do: create a lifetime supply of bad-luck potion, so I can spread it around wherever I go. I have been trying to make the potion since I was very young. When I was only a witch in training, I pulled hair from a black cat for one of my attempts, and that is how I ended up with these scars. But some ingredients were impossible to obtain. I could never capture a wild dragon, and pet dragons are ridiculously expensive. I should have thought of looking for a magical animal adoption agency years ago. And imagine my delight to find YOU there as well!"

As she spoke, she popped the objects on the table one by one into the pot. When the tabletop was nearly cleared, she swept a handful of sparkly hairs off it, counted them out until she reached thirteen, then threw them into the pot too. They sizzled.

"Those are Moondrop's hairs!" cried Clover.

The witch smiled a twisted smile and took the last item off the table: a long green claw.

"And that's Snort's claw!"

The witch smiled again, then tossed it into the cauldron and watched the brew bubble. "At last, it is ready for the final and most challenging ingredient. The blood of an unlucky child. That's you, my dear."

"No!" cried Clover. She struggled once again to free her hands, pulling and tugging, but the ropes didn't give.

"There is no point in fighting. You know you are unlucky, and anything you do will simply worsen your situation." Ms. Wickity drew out her wand and pointed it at Clover. *"Free, free, stand by me."* The ropes magically fell from Clover's wrists and, as though someone was controlling her limbs, Clover jerked to her feet and whooshed next to Ms. Wickity, landing with such force she nearly tumbled into the pot.

Now untied, Clover knew this was her chance to escape, but before she could make a move, Ms. Wickity's cold, scaly fingers wrapped around her wrist like the coils of a snake. With her other hand, Ms. Wickity pulled a pin from her hat. Clover struggled, but Ms. Wickity held her fast, and jabbed the pin deep into Clover's thumb.

"Ouch!" yelled Clover.

"Silence!" snapped Ms. Wickity, stretching Clover's hand over the brew.

The steam scalded Clover's skin as Ms. Wickity squeezed three drops of blood into the pot.

The moment the last drop touched the potion, a green-and-white mist rose up. Ms. Wickity shoved Clover away, saying, *"Tie, tie, stay there till you die."* Clover flew back to the chair, powerless against the spell, and the rope twisted around her wrists, tighter than before.

Ms. Wickity removed the pot from over the fire and set it on the table. With a ladle she scooped some of the brew into a small spray bottle that looked like one of Clover's mother's perfume bottles, except it was made from glass as black as smoke.

"Now to test it. It's so powerful just one mist will change this pathetic white cat into an unlucky black one, truly wicked and fit for a witch."

"You're not going to use it on the kitten!" gasped Clover.

Ms. Wickity just laughed and put the nozzle of the bottle in through the bars of the cage and aimed it at the kitten's head.

The kitten mewed pitifully.

"You stupid little misfit. This will actually help you. Don't you want to be a proper witch's cat?"

The tiny kitten backed into the far corner of the cage.

Ms. Wickity sprayed a puff of the potion. The kitten sneezed . . . then froze. His tail stuck straight up in the air like an exclamation point.

Clover couldn't bear to watch.

She closed her eyes.

When she opened them again, she blinked in surprise.

The kitten wasn't white anymore.

But it wasn't black either.

The kitten had turned a beautiful green!

10

Serendipity

It was the loveliest color Clover had ever seen—the color of new grass, peas, peppermint leaves, and emeralds. The color of clovers.

The little kitten looked pleased and licked the green fur on the back of his paw.

"WHAT?" Ms. Wickity screeched. "Impossible!" She pointed her finger at Clover. "You told me you were unlucky, but green is the LUCKIEST of colors! You lied to me. You must be a LUCKY child."

"No! I'm not lucky!" said Clover.

Ms. Wickity spun around and threw open a cupboard, grabbing a recipe book to double-check her ingredients.

Meanwhile, Clover's mind was spinning. A LUCKY child? Her? Then she thought about it, and something remarkable occurred to her. . . .

If she HADN'T messed up with Ms. Wickity, Moondrop and Snort wouldn't have been adopted by Susie and Henry—and they were perfect matches.

If she HADN'T lost Penny, she would NEVER have come to the M.A.A.A. and met Moondrop and Snort and all the wonderful magical animals in the first place. And she would never have been able to help Mr. Jams so he could leave on his rescue mission (even if he hadn't come back yet), or have been able to help animals herself.

Maybe she wasn't so unlucky after all!

The kitten mewed.

Clover needed to rescue the kitten. The witch was still bent over her book, muttering and swearing to herself, but who knew what she might do next.

Clover pulled against the ropes again and felt something dig into her skin. The key! Around her wrist was the Agency key—carved from a tooth, with sharp teeth of its own. If she HADN'T tied the key around her wrist it wouldn't be here to help her now. And, amazingly, Ms. Wickity hadn't noticed it.

Suddenly, Clover felt powerful.

She felt lucky!

She struggled to grasp the key with her opposite hand. She twisted and wiggled until her grip grew firm, and then she scraped the key's sharp edge across the rope—back and forth, back and forth. At first, it seemed like nothing was happening, but then she felt one strand of the rope snap. She sawed furiously, thankful that the witch was absorbed in her book.

Just as Clover felt the last strand of the rope give, Ms. Wickity looked up at the kitten. "Maybe the cat just needs MORE potion. Yes, that has to be it. I'll spray the beast again!"

"Leave that kitten alone!" Clover yelled. She leapt out of the chair and grabbed the pot from the table, throwing its entire contents at the witch.

SPLASH!

Ms. Wickity shrieked and jumped back, but not quite in time. The potion splashed across her hands, drenching them. Instantly her fingers turned from crooked and bony to straight and beautiful. Her cracked, yellow nails became smooth and bright green. "My hands!" screeched Ms. Wickity. While the witch frantically wiped her hands on her cloak, Clover grabbed the cage

121

with the kitten inside and hugged it close to her chest.

"You're not going anywhere!" Ms. Wickity pulled her wand from her pocket and pointed it at Clover. *"Sleep, sleep, fall into a heap!"*

Clover blinked. Instead of feeling sleepy, she felt exactly the opposite—awake and energetic. She hurried toward the door.

Ms. Wickity shouted another spell, pointing her wand at her broom: *"Tip, flip, make her trip!"*

But instead of the broom falling down and tripping Clover, it fell onto the handle of the door and pushed it open.

Something was really wrong with Ms. Wickity's spells.

Ms. Wickity's eyes went wide with horror as she cried out another one, *"Bam, bam, door slam!"*

A whoosh of wind escaped from the witch's wand, and pushed the door farther open instead.

"That potion!" shrieked Ms. Wickity, her face now furious red. "It's making me cast lucky spells! The terrible prophecy has come true!"

Clover was off and running down the path. Ms. Wickity chased behind her, still crying out spells: *"Spike, spike, lightning strike!"* and *"Sting, sting, bees take wing!*" When Clover looked back, instead of lightning and bees, rainbows and butterflies were flying out of the open door.

♣

Clover ran the whole way back to the Agency, hugging the cage with the kitten in it. She glimpsed a yellow bird as she was running and wondered if it might be Penny, but she was afraid the witch was after her and didn't stop. She ran past the oak tree, past the ring of mushrooms. It wasn't long before she emerged into the clearing, panting and hot.

The Agency was just up ahead, crooked and moss-covered as ever. The sight of it filled Clover with happiness.

She hurried up the path that curved like a dragon's tail. When she reached the garden gnome, standing by the door with his arms crossed, she patted him on the head.

"Good job," she said.

With a grunt, the gnome fell asleep at once.

Clover unlocked the door and took a deep breath. The building still smelled very strongly of smoke, a

reminder of Snort. She could hear the unicorns neighing from the back. They were hungry.

Boy, do I have a lot of work to do, thought Clover.

First she freed the kitten from the cage. He leapt out happily and joined her as she fed the animals. They were so hungry, one of the unicorns even nibbled at her hair! Then she began to clean up the Agency. She found a hammer and nails in the storage room and fixed Moondrop's stall door. Every time she had used a hammer before she had hit her fingers, but this time she wasn't nervous. She confidently pounded away, and didn't strike herself once. She changed the hay in the unicorns' stables, and vigorously cleaned Moondrop's and Snort's pens so they were ready for new animals. She moved on to the front room. With a bucket and mop and an armful of rags, she scrubbed the floor, and dusted the tables and bookshelves. She beat the rug again, making sure it was as clean as it could be, and she put a vase of flowers over the burnt spot on the table. When she was done, the entire Agency sparkled.

Everything was in order. She even wrote out all her questions for Mr. Jams (like *What is a hippogriff?* and *What is the stardust for?*) so she wouldn't forget them. Then she put on the kettle and brewed a cup of green tea, in honor of the little kitten, and together she and the kitten curled up on the couch in the front room.

As she stroked the kitten and waited for the tea to cool, she thought about how strange it was that Ms. Wickity had made her own fortune come true. Clover almost felt sorry for the witch; but then the kitten purred in her lap, and she was so glad that the awful witch never would, never COULD, do harm again.

In the last few days, so much had changed. Her friendless, luckless summer had transformed into one filled with enchantment and excitement. Just days ago, she hadn't been certain magic existed. Now she knew it did. It was her bad luck that she didn't believe in anymore.

Things happened. Bad things. Good things. It was what you did with them that mattered. And so far, Clover was proud of what she had done. She was proud of all the matches she had made, proud of keeping the Agency safe, proud of saving the kitten. Those were lucky happenings of her own making.

Although she could never share these things with her parents, she knew they would be extra proud of her. Her mom was right—being plucky *had* made her lucky.

Dipping a spoonful of honey into her tea, she had an idea.

"I'll call you Dipity," Clover announced to the kitten. "Short for 'Serendipity,' which means 'lucky happenings.' That's a good name for you."

The kitten flicked his green tail in approval.

She hoped Mr. Jams would let her keep him.

And just as she thought of Mr. Jams, she heard the front door creak open and Mr. Jams's voice: "Clover, I've returned!"

He pushed through the door. Dipity leapt off Clover's lap and hid under the couch.

Mr. Jams's pointed beard was tangled with bits of twigs, and one knee of his pants was ripped. His boots were covered in muck and his jacket was torn and stained. But his blue eyes twinkled with excitement. He smiled as he glanced at the room. "Very neat and calm in here, I must say. Not a horse feather out of place. Nothing much happened, then? No problems? I'm sorry I am a little late. There was no way around it. But I knew you could handle it. I'm lucky you were here to help."

"Well . . ." started Clover. "There were a *few* things that happened."

"And I can't wait to hear about them. But first, no time to delay. Come outside—I need your help bringing it in."

"*It?* What is it? What animal did you rescue?"

"It's not really an animal. At least not yet. But it will be. Beaks and eggshells, will it ever."

"What do you mean?" Clover's heart started to pound with excitement.

But Mr. Jams had already turned around and hurried out the door.

As Clover hurried after him, she realized she was walking with a bounce in her step. This time, she didn't change it.

ACKNOWLEDGMENTS

To a large degree, I believe, like Clover does at the end of this book, that you make your own luck. But when it comes to all the people who helped me bring this book to life, I have been completely and totally lucky beyond my own making. Thank you to all those people: my dad, who is Mr. Jams; my mom and my family; my writing soul mate, Vikki Vansickle; my writing group, the Inkslingers—Rachelle Delaney, Tanya Lloyd Kyi, Lori Sherritt-Fleming, Maryn Quarless, Shannon Ozirny, and Christy Goerzen; Lee Edward Fodi, who was there when this story was born; Dimiter Savoff, for believing in my writing; my writing friends James and KC, and the whole Storm Crow gang; my wonderful

Disney • Hyperion team, especially Stephanie Lurie, editors Catherine Onder and Rotem Moscovich, editorial assistant Julie Moody, and designers Sara Gillingham and Joann Hill; my wonderful HarperCollins Canada team, especially editor Hadley Dyer; and the talented Alexandra Boiger. Special thanks to my amazing agent, Emily Van Beek; to my dear husband, Luke; and finally, most of all, to Tiffany Stone for her utterly thoughtful edits and ideas and time (and her whole family for putting up with Clover). Tiff, you are the best.

KALLIE GEORGE works as an author and editor in Vancouver, Canada, and she holds a master's degree in children's literature from the University of British Columbia. In addition to writing and editing, Kallie is a speaker and leads workshops for aspiring writers. She dreams of one day adopting a fairy horse. Visit her online at kalliegeorge.com.

ALEXANDRA BOIGER grew up in Munich, Germany, where she studied graphic design, and then began a career in feature animation, allowing her to work for Warner Bros. UK and DreamWorks. After transitioning to children's book illustration, she has worked on numerous popular titles, including the Tallulah series. She lives with her husband and daughter in northern California. See more of her work online at alexandraboiger.com.

The text for this book is set in 11.5-point Janson Text.
Janson is based on late-17th century type designed
by the Hungarian printer Nicholas Kis.

The illustrations for this book were created
using graphite on paper, then spot colored
digitally using various textures.

NATIONAL PARK

YOSEMITE VALLEY

Legend:
- ▲ Campground
- ▫ Picnic Area
- ◖ Overlook and Parking
- ▬ Road
- ┄ Trail

Upper Yosemite Fall

Yosemite Point
6,936

Eagle Peak
7,779

YOSEMITE VILLAGE

North Dome
7,542

Lower Yosemite Fall

VISITORS CENTER

STORES
POST OFFICE
RESTAURANT

PARK HEADQUARTERS

HOSPITAL

Royal Arch Cascade

YOSEMITE LODGE

GAS

AHWAHNEE HOTEL

Ribbon Fall

ROYAL ARCHES   Mirror Lake

El Capitan
7,569

Rocky Point
Picnic Area

GAS

ONE WAY

Washington
Column

THREE BROTHERS

EAGLE CR.

RIBBON CR.

ROYAL ARCH CR.

TENAYA CR.

to Tioga Pass,
Merced & Stockton

El Capitan
Picnic Area

CHAPEL
SENTINEL BRIDGE

ONE WAY

Indian Caves

CURRY VILLAGE

STABLES

Half Dome
8,842

NORTH VALLEY ROAD

MERCED R.

Union Point
6,314

Moran Point
6,300

GAS

SENTINEL CR.

hedral Rocks

South Valley Road

Sentinel Rock
7,083

Glacier Point
7,214

idalveil
Fall

5,909

Sentinel Fall

Cathedral Spires
6,118

Profile Cliffs
7,503

Sentinel Dome
8,122

JOHN MUIR TRAIL

MERCED R.

Emerald
Pool

DALVEIL CR.

Vernal Fall

MIST
TRAIL

ZIG-ZAG TRAIL

Taft Point
7,480

Illilouette Fall

ILLILOUETTE CR.

Nevada Fall

0   Miles   1

The Magnificent West: YOSEMITE

The Magnificent West: YOSEMITE

By Milton Goldstein

With 60 Photographs in Color

Doubleday & Company, Inc., Garden City, New York

ISBN: 0-385-03296-X
Library of Congress Catalog Card Number: 72-85054
All Rights Reserved
Printed in Japan

9   8   7   6   5   4   3   2

To The Memory
of
My Beloved Daughter,

DORINA,

Courageous, Noble,
Vibrant with the Joy of
Thinking and Feeling,
Who Loved Yosemite
In All Its
Magnificence

Preface

T HIS book is a love story—a story of my love for Yosemite and my attempt to portray its magnificence in photography. Essentially, as Thoreau put it, "All that a man has to say or do that can possibly concern mankind, is in some shape or other to tell the story of his love."

To me, the magnificent West of the United States is a thrilling vision—of beauty, strength, and nobility—in a world increasingly permeated with the fashionable, the petty, and the ugly. And Yosemite is the most inspiring of all the many treasures of the West.

My passionate attachment to Yosemite derives from the death of my mother. I had grown up loving and worshiping my mother—a magnificent person, noble in character, passionate in emotion, devoted in love, and zestful in living. My mother's death , in consequence of a stroke that left her helpless for years, left me disturbed. It was easy to understand—all things pass and death comes to us all—but impossible to accept.

The healing process of time slowly changed aggression to depression and then apathy—and even some glimmerings of satisfaction. And then, about two years after her death, I found Yosemite, and, instantaneously, joy returned to my life: I had found another ideal to love and worship.

The need to worship runs deep in me, and I can say with Thoreau, "I would fain improve every opportunity to wonder and worship, as a sunflower welcomes the light. The more thrilling, wonderful, divine objects I behold in a day, the more expanded and immortal I become."

Since I discovered Yosemite, a little over seven years ago, the mountains of the West have been my home, and the central meaning of my life has been a mystic identification with their magnificence and an attempt to express my vision of that magnificence in photography.

What I have tried to do with my camera is to express that vision in an ideal form reflecting the fundamental values of my life. Not ideal in the sense of nature prettified or distorted, but ideal in the sense of nature purified and exalted.

Contents

List of the Photographs   x

Part I.   Introduction   1

Part II.   The Photographs   33

    Entrance to the Yosemite Valley   34

    The Great Rocks   50

    The Falls   92

    The River   110

    The Trees   120

    Half Dome, from Sentinel Bridge   128

    The High Country   136

Part III.   Appendixes   155

    A.   A Guide to Yosemite National Park   157

    B.   Camping Accommodations in the National Parks   175

    C.   Addresses of the National Parks   181

    D.   Camping Accommodations in the National Monuments   183

    E.   Glossary of Geologist's and Naturalist's Terms   187

    F.   Selected Bibliography   197

    G.   John Muir, Ecological Prophet   203

Index   207

LIST OF THE PHOTOGRAPHS

Entrance to the Yosemite Valley   34

1. Tunnel View, Peaks and Clouds   34
2. Tunnel View, Dark Sunset   36
3. Tunnel View, Winter Sunset   38
4. Tunnel View, Autumn Sunset   40
5. Valley View, Pre-Sunrise   42
6. Valley View, Pre-Sunrise Colors   44
7. Valley View, Bright   46
8. Valley View, Post-Sunset   48

The Great Rocks   50

9. El Capitan, Massive   50
10. El Capitan, Pretty   52
11. El Capitan, Storm   54
12. El Capitan, Lyric, Cool   56
13. El Capitan, Shoulder, Sunset   58
14. El Capitan and El Capitan Fall   60
15. Half Dome, Peak, from Mirror Lake   62
16. Half Dome from Rocky Point Picnic Area   64
17. Half Dome from a Point near the Chapel   66
18. North Dome from Happy Isles   68
19. Sentinel Rock, Sunset   70
20. Half Dome and North Dome, Reflections   72
21. Lost Arrow from Yosemite Lodge   74
22. Profile Cliffs from El Capitan Meadow   76
23. Three Brothers from the Merced River   78
24. Middle Brother, Peak, Sharp   80
25. Middle Brother, Peak, Mystical   82
26. Royal Arches, Washington Column, and North Dome   84
27. Royal Arches, Washington Column, and North Dome   86
28. Glacier Point Cliff   88
29. Valley Sunset   90

The Falls   92
   30. Yosemite Falls, Winter   92
   31. Lower Yosemite Fall   94
   32. Upper Yosemite Fall, Rainbow   96
   33. Upper Yosemite Fall Mist, Rainbow   98
   34. Vernal Fall from Lady Franklin Rock   100
   35. Vernal Fall from the Mist Trail, Blue   102
   36. Vernal Fall from the Mist Trail, Beige   104
   37. Vernal Fall from the Mist Trail, Rainbow 106
   38. Nevada Fall from the Zig-Zag Trail   108

The River   110
   39. Happy Isles   110
   40. Mirror Lake   112
   41. Merced River, Winter   114
   42. Merced River, Autumn   116
   43. Merced River, Abstract   118

The Trees   120
   44. Sequoia Tree "Grizzly Giant," Mariposa Grove   120
   45. Ponderosa Pine Tree, Bark   122
   46. Incense Cedar Tree at Valley View   124
   47. Cottonwood Tree and Merced River   126

Half Dome from Sentinel Bridge   128
   48. Half Dome from Sentinel Bridge, Spring Morning   128
   49. Half Dome from Sentinel Bridge, Autumn Afternoon   130
   50. Half Dome from Sentinel Bridge, Summer Evening   132
   51. Half Dome from Sentinel Bridge, Winter Sunset   134

The High Country   136
   52. Mt. Dana and Mt. Gibbs, Tuolumne Meadows 136
   53. Mt. Dana and Mt. Gibbs, near Tioga Pass 138
   54. Half Dome from Tioga Road   140
   55. Tenaya Lake, Spring, Winter Snow   142
   56. Polly Dome, Tenaya Lake   144
   57. Jeffrey Pine Tree, Sentinel Dome   146
   58. View from Glacier Point   148
   59. Glacier Point, Sunset, Half Dome   150
   60. Glacier Point, Sunset, Mt. Starr King   152

I INTRODUCTION

Entrance to the Yosemite Valley

P ERHAPS the most enthusiastic celebrant of western magnificence was John Muir, whose love affair with Yosemite is famous. Muir's words about Yosemite still ring true:

> Yosemite Park is a place of rest, a refuge from the roar and dust and weary, nervous, wasting work of the lowlands, in which one gains the advantages of both solitude and society. Nowhere will you find more company of a soothing peace-be-still kind. Your animal fellow-beings, so seldom regarded in civilization, and every rock-brow and mountain, stream, and lake, and every plant soon come to be regarded as brothers; even one learns to like the storms and clouds and tireless winds. This one noble park is big enough and rich enough for a whole life of study and aesthetic enjoyment. It is good for everybody, no matter how benumbed with care, encrusted with a mail of business habits like a tree with bark. None can escape its charms. Its natural beauty cleanses and warms like fire, and you will be willing to stay forever in one place like a tree.

Every imposing work of architecture, whether the architect be human or divine, should have an appropriately imposing entrance. Yosemite has two such entrances—first to the Sierra Nevada mountain range as a whole, of which Yosemite is the gleaming crown, and then to the Yosemite Valley, the heart of Yosemite National Park.

The approach to the Sierra is described by Muir this way:

> Making your way through the mazes of the Coast Range to the summit of any of the inner peaks or passes opposite San Francisco, in the clear springtime, the grandest and most telling of all California landscapes is outspread before you. At your feet lies the great Central Valley glowing golden in the sunshine, extending north and south farther than the eye can reach, one smooth, flowery, lake-like bed of fertile soil. Along its eastern margin rises the mighty Sierra, miles in height, reposing like a smooth cumulous cloud in the sunny sky, and so gloriously colored, and so luminous, it seems to be not clothed with light, but wholly composed of it, like the wall of some celestial city. Along the top, and extending a good way down, you see a pale, pearl-gray belt of snow; and below it a belt of blue and dark purple, marking the extension of the forests; and along the base of the range a broad belt of rose-purple and yellow, where lie the miner's gold-fields and the foot-hill gardens. All these colored belts blending smoothly make a wall of light ineffably fine, and as beautiful as a rainbow, yet firm as adamant.

> When I first enjoyed this superb view, one glowing April day, from the summit of the Pacheco Pass, the Central Valley, but little trampled or plowed as yet, was one furred, rich sheet

of golden compositae, and the luminous wall of the mountains shone in all its glory. Then it seemed to me the Sierra should be called not the Nevada, or Snowy Range, but the Range of Light. And after ten years spent in the heart of it, rejoicing and wondering, bathing in its glorious floods of light, seeing the sunbursts of morning among the icy peaks, the noonday radiance on the trees and rocks and snow, the flush of the alpenglow, and a thousand dashing waterfalls with their marvelous abundance of irised spray, it still seems to me above all others the Range of Light, the most divinely beautiful of all the mountain-chains I have ever seen.

The Sierra is about 500 miles long, 70 miles wide, and from 7000 to nearly 15,000 feet high. In general views, no mark of man is visible on it, nor anything to suggest the richness of the life it cherishes, or the depth and grandeur of its sculpture. None of its magnificent forest-crowned ridges rises much above the general level to publish its wealth. No great valley or lake is seen, or river, or group of well-marked features of any kind, standing out in distinct pictures. Even the summit-peaks, so clear and high in the sky, seem comparatively smooth and featureless. Nevertheless, glaciers are still at work in the shadows of the peaks, and thousands of lakes and meadows shine and bloom beneath them, and the whole range is furrowed with canyons to a depth of from 2000 to 5000 feet, in which once flowed majestic glaciers, and in which now flow and sing a band of beautiful rivers.

Yosemite National Park is almost 1200 square miles in area. Only a small part is occupied by Yosemite Valley, which is about seven miles long, up to a mile high, and a mile wide. But this limited area has always been the mecca of lovers of Yosemite. The rest of the park—especially the High Country—has wonders enough, but the concentration of many fantastically beautiful and incredibly inspiring mountains, trees, and waterfalls in the valley itself explains its pre-eminent position in the world of natural beauty.

The Yosemite Valley has two approaches, each with its own inspiring view. Valley View, on the road from Merced, is sheer enchantment, with the colorful Merced River lighting up the array of meadow, forest, and imposing cliffs and peaks surrounding the valley. Tunnel View, on the road from Fresno, bursts into sight as one leaves the Wawona tunnel through the Yosemite cliff; it is the greatest cathedral on earth. The granite pillars of this cathedral—all cliffs, peaks, or domes from three to five thousand feet high, rising steeply from the valley floor—are names to conjure with: El Capitan, Clouds Rest, Half Dome, Sentinel Dome, Sentinel Rock, Cathedral Rocks. My first view of the Yosemite Valley, as I came out of the Wawona tunnel, was an overwhelming illumination; my spirit soared and my life assumed new meaning.

The Great Rocks

The central theme that I find in nature is its infinite variety of beauty—in form, in color, in light, in texture, in mood, and in reflection—not only in nature as a whole, or in every great scene, but even in an individual object: a mountain, a peak, a cliff, a rock.

To me, Half Dome is not a static, inorganic object: it is alive with vibrant significance, constantly changing in every aspect of its appearance and mood with the time of the day, the season of the year, and the position of the viewer, as well as with every minuscule change in the tone and color of the light.

The same scene, at different times, can be cold or warm, harsh or gentle, boisterous or soothing, dramatic or mystical. The middle cliff of Three Brothers may be a fantastically beautiful twist of hard rock, or a mystically enchanting dream. The great triumvirate of Royal Arches, Washington Column, and North Dome can be an idyllic sylvan vision or a blazing splendor of rock. In any event, I feel that all the emotions of man can be shared with nature in a mystical union.

Many of my reflections on nature were beautifully expressed by Wordsworth in his poem *Tintern Abbey:*

Five years have past; five summers, with the length
Of five long winters! and again I hear
These waters, rolling from their mountain-springs
With a soft inland murmur.—Once again
Do I behold these steep and lofty cliffs,
That on a wild secluded scene impress
Thoughts of more deep seclusion, and connect
The landscape with the quiet of the sky.

· ·

These beauteous forms,
Through a long absence, have not been to me
As is a landscape to a blind man's eye:
But oft, in lonely rooms, and 'mid the din
Of towns and cities, I have owed to them,
In hours of weariness, sensations sweet,
Felt in the blood, and felt along the heart;
And passing even into my purer mind,
With tranquil restoration: —feelings too
Of unremembered pleasure: such, perhaps,
As have no slight or trivial influence
On that best portion of a good man's life,
His little, nameless, unremembered acts
Of kindness and of love. Nor less, I trust,
To them I may have owed another gift,
Of aspect more sublime; that blessed mood,
In which the burden of the mystery,
In which the heavy and the weary weight
Of all this unintelligible world,
Is lightened: . . .

· ·

Oh! how oft—
In darkness and amid the many shapes
Of joyless daylight; when the fretful stir

Unprofitable, and the fever of the world,
Have hung upon the beatings of my heart—
How oft, in spirit, have I turned to thee,

. . . .

While here I stand, not only with the sense
Of present pleasure, but with pleasing thoughts
That in this moment there is life and food
For future years. And so I dare to hope,
Though changed, no doubt, from what I was when first
I came among these hills;

. . . .

For nature then

. . . .

To me was all in all.—I cannot paint
What then I was. The sounding cataract
Haunted me like a passion: the tall rock,
The mountain, and the deep and gloomy wood,
Their colours and their forms, were then to me
An appetite; a feeling and a love,
That had no need of a remoter charm
By thoughts supplied, nor any interest
Unborrowed from the eye.

. . . .

I have learned
To look on nature, not as in the hour
Of thoughtless youth; but hearing oftentimes
The still, sad music of humanity,
Nor harsh nor grating, though of ample power
To chasten and subdue. And I have felt
A presence that disturbs me with the joy
Of elevated thoughts; a sense sublime
Of something far more deeply interfused,
Whose dwelling is the light of setting suns,
And the round ocean, and the living air,
And the blue sky, and in the mind of man:
A motion and a spirit, that impels
All thinking things, all objects of all thought,
And rolls through all things. Therefore am I still
A lover of the meadows and the woods,
And mountains; and of all that we behold
From this green earth;

. . . .

Knowing that Nature never did betray
The heart that loved her . . .

The great rocks of Yosemite—the cliffs and peaks—were described by Muir with a lover's ardor:

> Though of such stupendous depth, these famous canyons are not raw, gloomy, jagged-walled gorges, savage and inaccessible. With rough passages here and there they still make delightful pathways for the mountaineer, conducting from the fertile lowlands to the highest icy fountains, as a kind of mountain streets full of charming life and light, graded and sculptured by the ancient glaciers, and presenting, throughout all their courses, a rich variety of novel and attractive scenery, the most attractive that has yet been discovered in the mountain-ranges of the world.
>
> In many places, especially in the middle region of the western flank of the range, the main canyons widen into spacious valleys or parks, diversified like artificial landscape-gardens, with charming groves and meadows, and thickets of blooming bushes, while the lofty, retiring walls, infinitely varied in form and sculpture, are fringed with ferns, flowering-plants of many species, oaks, and evergreens, which find anchorage on a thousand narrow steps and benches; while the whole is enlivened and made glorious with rejoicing streams that come dancing and foaming over the sunny brows of the cliffs to join the shining river that flows in tranquil beauty down the middle of each one of them.
>
> The most famous and accessible of these canyon valleys, and also the one that presents their most striking and sublime features on the grandest scale, is the Yosemite, situated in the basin of the Merced River at an elevation of 4000 feet above the level of the sea. It is about seven miles long, half a mile to a mile wide, and nearly a mile deep in the solid granite flank of the range.
>
> The walls of these park valleys of the Yosemite kind [yosemite—a glacially carved, U-shaped, steep-walled canyon] are made up of rocks, mountains in size, partly separated from each other by narrow gorges and side-canyons; and they are so sheer in front, and so compactly built together on a level floor, that, comprehensively seen, the parks they inclose look like immense halls or temples lighted from above. Every rock seems to glow with life. Some lean back in majestic repose; others, absolutely sheer, or nearly so, for thousands of feet, advance their brows in thoughtful attitudes beyond their companions, giving welcome to storms and calms alike, seemingly conscious yet heedless of everything going on about them, awful in stern majesty, types of permanence, yet associated with beauty of the frailest and most fleeting forms; their feet set in pine-groves and gay emerald meadows, their brows in the sky; bathed in light, bathed in floods of singing water, while snow-clouds, avalanches, and the winds shine and surge and wreathe about them as the years go by, as if into these mountain mansions Nature had taken pains to gather her choicest treasures to draw her lovers into close and confiding communion with her.

But Muir was not content simply to enjoy the grandeur of the great canyons and rocks of Yosemite; he was fascinated by the problem of the origin of the stupendous Yosemite forms, and refused to accept the cataclysmic theory advocated by the distinguished academic geologists of the day. Passionately curious, he explored the mountains with unprejudiced observation and a sharp mind, and developed the glacial theory of the origin of the Yosemite canyons and rocks, which, in its basic terms, is the generally accepted theory today.

To read Muir's account of the development of his glacial theory is to share with him some of the thrill of pioneer discovery.

The greatest obstacle in the way of reading the history of yosemite valleys is not its complexity or obscurity, but simply the magnitude of the characters in which it is written. It would require years of enthusiastic study to master the English alphabet if it were carved upon the flank of the Sierra in letters sixty or seventy miles long, their bases set in the foothills, their tops leaning back among the glaciers and shattered peaks of the summit, often veiled with forests and thickets, and their continuity often broken by cross gorges and hills. So also the sculptured alphabet canyons of the Sierra are magnificently simple, yet demand years of laborious research for their apprehension. A thousand blurred fragments must be conned and brooded over with studious care, and kept vital and formative on the edges, ready to knit like broken living bones, while a final judgment is being bravely withheld until the entire series of phenomena has been weighed and referred to an all-unifying, all-explaining law. To one who can leisurely contemplate Yosemite from some commanding outlook, it offers, as a whole, a far more natural combination of features than is at all apparent in partial views obtained from the bottom. Its stupendous domes and battlements blend together and manifest delicate compliance to law, for the mind is then in some measure emancipated from the repressive and enslaving effects of their separate magnitudes, and gradually rises to a comprehension of their unity and of the poised harmony of their general relations.

Nature is not so poor as to possess only one of anything, nor throughout her varied realms has she ever been known to offer an exceptional creation, whether of mountain or valley. When, therefore, we explore the adjacent Sierra, we are not astonished to find that there are many yosemite valleys identical in general characters, each presenting on a varying scale the same species of mural precipices, level meadows, and lofty waterfalls. The laws which preside over their distribution are as constant and apparent as those governing the distribution of forest trees. They occur only in the middle region of the chain, where the declivity is considerable and where the granite is similar in its internal structure. The position of each valley upon the yosemite zone indicates a marked and inseparable relation to the ancient glaciers, which, when fully deciphered, amounts to cause and effect. So constant and obvious is this connection between the various yosemites and the *névé* amphitheaters which fountained the ancient ice rivers, that an observer, inexperienced in these phenomena, might easily anticipate the position and size of any yosemite by a study of the glacial fountains above it, or the position and size of the fountains by a study of their complementary yosemite. *All yosemites occur at the junction of two or more glacial canyons.* Thus the greater and lesser yosemites of the Merced, Hetch Hetchy, and those of the upper Tuolumne, those of Kings River, and the San Joaquin, all occur immediately below the confluences of their ancient glaciers. If, in following down the canyon channel of the Merced Glacier, from its origin in the *névé* amphitheaters of the Lyell group, we should find that its sudden expansion and deepening at Yosemite occurs without a corresponding union of glacial tributary canyons, and without any similar expansion elsewhere, then we might well be driven to the doctrine of special marvels. But this emphatic deepening and widening becomes harmonious when we observe smaller yosemites occurring at intervals all the way down, across the yosemite zone, *wherever a tributary canyon unites with the trunk,* until, on reaching Yosemite, where the enlargement is greatest, we find the number of confluent glacier canyons is also greatest. . . . Still further, the aggregate area of their cross sections is approximately equal to the area of the cross sections of the several resulting yosemites, just as the cross section of a tree trunk is about equal to the sum of the sections of its branches. *Furthermore, the trend of yosemite valleys is always a direct resultant of the sizes, directions, and declivities of their confluent canyons,* modified by peculiarities of structure in their rocks. Now, all the canyons mentioned above are the abandoned channels of glaciers; therefore, these yosemites and their glaciers are inseparably related. Instead of being local in character, or formed by obscure and lawless forces, *these valleys are the only great sculpture phenomena whose existence and exact positions we may confidently anticipate.*

The Valley, now filled with sunshine, was once filled with ice, when the grand old Yosemite Glacier, flowing river-like from its distant fountains, swept through it, crushing, grinding, wearing its way ever deeper, developing and fashioning these sublime rocks.

The carving processes of ice, which produced the incomparable magnificence of Yosemite (and the Sierra Nevada, of which Yosemite is a part), were clearly shown by Muir, in his pioneering work *Studies in the Sierra,* to explain the profusion as well as the beauty of the great yosemite forms characteristic of the Sierra Nevada.

This study of mountain building refers particularly to that portion of the range embraced between latitudes 36° 30′ and 39°. It is about 200 miles long, sixty wide, and attains an elevation along its axis of from 8000 to nearly 15,000 feet above the level of the sea. The individual mountains that are distributed over this vast area, whether the lofty and precipitous alps of the summit, the more beautiful and highly specialized domes and mounts dotted over the undulating flanks, or the huge bosses and angles projecting horizontally from the sides of canyons and valleys, have all been sculptured and brought into relief during the glacial epoch by the direct mechanical action of the ice sheet, with the individual glaciers into which it afterward separated. Our way to a general understanding of all this has been made clear by previous studies of valley formations—studies of the physical characters of the rocks out of which the mountains under consideration have been made, and of the widely contrasted methods and quantities of glacial and post-glacial denudation.

Notwithstanding the accessibility and imposing grandeur of the summit alps, they remain almost wholly unexplored. A few nervous raids have been made among them from random points adjacent to trails, and some of the more easily accessible, such as mounts Dana, Lyell, Tyndall, and Whitney, have been ascended, while the vast wilderness of mountains in whose fastnesses the chief tributaries of the San Joaquin and Kings rivers take their rise, have been beheld and mapped from a distance, without any attempt at detail. Their echoes are never stirred even by the hunter's rifle, for there is no game to tempt either Indian or white man as far as the frosty lakes and meadows that lie at their bases, while their avalanche-swept and crevassed glaciers, their labyrinths of yawning gulfs and crumbling precipices, offer dangers that only powerful motives will induce anyone to face.

The view southward from the colossal summit of Mount Humphreys is indescribably sublime. Innumerable gray peaks crowd loftily into the keen azure, infinitely adorned with light and shade; lakes glow in lavish abundance around their bases; torrents whiten their denuded gorges; while many a glacier and bank of fountain *névé* leans back in their dark recesses. Awe-inspiring, however, as these vast mountain assemblies are, and incomprehensible as they may at first seem, their origin and the principal facts of their individual histories are problems easily solved by the patient student.

Beginning with pinnacles, which are the smallest of the summit mountainets: no geologist will claim that these were formed by special upheavals, nor that the little chasms which separated them were formed by special subsidences or rivings asunder of the rock; because many of these chasms are as wide at the bottom as at the top, and scarcely exceed a foot in depth; and many may be formed artificially by simply removing a few blocks that have been loosened.

The Sierra pinnacles are from less than a foot to nearly a thousand feet in height, and in all the cases that have come under my observation their forms and dimensions have been determined, not by cataclysmic fissures, but by the gradual development of orderly joints and cleavage planes. . . . Magnificent crests tipped with leaning pinnacles adorn the jagged flanks of Mount Ritter, and majestic examples of vertical pinnacle architecture abound among the lofty mountain cathedrals on the heads of Kings and Kern rivers. The Minarets to the south of Mount Ritter are an imposing series of partially separate pinnacles about 700 feet in height, set upon the main axis of the range. Glaciers are still grinding their eastern bases, illustrating in the plainest manner the blocking out of these imposing features from the solid. The formation of small peaklets that roughen the flanks of large peaks may in like manner be shown to depend, not upon any up-thrusting or down-thrusting forces, but upon the orderly erosion and transportation of the material that occupied the intervening notches and gorges.

The same arguments we have been applying to peaklets and pinnacles are found to be entirely applicable to the main mountain peaks; for careful detailed studies demonstrate that as pinnacles are separated by eroded chasms, and peaklets by notches and gorges, so the main peaks are separated by larger chasms, notches, gorges, valleys, and wide ice-womb amphitheaters. When across hollows we examine contiguous sides of mountains, we perceive that the same mechanical structure is continued across intervening spaces of every kind, showing that there has been a removal of the material that once filled them. . . . We frequently find rows of pinnacles set upon a base, the cleavage of which does not admit of pinnacle formation, and in an analogous way we find immense slate mountains, like Dana and Gibbs, resting upon a plain granite pavement, as if they had been formed elsewhere, transported and set down in their present positions, like huge erratic boulders. It appears, therefore, that the loftiest mountains as well as peaklets and pinnacles of the summit region are residual masses of the once solid wave of the whole range, and that all that would be required to unbuild and obliterate these imposing structures would simply be the filling up of the labyrinth of intervening chasms, gorges, canyons, etc., which divide them, by the restoration of rocks that have disappeared. Here the important question comes up, What has become of the missing material, not the millionth part of which is now to be seen? It has not been engulfed, because the bottoms of all the dividing valleys and basins are unmistakably solid. It must, therefore, have been carried away; and because we find portions of it scattered far and near in moraines, easily recognized by peculiarities of mineralogical composition, we infer that glaciers were the transporting agents. That glaciers have brought out the summit peaks from the solid with all their imposing architecture, simply by the formation of the valleys and basins in which they flowed, is a very important proposition, and well deserves careful attention.

We have already shown that all the valleys of the region under consideration, from the minute striae and scratches of the polished surfaces less than the hundredth part of an inch in depth, to the yosemite gorges half a mile or more in depth, were all eroded by glaciers, and that post-glacial streams, whether small glancing brooklets or impetuous torrents, had not yet lived long enough to fairly make their mark, no matter how unbounded their eroding powers may be. Still, it may be conjectured that pre-glacial rivers furrowed the range long ere a glacier was born, and that when at length the ice winter came on with its great skyfuls of snow, the young glaciers crept into these river channels, overflowing their banks, and deepening, widening, grooving, and polishing them without destroying their identity. For the destruction of this conjecture it is only necessary to observe that the trends of the present valleys are strictly glacial, and glacial trends are extremely different from water trends; pre-glacial rivers could not, therefore, have exercised any appreciable influence upon their formation.

Neither can we suppose fissures to have wielded any determining influence, there being no conceivable coincidence between the zigzag and apparently accidental trends of fissures and the exceedingly specific trends of ice currents. The same argument holds good against primary foldings of the crust, dislocations, etc. Finally, if these valleys had been hewn or dug out by any pre-glacial agent whatever, traces of such agent would be visible on mountain masses which glaciers have not yet segregated; but no such traces of valley beginnings are anywhere manifest. The heads of valleys extend back into mountain masses just as far as glaciers have gone and no farther.

Granting, then, that the greater part of the erosion and transportation of the material missing from between the mountains of the summit was effected by glaciers, it yet remains to be considered what agent or agents shaped the upper portions of these mountains, which bear no traces of glacial action, and which probably were always, as they now are, above the reach of glaciers. Even here we find the glacier to be indirectly the most influential agent, constantly eroding backward, thus undermining their bases, and enabling gravity to drag down large masses, and giving greater effectiveness to the winter avalanches that sweep and furrow their sides. All the summit peaks present a crumbling, ruinous, unfinished aspect. Yet they have suffered very little change since the close of the glacial period, for if denudation had been extensively carried on, their separating pits and gorges would be choked with debris; but, on the contrary, we find only a mere sprinkling of post-glacial detritus, and that the streams could not have carried much of this away is conclusively shown by the fact that the small lake bowls through which they flow have not been filled up. . . .

Regarded as measures of mountain-building forces, the results of erosion are negative rather than positive, expressing more directly what has *not* been done than what *has* been done. The difference between the peaks and the passes is not that the former are elevations, the latter depressions; both are depressions, differing only in degree. The abasement of the peaks having been effected at a slower rate, they were, of course, left behind as elevations.

The transition from the spiky, angular summit mountains to those of the flanks with their smoothly undulated outlines is exceedingly well marked; weak towers, pinnacles, and crumbling, jagged crests at once disappear, leaving only hard, knotty domes and ridge waves as geological illustrations, on the grandest scale, of the survival of the strongest. . . . As we descend from the alpine summits on the smooth pathways of the ancient ice currents, noting where they have successively denuded the various rocks—first the slates, then the slaty-structured granites, then the curved granites—we detect a constant growth of specialization and ascent into higher forms. Angular masses, cut by cleavage planes, begin to be comprehended in flowing curves. These masses, in turn, become more highly organized, giving rise by the most gradual approaches to that magnificent dome scenery for which the Sierra is unrivaled. In the more strongly specialized granite regions, the features, and, indeed, the very existence, of the over-flowed mountains are in great part due neither to ice, water, nor any eroding agent whatsoever, but to building forces—crystalline, perhaps—which put them together and bestowed all that is more special in their architectural physiognomy, while they yet lay buried in the common fountain mass of the range.

The same silent and invisible mountain builders performed a considerable amount of work upon the down-flowed mountains of the summit, but these were so weakly put together that the heavy hand of the glacier shaped and molded, without yielding much compliance to their undeveloped forms. Had the unsculptured mass of the range been every way homogeneous, glacial denudation would still have produced summit mountains, differing not essentially from those we now find, but the rich profusion of flank mountains and mountainets, so marvelously individualized, would have had no existence, as the whole surface would evidently have been planed down into barren uniformity.

Thus the want of individuality which we have been observing among the summit mountains is obviously due to the comparatively uniform structure and erodibility of the rocks out of which they have been developed; their forms in consequence being greatly dependent upon the developing glaciers; whereas the strongly structured and specialized flank mountains, while accepting the ice currents as developers, still defended themselves from their destructive and form-bestowing effects.

The wonderful adaptability of ice to the development of buried mountains, possessing so wide a range of form and magnitude, seems as perfect as if the result of direct plan and forethought. Granite crystallizes into landscapes; snow crystallizes above them to bring their beauty to the light. The grain of no mountain oak is more gnarled and interfolded than that of Sierra granite, and the ice sheet of the glacial period is the only universal mountain eroder that works with reference to the grain. Here it smooths a pavement by slipping flatly over it, removing inequalities like a carpenter's plane; again it *makes* inequalities, gliding moldingly over and around knotty dome clusters, groping out every weak spot, sparing the strong, crushing the feeble, and following lines of predestined beauty obediently as the wind.

Rocks are brought into horizontal relief on the sides of valleys wherever superior strength of structure or advantageousness of position admits of such development, just as they are elsewhere in a vertical direction. Some of these projections are of a magnitude that well deserves the name of *horizontal mountain*. That the variability of resistance of the rocks themselves accounts for the variety of these horizontal features is shown by the prevalence of this law. *Where the uniformity of glacial pressure has not been disturbed by the entrance of tributaries, we find that where valleys are narrowest their walls are strongest; where widest, weakest.*

In the case of valleys with sloping walls, their salient features will be mostly developed in an oblique direction; but neither horizontal nor oblique mountainets or mountains can ever reach as great dimensions as the vertical, because the retreating curves formed in weaker portions of valley walls are less eroded the deeper they become, on account of receiving less and less pressure, while the alternating salient curves are more heavily pressed and eroded the farther they project into the past-squeezing glacier; thus tending to check irregularity of surface beyond a certain limit, which limit is measured by the resistance offered by the rocks to the glacial energy brought to bear upon them. So intense is this energy in the case of large steeply inclined glaciers, that many salient bosses are broken off on the lower or downstream side with a fracture like that produced by blasting. These fractures occur in all deep yosemite canyons, forming the highest expressions of the intensity of glacial force I have observed.

The same tendency toward maintaining evenness of surface obtains to some extent in vertical erosion also; as when hard masses rise abruptly from a comparatively level area exposed to the full sweep of the overpassing current. If vertical cleavage be developed in such rocks, moutonnéed forms will be produced with a split face turned away from the direction of the flow. These forms, measuring from a few inches to a thousand feet or more in height, abound in hard granitic regions. If no cleavage be developed, then long ovals will be formed, with their greater diameters extended in the direction of the current. The general tendency, however, in vertical erosion is to make the valleys deeper and ridges relatively higher, the ice currents being constantly attracted to the valleys, causing erosion to go on at an accelerated rate, and drawn away from the resisting ridges until they emerge from the ice sheet and cease to be eroded; the law here applicable being, "to him that hath shall be given."

Thus it appears that, no matter how the pre-glacial mass of the range came into existence, all the separate mountains distributed over its surface between latitudes 36° 30′ and 39°, whether the lofty alps of the summit, or richly sculptured dome clusters of the flank, or the burnished bosses and mountainets projecting from the sides of valleys—all owe their development to the ice sheet of the great winter and the separate glaciers into which it afterward separated. In all this sublime fulfillment there was no upbuilding, but a universal razing and dismantling, and of this every mountain and valley is the record and monument.

The Falls

Were Yosemite merely an unparalleled congregation of canyons, peaks, cliffs, domes, pinnacles, and spires, it would be enough to stagger the imagination into disbelief—short of the reassurance of repeated observation. But when the incredible array of waterfalls is added to the rock, Yosemite seems a visual paradise.

Yosemite has neither the highest nor the widest fall in the world; it simply has the greatest number and variety of beautiful waterfalls. To call the roll of the lesser-known waterfalls of Yosemite is to recite an aggregate of waterfall beauty unequaled in the world—Ribbon Fall, Cascade Falls, El Capitan Fall, Staircase Falls, Illilouette Fall, Sentinel Fall, etc. However, the crowning waterfalls are Yosemite Falls, Vernal Fall, Nevada Fall, and Bridalveil Fall—each uniquely and superbly beautiful.

Yosemite Falls, the most popular of all, is a symphony of flowing form. From the wild leap of the Upper Fall (1430 feet) to the tumultuous, rock-gouging, churning Middle Cascade (675 feet) and the classic smashing climax of the Lower Fall (320 feet), it pours forth an ode to joyous abandon.

Vernal Fall (317 feet) is a vision of loveliness in form and color. Sliding smoothly over the lip of a great, dark cliff, it crashes into giant rocks below, generating a spray of heavenly rainbows, when the light is right, that seem to envelop the viewer on the Mist Trail in an unearthly bliss.

Nevada Fall (594 feet) is a display of the fury of water in motion, as it plunges through a narrow channel of rock that thrusts it forth in violent bursts of vaulting form and shifting light.

Bridalveil Fall (620 feet), nourished by a lush hanging valley, is a dream of wind-tossed water (resembling a bridal veil) that seems to dissolve in a shifting mist. One of the standard joys of Yosemite is to watch the afternoon rainbow climb the column of Bridalveil Fall, varying its shape and color as it ascends.

Muir's love for the waterfalls of Yosemite was eloquently expressed:

The upper branches of the Yosemite streams are buried every winter beneath a heavy mantle of snow, and set free in the spring in magnificent floods. Then, all the fountains, full and overflowing, every living thing breaks forth into singing, and the glad exulting streams, shining and falling in the warm sunny weather, shake everything into music, making all the mountain-world a song.

After the highest point on the lower division of the trail to Yosemite Falls is gained it leads up into the deep recess occupied by the great fall, the noblest display of falling water to be found in the Valley, or perhaps in the world. When it first comes in sight it seems almost within reach of one's hand, so great in the spring is its volume and velocity, yet it is still nearly a third of a mile away and appears to recede as we advance. The sculpture of the walls about it is on a scale of grandeur, according nobly with the fall—plain and massive, though elaborately finished, like all the other cliffs about the Valley. When the afternoon sunshine is streaming through the throng of comets, ever wasting, ever renewed, the marvelous fineness, firmness and variety of their forms are beautifully revealed. At the top of the fall they seem to burst forth in irregular spurts from some grand, throbbing mountain heart. Now and then one mighty throb sends forth a mass of solid water into the free air far beyond the others, which rushes alone to the bottom of the fall with long streaming tail, like combed silk, while the others, descending in clusters, gradually mingle and lose their identity. But they all rush past us with amazing velocity and display of power, though apparently drowsy and deliberate in their movements when observed from a distance of a mile or two. The heads of these comet-like masses are composed of nearly solid water, and are dense white in color like pressed snow, from the friction they suffer in rushing through the air, the portion worn off forming the tail, between the white lustrous threads and films of which faint, grayish pencilings appear, while the outer, finer sprays of water-dust, whirling in sunny eddies, are pearly gray throughout. At the bottom of the fall there is but little distinction of form visible. It is mostly a hissing, clashing, seething, upwhirling mass of scud and spray, through which the light sifts in gray and purple tones, while at times when the sun strikes at the required angle, the whole wild and apparently lawless, stormy, striving mass is changed to brilliant rainbow hues, manifesting finest harmony. The middle portion of the fall is the most openly beautiful; lower, the various forms into which the waters are wrought are more closely and voluminously veiled, while higher, towards the head, the current is comparatively simple and undivided. But even at the bottom, in the boiling clouds of spray, there is no confusion, while the rainbow light makes all divine, adding glorious beauty and peace to glorious power. This noble fall has far the richest, as well as the most powerful, voice of all the falls of the Valley, its tones varying from the sharp hiss and rustle of the wind in the glossy leaves of the live-oaks and the soft, sifting, hushing tones of the pines, to the loudest rush and roar of storm winds and thunder among the crags of the summit peaks. The low bass, booming, reverberating tones, heard under favorable circumstances five or six miles away, are formed by the dashing and exploding of heavy masses mixed with air upon two projecting ledges on the face of the cliff, the one on which we are standing and another about 200 feet above it. The torrent of massive comets is continuous at time of high water, while the explosive, booming notes are wildly intermittent, because, unless influenced by the wind, most of the heavier masses shoot out from the face of the precipice, and pass the ledges upon which at other times they are exploded. Occasionally the whole fall is swayed away from the front of the cliff, then suddenly dashed flat against it, or vibrated from side to side like a pendulum, giving rise to endless variety of forms and sounds.

The Vernal, about a mile below the Nevada, is 400 feet high, a staid, orderly, graceful, easy-going fall, proper and exact in every movement and gesture, with scarce a hint of the passionate enthusiasm of the Yosemite or of the impetuous Nevada, whose chafed and twisted waters hurrying over the cliff seem glad to escape into the open air, while its deep, booming, thunder-tones reverberate over the listening landscape. Nevertheless it is a favorite with most visitors, doubtless because it is more accessible than any other, more closely approached and better seen and heard. A good stairway ascends the cliff beside it and the level plateau at the head enables one to saunter safely along the edge of the river as it comes from Emerald Pool and to watch its waters, calmly bending over the brow of the precipice, in a sheet eighty feet wide, changing in color from green to purplish gray and white until dashed on a boulder talus. Thence issuing from beneath its fine broad spray-clouds we see the tremendously adventurous river still unspent, beating its way down the wildest and deepest of all its canyons in gray roaring rapids, dear to the ouzel, and below the confluence of the Illilouette, sweeping around the shoulder of the Half Dome on its approach to the head of the tranquil levels of the Valley.

The Nevada Fall is 600 feet high and is usually ranked next to the Yosemite in general interest among the five main falls of the Valley. Coming through the Little Yosemite in tranquil reaches, the river is first broken into rapids on a moraine boulder-bar that crosses the lower end of the valley. Thence it pursues its way to the head of the fall in a rough, solid rock channel, dashing on side angles, heaving in heavy surging masses against elbow knobs, and swirling and swashing in potholes without a moment's rest. Thus, already chafed and dashed to foam, over-folded and twisted, it plunges over the brink of the precipice as if glad to escape into the open air. But before it reaches the bottom it is pulverized yet finer by impinging upon a sloping portion of the cliff about half-way down, thus making it the whitest of all the falls of the Valley, and altogether one of the most wonderful in the world.

On the north side, close to its head, a slab of granite projects over the brink, forming a fine point for a view, over its throng of streamers and wild plunging, into its intensely white bosom, and, through the broad drifts of spray, to the river far below, gathering its spent waters and rushing on again down the canyon in glad exultation into Emerald Pool, where at length it grows calm and gets rest for what still lies before it. All the features of the view correspond with the waters in grandeur and wildness. The glacier-sculptured walls of the canyon on either hand, with the sublime mass of the Glacier Point Ridge in front, form a huge triangular pit-like basin, which, filled with the roaring of the falling river, seems as if it might be the hopper of one of the mills of the gods in which the mountains were being ground.

The River

Among the great rivers of the West, the Merced would seem to have no special excellence, except for the stunning waterfalls and cascades it generates. It is simply another beautiful, clear Sierra stream, smoothly winding its way through meadow, forest, and cliff. However, as it reflects the colors of meadow, forest, cliff, and sky and boldly mirrors the great forms, adding its own various moods to those about it, the Merced enhances the glories of Yosemite.

Among the many Yosemite streams is Tenaya Creek, famous for its Mirror Lake, which reflects serene images of Mt. Watkins, Clouds Rest, and Half Dome. The Yosemite streams were characterized by Muir with joyous appreciation:

Down through the middle of the Valley flows the crystal Merced, River of the onlooking rocks; things frail and fleeting and types of endurance meeting here and blending in countless forms, as if into this one mountain mansion Nature had gathered her choicest treasures, to draw her lovers into close and confiding communion with her.

In the spring, after all the avalanches are down and the snow is melting fast, then all the Yosemite streams, from their fountains to their falls, sing their grandest songs. Countless rills make haste to the rivers, running and singing soon after sunrise, louder and louder with increasing volume until sundown; then they gradually fail through the frosty hours of the night. In this way the volume of the upper branches of the river is nearly doubled during the day, rising and falling as regularly as the tides of the sea. Then the Merced overflows its banks, flooding the meadows, sometimes almost from wall to wall in some places, beginning to rise towards sundown just when the streams on the fountains are beginning to diminish, the difference in time of the daily rise and fall being caused by the distance the upper flood streams have to travel before reaching the Valley. In the warmest weather they seem fairly to shout for joy and clash their upleaping waters together like clapping of hands; racing down the canyons with white manes flying in glorious exuberance of strength, compelling huge, sleeping boulders to wake up and join in their dance and song, to swell their exulting chorus.

In early summer, after the flood season, the Yosemite streams are in their prime, running crystal clear, deep and full but not overflowing their banks—about as deep through the night as the day, the difference in volume so marked in spring being now too slight to be noticed. Nearly all the weather is cloudless and everything is at its brightest—lake, river, garden and forest with all their life. Most of the plants are in full flower. The blessed ouzels have built their mossy huts and are now singing their best songs with the streams.

In tranquil, mellow autumn, when the year's work is about done and the fruits are ripe, birds and seeds out of their nests, and all the landscape is glowing like a benevolent countenance, then the streams are at their lowest ebb, with scarce a memory left of their wild spring floods.

The Trees

The trees of Yosemite are varied in their beauty—the massive Sequoias, the tall pines and firs, the broad-leafed oaks, maples, and cottonwoods, among many others. The Sequoias, reaching toward the sky, are a dramatic reminder that magnificence is real. Gutted by lightning, scarred by fire, torn by wind, snow, and ice, but broadly rooted in the earth and caressed by the sun, they are a triumph of massive strength. Muir paid tribute to all the coniferous trees of Yosemite in his inimitable way:

The coniferous forests of the Sierra are the grandest and most beautiful in the world, and grow in a delightful climate on the most interesting and accessible of mountain-ranges, yet strange to say they are not well known. More than sixty years ago David Douglas, an enthusiastic botanist and tree lover, wandered alone through fine sections of the Sugar Pine and Silver Fir woods wild with delight. A few years later, other botanists made short journeys from the coast into the lower woods. Then came the wonderful multitude of miners into the foot-hill zone, mostly blind with gold-dust, soon followed by "sheepmen," who, with wool over their eyes, chased their flocks through all the forest belts from one end of the range to the other. Then the Yosemite Valley was discovered, and thousands of admiring tourists passed through sections of the lower and middle zones on their way to that wonderful park, and gained fine glimpses of the Sugar Pines and Silver Firs along the edges of dusty trails and roads. But few indeed, strong and free with eyes undimmed with care, have gone far enough and lived long enough with the trees to gain anything like a loving conception of their grandeur and significance as manifested in the harmonies of their distribution and varying aspects throughout the seasons, as they stand arrayed in their winter garb rejoicing in storms, putting forth their fresh leaves in the spring while steaming with resiny fragrance, receiving the thunder-showers of summer, or reposing heavy-laden with ripe cones in the rich sun-gold of autumn. For knowledge of this kind one must dwell with the trees and grow with them, without any reference to time in the almanac sense.

The distribution of the general forest in belts is readily perceived. These, as we have seen, extend in regular order from one extremity of the range to the other; and however dense and somber they may appear in general views, neither on the rocky heights nor down in the leafiest hollows will you find anything to remind you of the dank, malarial selvas of the Amazon and Orinoco, with their "boundless contiguity of shade," the monotonous uniformity of the Deodar forests of the Himalaya, the Black Forest of Europe, or the dense dark woods of Douglas Spruce where rolls the Oregon. The giant pines, and firs, and Sequoias hold their arms open to the sunlight, rising above one another on the mountain benches, marshaled in glorious array, giving forth the utmost expression of grandeur and beauty with inexhaustible variety and harmony.

The inviting openness of the Sierra woods is one of their most distinguishing characteristics. The trees of all the species stand more or less apart in groves, or in small, irregular groups, enabling one to find a way nearly everywhere, along sunny colonnades and through openings that have a smooth, park-like surface, strewn with brown needles and burs. Now you cross a wild garden, now a meadow, now a ferny, willowy stream; and ever and anon you emerge from all the groves and flowers upon some granite pavement or high, bare ridge commanding superb views above the waving sea of evergreens far and near.

One would experience but little difficulty in riding on horseback through the successive belts all the way up to the storm-beaten fringes of the icy peaks. The deep canyons, however, that extend from the axis of the range, cut the belts more or less completely into sections, and prevent the mounted traveler from tracing them lengthwise.

This simple arrangement in zones and sections brings the forest, as a whole, within the comprehension of every observer. The different species are ever found occupying the same relative positions to one another, as controlled by soil, climate, and the comparative vigor of each species in taking and holding the ground; and so appreciable are these relations, one need never be at a loss in determining, within a few hundred feet, the elevation above sea-level by the trees alone; for, notwithstanding some of the species range upward for several thousand feet, and all pass one another more or less, yet even those possessing the greatest vertical range are available in this connection, in as much as they take on new forms corresponding with the variations in altitude.

Crossing the treeless plains of the Sacramento and San Joaquin from the west and reaching the Sierra foot-hills, you enter the lower fringe of the forest, composed of small oaks and pines, growing so far apart that not one twentieth of the surface of the ground is in shade at clear noonday. After advancing fifteen or twenty miles, and making an ascent of from two to three thousand feet, you reach the lower margin of the main pine belt, composed of the gigantic Sugar Pine, Yellow Pine, Incense Cedar, and Sequoia. Next you come to the magnificent Silver Fir belt, and lastly to the upper pine belt, which sweeps up the rocky acclivities of the summit peaks in a dwarfed, wavering fringe to a height of from ten to twelve thousand feet.

This general order of distribution, with reference to climate dependent on elevation, is perceived at once, but there are other harmonies, as far-reaching in this connection, that become manifest only after patient observation and study. Perhaps the most interesting of these is the arrangement of the forests in long, curving bands, braided together into lacelike patterns, and outspread in charming variety. The key to this beautiful harmony is the ancient glaciers; where they flowed the trees followed, tracing their wavering courses along canyons, over ridges, and over high, rolling plateaus. The Cedars of Lebanon, says Hooker, are growing upon one of the moraines of an ancient glacier. All the forests of the Sierra are growing upon moraines. But moraines vanish like the glaciers that make them. Every storm that falls upon them wastes them, cutting gaps, disintegrating boulders, and carrying away their decaying material into new formations, until at length they are no longer recognizable by any save students, who trace their transitional forms down from the fresh moraines still in process of formation, through those that are more and more ancient, and more and more obscured by vegetation and all kinds of post-glacial weathering.

Had the ice-sheet that once covered all the range been melted simultaneously from the foot-hills to the summits, the flanks would, of course, have been left almost bare of soil, and these noble forests would be wanting. Many groves and thickets would undoubtedly have grown up on lake and avalanche beds, and many a fair flower and shrub would have found food and a dwelling-place in weathered nooks and crevices, but the Sierra as a whole would have been a bare, rocky desert.

It appears, therefore, that the Sierra forests in general indicate the extent and positions of the ancient moraines as well as they do lines of climate. For forests, properly speaking, cannot exist without soil; and, since the moraines have been deposited upon the solid rock, and only upon elected places, leaving a considerable portion of the old glacial surface bare, we find luxuriant forests of pine and fir abruptly terminated by scored and polished pavements on which not even a moss is growing, though soil alone is required to fit them for the growth of trees 200 feet in height.

Half Dome, from Sentinel Bridge

Each of the great mountains of the world has a complex personality, as varied in its aspects and moods as any human being. A slight variation in viewpoint, light, or time of day, as well as a change of seasons (or a change in the mood of the viewer), may produce a totally different effect.

Muir called Half Dome "the most beautiful and most sublime of all the wonderful Yosemite rocks," and I have been fascinated by its various essences and appearances. From Mirror Lake it is an overpowering mass; from Glacier Point it is a soaring, proud dome; from Sentinel Bridge it is majestic and serene.

Capturing the moods of Half Dome from Sentinel Bridge has been one of my favorite preoccupations. From scores of pictures, I have chosen four to illustrate the moods of Half Dome as seen in the four seasons.

I feel of Half Dome (and of nature) as Bryant wrote in *Thanatopsis:*

> To him who in the love of Nature holds
> Communion with her visible forms, she speaks
> A various language; for his gayer hours
> She has a voice of gladness, and a smile
> And eloquence of beauty, and she glides
> Into his darker musings, with a mild
> And healing sympathy, that steals away
> Their sharpness, ere he is aware. . . .

The High Country

Outside the valley, the great favorite of Yosemite lovers is the High Country, roughly the region over 7000 feet high. There are a few famous High Country scenes—among them the views of the Sierra peaks and domes from Glacier Point and Sentinel Dome. But, more than individual scenes of great beauty, the High Country offers a different world, in which the air is cleaner, the sky is bluer, the light is more dazzling, and nature is alive with challenge.

Muir describes the view from the summit of Fairview Dome, about 10,000 feet high, which is near Tenaya Lake:

> The general view from the summit consists of a sublime assemblage of ice-born rocks and mountains, long wavering ridges, meadows, lakes, and forest-covered moraines, hundreds of square miles of them. The lofty summit-peaks rise grandly along the sky to the east, the gray pillared slopes of the Hoffmann Range toward the west, and a billowy sea of shining rocks like the Monument, some of them almost as high and which from their peculiar sculpture seem to be rolling westward in the middle ground, something like breaking waves. Immediately beneath you are the Big Tuolumne Meadows, smooth lawns with large breadths of woods on either side, and watered by the young Tuolumne River, rushing cool and clear from its many snow- and ice-fountains. Nearly all the upper part of the basin of the Tuolumne Glacier is in sight, one of the greatest and most influential of all the Sierra ice-rivers. Lavishly flooded by many a noble affluent from the ice-laden flanks of Mounts Dana, Lyell, McClure, Gibbs, Conness, it poured its majestic outflowing current full against the end of the Hoffmann Range, which divided and deflected it to right and left, just as a river of water is divided against an island in the middle of its channel. Two distinct glaciers were thus formed, one of which flowed through the great Tuolumne Canyon and Hetch Hetchy Valley, while the other swept upward in a deep current two miles wide across the divide, five hundred feet high between the basins of the Tuolumne and Merced, into the Tenaya Basin, and thence down through the Tenaya Canyon and Yosemite.
>
> The map-like distinctness and freshness of this glacial landscape cannot fail to excite the attention of every beholder, no matter how little of its scientific significance may be recognized.

These bald, westward-leaning rocks, with their rounded backs and shoulders toward the glacier fountains of the summit-mountains, and their split, angular fronts looking in the opposite direction, explain the tremendous grinding force with which the ice-flood passed over them, and also the direction of its flow. And the mountain peaks around the sides of the upper general Tuolumne Basin, with their sharp unglaciated summits and polished rounded sides, indicate the height to which the glaciers rose. . . .

Among the glories of the High Country are its glacier lakes and meadows, whose origins and destinies are celebrated by Muir:

Among the many unlooked-for treasures that are bound up and hidden away in the depths of Sierra solitudes, none more surely charm and surprise all kinds of travelers than the glacier lakes. The forests and the glaciers and the snowy fountains of the streams advertise their wealth in a more or less telling manner even in the distance, but nothing is seen of the lakes until we have climbed above them. All the upper branches of the rivers are fairly laden with lakes, like orchard trees with fruit. They lie embosomed in the deep woods, down in the grovy bottoms of canyons, high on bald tablelands, and around the feet of the icy peaks, mirroring back their wild beauty over and over again. Some conception of their lavish abundance may be made from the fact that, from one standpoint on the summit of Red Mountain, a day's journey to the east of Yosemite Valley, no fewer than forty-two are displayed within a radius of ten miles. The whole number in the Sierra can hardly be less than fifteen hundred, not counting the smaller pools and tarns, which are innumerable. Perhaps two thirds or more lie on the western flank of the range, and all are restricted to the alpine and subalpine regions. At the close of the last glacial period, the middle and foot-hill regions also abounded in lakes, all of which have long since vanished as completely as the magnificent ancient glaciers that brought them into existence.

Though the eastern flank of the range is excessively steep, we find lakes pretty regularly distributed throughout even the most precipitous portions. They are mostly found in the upper branches of the canyons, and in the glacial amphitheaters around the peaks.

Occasionally long, narrow specimens occur upon the steep sides of dividing ridges, their basins swung lengthwise like hammocks, and very rarely one is found lying so exactly on the summit of the range at the head of some pass that its waters are discharged down both flanks when the snow is melting fast. But, however situated, they soon cease to form surprises to the studious mountaineer; for, like all the love-work of Nature, they are harmoniously related to one another, and to all the other features of the mountains. It is easy, therefore, to find the bright lake-eyes in the roughest and most ungovernable-looking topography of any landscape countenance. Even in the lower regions, where they have been closed for many a century, their rocky orbits are still discernible, filled in with the detritus of flood and avalanche. A beautiful system of grouping in correspondence with the glacial fountains is soon perceived; also their extension in the direction of the trends of the ancient glaciers; and in general their dependence as to form, size, and position upon the character of the rocks in which their basins have been eroded, and the quantity and direction of application of the glacial force expended upon each basin.

In the upper canyons we usually find them in pretty regular succession, strung together like beads on the bright ribbons of their feeding-streams, which pour, white and gray with foam and spray, from one to the other, their perfect mirror stillness making impressive contrasts with the grand blare and glare of the connecting cataracts. In Lake Hollow, on the north side of the Hoffmann spur, immediately above the great Tuolumne canyon, there are ten lovely lakelets lying near together in one general hollow, like eggs in a nest. Seen from above, in a general view, feathered with Hemlock Spruce, and fringed with sedge, they seem to me the most singularly beautiful and interestingly located lake-cluster I have ever yet discovered. . . .

In the basin of the Merced River, I counted 131 [lakes], of which 111 are upon the tributaries that fall so grandly into Yosemite Valley. Pohono Creek, which forms the fall of that name, takes its rise in a beautiful lake, lying beneath the shadow of a lofty granite spur that puts out from Buena Vista peak. This is now the only lake left in the whole Pohono Basin. The Illilouette has sixteen, the Nevada no fewer than sixty-seven, the Tenaya eight, Hoffmann Creek five, and Yosemite Creek fourteen. There are but two other lake-bearing affluents of the Merced, viz., the South Fork with fifteen, and Cascade Creek with five, both of which unite with the main trunk below Yosemite.

The Merced River, as a whole, is remarkably like an elm-tree, and it requires but little effort on the part of the imagination to picture it standing upright, with all its lakes hanging upon its spreading branches, the topmost eighty miles in height. Now add all the other lake-bearing rivers of the Sierra, each in its place, and you will have a truly glorious spectacle—an avenue the length and width of the range; the long, slender, gray shafts of the main trunks, the milky way of arching branches, and the silvery lakes, all clearly defined and shining on the sky. How excitedly such an addition to the scenery would be gazed at! Yet these lakeful rivers are still more excitingly beautiful and impressive in their natural positions to those who have the eyes to see them as they lie imbedded in their meadows and forests and glacier-sculptured rocks.

When a mountain lake is born—when, like a young eye, it first opens to the light—it is an irregular, expressionless crescent, inclosed in banks of rock and ice—bare, glaciated rock on the lower side, the rugged snout of a glacier on the upper. In this condition it remains for many a year, until at length, toward the end of some auspicious cluster of seasons, the glacier recedes beyond the upper margin of the basin, leaving it open from shore to shore for the first time, thousands of years after its conception beneath the glacier that excavated its basin. The landscape, cold and bare, is reflected in its pure depths; the winds ruffle its glassy surface, and the sun fills it with throbbing spangles, while its waves begin to lap and murmur around its leafless shores—sun-spangles during the day and reflected stars at night its only flowers, the winds and the snow its only visitors. Meanwhile, the glacier continues to recede, and numerous rills, still younger than the lake itself, bring down glacier-mud, sand-grains, and pebbles, giving rise to margin-rings and plats of soil. To these fresh soil-beds come many a waiting plant. First, a hardy carex with arching leaves and a spike of brown flowers; then, as the seasons grow warmer, and the soil-beds deeper and wider, other sedges take their appointed places, and these are joined by blue gentians, daisies, dodecatheons, violets, honeyworts, and many a lowly moss. Shrubs also hasten in time to the new gardens—kalmia with its glossy leaves and purple flowers, the arctic willow, making soft woven carpets, together with the heathy bryanthus and cassiope, the fairest and dearest of them all. Insects now enrich the air, frogs pipe cheerily in the shallows, soon followed by the ouzel, which is the first bird to visit a glacier lake, as the sedge is the first of plants.

So the young lake grows in beauty, becoming more and more humanly lovable from century to century. Groves of aspen spring up, and hardy pines, and the Hemlock Spruce, until it is richly overshadowed and embowered. But while its shores are being enriched, the soil-beds creep out with incessant growth, contracting its area, while the lighter mud-particles deposited on the bottom cause it to grow constantly shallower, until at length the last remnant of the lake vanishes—closed forever in ripe and natural old age. And now its feeding-stream goes winding on without halting through the new gardens and groves that have taken its place.

The length of the life of any lake depends ordinarily upon the capacity of its basin, as compared with the carrying power of the streams that flow into it, the character of the rocks over which these streams flow, and the relative position of the lake toward other lakes. In a series whose basins lie in the same canyon, and are fed by one and the same main stream, the uppermost will, of course, vanish first unless some other lake-filling agent comes in to modify the result; because at first it receives nearly all of the sediments that the stream brings down, only the finest of the mud-particles being carried through the highest of the series to the next below. Then the next higher, and the next would be successively filled, and the lowest would be the last to vanish. But this simplicity as to duration is broken in upon in various ways, chiefly through the action of side-streams that enter the lower lakes direct. For, notwithstanding many of these side tributaries are quite short, and, during late summer, feeble, they all become powerful torrents in springtime when the snow is melting, and carry not only sand and pine-needles, but large trunks and boulders tons in weight, sweeping them down their steeply inclined channels and into the lake basins with astounding energy. Many of these side affluents also have the advantage of access to the main lateral moraines of the vanished glacier that occupied the canyon, and upon these they draw for lake-filling material, while the main trunk stream flows mostly over clean glacier pavements, where but little moraine matter is ever left for them to carry. Thus a small rapid stream with abundance of loose transportable material within its reach may fill up an extensive basin in a few centuries, while a large perennial trunk stream, flowing over clean, enduring pavements, though ordinarily a hundred times larger, may not fill a smaller basin in thousands of years.

The comparative influence of great and small streams as lake-fillers is strikingly illustrated in Yosemite Valley, through which the Merced flows. The bottom of the valley is now composed of level meadow-lands and dry, sloping soil-beds planted with oak and pine, but it was once a lake stretching from wall to wall and nearly from one end of the valley to the other, forming one of the most beautiful cliff-bound sheets of water that ever existed in the Sierra. . . .

After the lakes on the High Sierra come the glacier meadows. They are smooth, level, silky lawns, lying embedded in the upper forests, on the floors of the valleys, and along the broad backs of the main dividing ridges, at a height of about 8000 to 9500 feet above the sea.

They are nearly as level as the lakes whose places they have taken, and present a dry, even surface free from rock-heaps, mossy bogginess, and the frowsy roughness of rank, coarse-leaved, weedy, and shrubby vegetation. The sod is close and fine, and so complete that you cannot see the ground; and at the same time so brightly enameled with flowers and butterflies that it may well be called a garden-meadow, or meadow-garden; for the plushy sod is in many places so crowded with gentians, daisies, ivesias, and various species of orthocarpus that the grass is scarcely noticeable, while in others the flowers are only pricked in here and there singly, or in small ornamental rosettes.

Glacier meadows abound throughout all the alpine and subalpine regions of the Sierra in still greater numbers than the lakes. Probably from 2500 to 3000 exist between latitude 36° 30′ and 39°, distributed, of course, like the lakes, in concordance with all the other glacial features of the landscape.

On the head waters of the rivers there are what are called "Big Meadows," usually about from five to ten miles long. These occupy the basins of the ancient ice-seas, where many tributary glaciers came together to form the grand trunks. Most, however, are quite small, averaging perhaps but little more than three fourths of a mile in length.

One of the very finest of the thousands I have enjoyed lies hidden in an extensive forest of the Two-leaved Pine, on the edge of the basin of the ancient Tuolumne Mer de Glace, about eight miles to the west of Mount Dana.

This is a perfect meadow, and under favorable circumstances exists without manifesting any marked changes for centuries. Nevertheless, soon or late it must inevitably grow old and vanish. During the calm Indian summer, scarce a sand-grain moves around its banks, but in flood-times and storm-times, soil is washed forward upon it and laid in successive sheets around its gently sloping rim, and is gradually extended to the center, making it dryer. Through a considerable period the meadow vegetation is not greatly affected thereby, for it gradually rises with the rising ground, keeping on the surface like water-plants rising on the swell of waves. But at length the elevation of the meadow-land goes on so far as to produce too dry a soil for the specific meadow-plants, when, of course, they have to give up their places to others fitted for the new conditions. The most characteristic of the newcomers at this elevation above the sea are principally sun-loving gilias, eriogonae, and compositae, and finally forest-trees. Henceforward the obscuring changes are so manifold that the original lake-meadow can be unveiled and seen only by the geologist.

Generally speaking, glacier lakes vanish more slowly than the meadows that succeed them, because, unless very shallow, a greater quantity of material is required to fill up their basins and obliterate them than is required to render the surface of the meadow too high and dry for meadow vegetation. Furthermore, owing to the weathering to which the adjacent rocks are subjected, material of the finer sort, susceptible of transportation by rains and ordinary floods, is more abundant during the meadow period than during the lake period. Yet doubtless many a fine meadow favorably situated exists in almost prime beauty for thousands of years, the process of extinction being exceedingly slow, as we reckon time. This is especially the case with meadows circumstanced like the one we have described—embosomed in deep woods, with the ground rising gently away from it all around, the network of tree-roots in which all the ground is clasped preventing any rapid torrential washing. But, in exceptional cases, beautiful lawns formed with great deliberation are overwhelmed and obliterated at once by the action of land-slips, earthquake avalanches, or extraordinary floods, just as lakes are.

Lovers of John Muir and Yosemite can share with him his joy in mountaineering in the High Country, as related in *Scribner's Monthly*, July 1880. His article is called "In the Heart of the California Alps":

Early one bright morning in the middle of Indian summer, while the glacier meadows were still crisp with frost crystals, I set out from the foot of Mount Lyell, on my way down to Yosemite Valley. I had spent the past summer, and many preceding ones, exploring the glaciers that lie on the headwaters of the San Joaquin, Tuolumne, Merced, and Owens rivers; measuring and studying their movements, trends, crevasses, moraines, etc., and the part they had played during the period of their greater extension in the creation and development of the landscapes of this alpine wonderland. Having been cold and hungry so many times, and worked so hard, I was weary, and began to look forward with delight to the approaching winter, when I would be warmly snowbound in my Yosemite cabin, with plenty of bread and books; but a tinge of regret came on when I considered that possibly I was now looking on all this fresh wilderness for the last time.

Pursuing my lonely way down the valley, I turned again and again to gaze on the glorious picture, throwing up my arms to enclose it as in a frame. After long ages of growth in the darkness beneath the glaciers, through sunshine and storms, it seemed now to be ready and waiting for the elected artist, like yellow wheat for the reaper; and I could not help wishing that I were that artist. I had to be content, however, to take it into my soul. At length, after rounding a precipitous headland that puts out from the west wall of the valley, every peak vanished from sight, and I pushed rapidly along the frozen meadows, over the divide between the waters of the Merced and Tuolumne, and down through the lower forests that clothe the slopes of Clouds Rest, arriving in Yosemite in due time—which, with me, is *any* time. And, strange to say, among the first human beings I met here were two artists, who were awaiting my return. Handing me letters of introduction, they inquired whether in the course of my explorations in the adjacent mountains I had ever come upon a landscape suitable for a large painting; whereupon I began a description of the one that had so lately excited my admiration. Then, as I went on further and further into details, their faces began to glow, and I offered to guide them to it, while they declared they would gladly follow, far or near, whithersoever I could spare the time to lead them.

Since storms might come breaking down through the fine weather at any time, burying the meadow colors in snow, and cutting off their retreat, I advised getting ready at once.

Our course lay out of the valley by the Vernal and Nevada falls, thence over the main dividing ridge to the Big Tuolumne Meadows, by the old Mono trail, and thence along the riverbank to its head. Toward the end of the second day, the Sierra Crown began to come into view, and when we had fairly rounded the projecting headland mentioned above, the whole picture stood revealed in the full flush of the alpenglow. Now their enthusiasm was excited beyond bounds, and the more impulsive of the two dashed ahead, shouting and gesticulating and tossing his arms in the air like a madman. Here, at last, was a typical alpine landscape.

After feasting awhile, I proceeded to make camp in a sheltered grove a little way back from the meadow, where pine boughs could be obtained for beds, while the artists ran here and there, along the river bends and up the side of the canyon, choosing foregrounds for sketches. After dark, when our tea was made and a rousing fire kindled, we began to make our plans. They decided to remain here several days, at the least, while I concluded to make an excursion in the meantime to the untouched summit of Ritter.

It was now about the middle of October, the springtime of snow-flowers. The first winter clouds had bloomed, and the peaks were strewn with fresh crystals, without, however, affecting the climbing to any dangerous extent. And as the weather was still profoundly calm, and the distance to the foot of the mountain only a little more than a day, I felt that I was running no great risk of being stormbound.

Ritter is king of our Alps, and had never been climbed. I had explored the adjacent peaks summer after summer, and, but for the tendency to reserve a grand masterpiece like this for a special attempt, it seemed strange that in all these years I had made no effort to reach its commanding summit. Its height above sea level is about 13,300 feet, and it is fenced round by steeply inclined glaciers, and canyons of tremendous depth and ruggedness, rendering it comparatively inaccessible. But difficulties of this kind only exhilarate the mountaineer.

Next morning, the artists went heartily to their work and I to mine. My general plan was simply this: to scale the canyon wall, cross over to the eastern flank of the range, and then make my way southward to the northern spurs of Mount Ritter in compliance with the intervening topography; for to push on directly southward from camp through the innumerable peaks and pinnacles that adorn this portion of the axis of the range is simply impossible.

Before I had gone a mile from camp, I came to the foot of a white cascade that beats its way down a rugged gorge in the canyon wall, from a height of about nine hundred feet, and pours its throbbing waters into the Tuolumne. Gladly I climbed along its dashing border, absorbing its divine music, and bathing from time to time in waftings of irised spray. Climbing higher, higher, new beauty came streaming on the sight: painted meadows, late-blooming gardens, peaks of rare architecture, lakes here and there, shining like silver, and glimpses of the forested lowlands seen far in the west. Over the summit, I saw the so-called Mono Desert lying dreamily silent in the thick, purple light—a desert of heavy sun glare beheld from a desert of ice-burnished granite. Here the mountain waters divide, flowing east to vanish in the volcanic sands and dry sky of the Great Basin; west, to flow through the Golden Gate to the sea.

Passing a little way down over the summit until I had reached an elevation of about 10,000 feet, I pushed on southward toward a group of savage peaks that stand guard about Ritter on the north and west, groping my way, and dealing instinctively with every obstacle as it presented itself. Here a huge gorge would be found cutting across my path, along the dizzy edge of which I scrambled until some less precipitous point was discovered where I might safely venture to the bottom and, selecting some feasible portion of the opposite wall, reascend with the same slow caution. Massive, flat-topped spurs alternate with the gorges, plunging abruptly from the shoulders of the snowy peaks, and planting their feet in the warm desert. These were everywhere marked and adorned with characteristic sculptures of the ancient glaciers that swept over this entire region like one vast ice-wind, and the polished surfaces produced by the ponderous flood are still so perfectly preserved that in many places the sunlight reflected from them is about as trying to the eyes as sheets of snow.

Now came the solemn, silent evening. Long, blue, spiky-edged shadows crept out across the snowfields, while a rosy glow, at first scarce discernible, gradually deepened and suffused every mountaintop, flushing the glaciers and the harsh crags above them. This was the alpenglow, to me one of the most impressive of all the terrestrial manifestations of God. At the touch of this divine light, the mountains seemed to kindle to a rapt, religious consciousness, and stood hushed like devout worshipers waiting to be blessed. Just before the alpenglow began to fade, two crimson clouds came streaming across the summit like wings of flame, rendering the sublime scene yet more intensely impressive; then came darkness and the stars.

Ritter was still miles away, but I could proceed no further that night. I found a good campground on the rim of a glacier basin about 11,000 feet above the sea. A small lake nestles in the bottom of it, from which I got water for my tea, and a storm-beaten thicket nearby furnished abundance of firewood. Somber peaks, hacked and shattered, circled halfway around the horizon, wearing a most savage aspect in the gloaming, and a waterfall chanted solemnly across the lake on its way down from the foot of a glacier.

I made my bed in a nook of the pine thicket, where the branches were pressed and crinkled overhead like a roof, and bent down around the sides. These are the best bedchambers our Alps afford—snug as squirrel nests, well ventilated, full of spicy odors, and with plenty of wind-played needles to sing one asleep. I little expected company, but, creeping in through a low side door, I found five or six birds nestling among the tassels. The night wind began to blow soon after dark; at first, only a gentle breathing, but increasing toward midnight to a violent gale that fell upon my leafy roof in ragged surges, like a cascade, and bearing strange sounds from the crags overhead. The waterfall sang in chorus, filling the old ice fountain with its solemn roar, and seeming to increase in power as the night advanced—fit voice for such a landscape. I had to creep out many times to the fire during the night; for it was biting cold and I had no blankets. Gladly I welcomed the morning star.

The dawn in the dry, wavering air of the desert was glorious. Everything encouraged my undertaking and betokened success. No cloud in the sky, no storm tone in the wind. Breakfast of bread and tea was soon made. I fastened a hard, durable crust to my belt by way of provision, in case I should be compelled to pass a night on the mountaintop; then, securing the remainder of my little stock from wolves and wood rats, I set forth free and hopeful.

On the southern shore of a frozen lake, I encountered an extensive field of hard, granular snow, up which I scampered in fine tone, intending to follow it to its head, and cross the rocky spur against which it leans, hoping thus to come direct upon the base of the main Ritter peak. The surface was pitted with oval hollows, made by stones and drifted pine needles that had melted themselves into the mass by the radiation of absorbed sun heat. These afforded good footholds, but the surface curved more and more steeply at the head, and the pits became shallower and less abundant, until I found myself in danger of being shed off like avalanching snow. I persisted, however, creeping on all fours, and shuffling up the smoothest places on my back, as I had often done on burnished granite, until, after slipping several times, I was compelled to retrace my course to the bottom, and make my way around the west end of the lake, and thence up to the summit of the divide between the headwaters of Rush Creek and the northernmost tributaries of the San Joaquin.

Arriving on the summit of this dividing crest, one of the most exciting pieces of pure wilderness was disclosed that the eye of man ever beheld. There, immediately in front, loomed the majestic mass of Mount Ritter, with a glacier swooping down its face nearly to my feet, then curving westward and pouring its frozen flood into a dark blue lake, whose shores were bound with precipices of crystalline snow; while a deep chasm drawn between the divide and the glacier separated the massive picture from everything else. Only the one sublime mountain in sight, the one glacier, and one lake; the whole veiled with one blue shadow—rock, ice, and water, without a single leaf.

Descending the divide in a hesitating mood, I picked my way across the yawning chasm at the foot, and climbed out upon the glacier.

I could not distinctly hope to reach the summit from this side, yet I moved on across the glacier as if driven by fate. Contending with myself, the season is too far spent, I said, and even should I be successful, I might be stormbound on the mountain; and in the cloud-darkness, with the cliffs and crevasses covered with snow, how could I escape? No; I must wait until next summer. I would only approach the mountain now, and inspect it, creep about its flanks, learn what I could of its history, holding myself ready to flee on the approach of the first storm cloud. But we little know until tried how much of the uncontrollable there is in us, urging across glaciers and torrents, and up dangerous heights, let the judgment forbid as it may.

I succeeded in gaining the foot of the cliff on the eastern extremity of the glacier, and discovered the mouth of a narrow avalanche gully, through which I began to climb, intending to follow it as far as possible, and at least obtain some fine wild views for my pains. Its general course is oblique to the plane of the mountain face, and the metamorphic slates of which it is built are cut by cleavage planes in such a way that they weather off in angular blocks, giving rise to irregular steps that greatly facilitate climbing on the sheer places. I thus made my way into a wilderness of crumbling spires and battlements, built together in bewildering combinations, and glazed in many places with a thin coating of ice, which I had to hammer off with a stone. The situation was becoming gradually more perilous; but, having passed several dangerous spots, I dared not think of descending; for, so steep was the entire ascent, one would inevitably fall to the glacier in case a single misstep were made.

At length, after attaining an elevation of about 12,800 feet, I found myself at the foot of a sheer drop in the bed of the avalanche channel I was tracing, which seemed absolutely to bar all further progress. It is only about forty-five or fifty feet high, and somewhat roughened by fissures and projections; but these seemed so slight and insecure, as footholds, that I tried hard to avoid the precipice altogether, by scaling the wall on either side. But, though less steep, the walls were smoother than the obstructing rock, and repeated efforts only showed that I must either go right ahead or turn back. The tried dangers beneath seemed even greater than that of the cliff in front; therefore, after scanning its face again and again, I began to scale it, picking my holds with intense caution. After gaining a point about halfway to the top, I was suddenly brought to a dead stop, with arms outspread, clinging close to the face of the rock, unable to move hand or foot either up or down. My doom appeared fixed. I *must* fall. There would be a moment of bewilderment, and then a lifeless rumble down the one general precipice to the glacier below.

When this final danger flashed upon me, I became nerve-shaken for the first time since setting foot on the mountain, and my mind seemed to fill with a stifling smoke. But this terrible eclipse lasted only a moment, when life blazed forth again with preternatural clearness. I seemed suddenly to become possessed of a new sense. The other self—the ghost of bygone experiences, Instinct, or Guardian Angel—call it what you will—came forward and assumed control. Then my trembling muscles became firm again, every rift and flaw in the rock was seen as through a microscope, and my limbs moved with a positiveness and precision with which I seemed to have nothing at all to do. Had I been borne aloft upon wings, my deliverance could not have been more complete.

Above this memorable spot, the face of the mountain is still more savagely hacked and torn. It is a maze of yawning chasms and gullies, in the angles of which rise beetling crags and piles of detached boulders that seem to have been gotten ready to be launched below. But the strange influx of strength I had received seemed inexhaustible. I found a way without effort, and soon stood upon the topmost crag in the blessed light.

Looking southward along the axis of the range, the eye is first caught by a row of exceedingly sharp and slender spires, which rise openly to a height of about a thousand feet, from a series of short, residual glaciers that lean back against their bases; their fantastic sculpture and the unrelieved sharpness with which they spring out of the ice rendering them peculiarly wild and striking. These are the Minarets, and beyond them you behold a most sublime wilderness of mountains, their snowy summits crowded together in lavish abundance, peak beyond peak, swelling higher, higher as they sweep on southward, until the culminating point of the range is reached on Mount Whitney, near the head of the Kern River, at an elevation of nearly 15,000 feet above the level of the sea.

Westward, the general flank of the range is seen flowing sublimely away from the sharp summits, in smooth undulations; a sea of huge gray granite waves dotted with lakes and meadows, and fluted with stupendous canyons that grow steadily deeper as they recede in the distance. Below this gray region lies the dark forest zone, broken here and there by upswelling ridges and domes; and yet beyond is a yellow, hazy belt, marking the broad plain of the San Joaquin, bounded on its further side by the blue mountains of the coast.

Turning now to the northward, there in the immediate foreground is the glorious Sierra Crown, with Cathedral Peak a few miles to the left—a temple of marvelous architecture, hewn from the living rock; the gray, giant form of Mammoth Mountain, 13,000 feet high; Mounts Ord, Gibbs, Dana, Conness, Tower Peak, Castle Peak, and Silver Mountain, stretching away in the distance, with a host of noble companions that are as yet nameless.

Eastward, the whole region seems a land of pure desolation covered with beautiful light. The torrid volcanic basin of Mono, with its one bare lake fourteen miles long; Owens Valley and the broad lava tableland at its head, dotted with craters, and the massive Inyo Range, rivaling even the Sierra in height. These are spread, map-like, beneath you, with countless ranges beyond, passing and overlapping one another and fading on the glowing horizon.

But in the midst of these fine lessons and landscapes, I had to remember that the sun was wheeling far to the west, while a new way had to be discovered, at least to some point on the timberline where I could have a fire; for I had not even burdened myself with a coat. I first scanned the western spurs, hoping some way might appear through which I might reach the northern glacier, and cross its snout; or pass around the lake into which it flows, and thus strike my morning track. This route was soon sufficiently unfolded to show that, if practicable at all, it would require so much time that reaching camp that night would be out of the question. I therefore scrambled back eastward, descending the southern slopes obliquely at the same time. Here the crags seemed less formidable, and the head of a glacier that flows northeast came in sight, which I determined to follow as far as possible, hoping thus to make my way to the foot of the peak on the east side, and thence across the intervening canyons and ridges to camp.

The inclination of the glacier is quite moderate at the head, and, as the sun had softened the *névé*, I made safe and rapid progress, running and sliding, and keeping up a sharp outlook for crevasses. About half a mile from the head, there is an ice cascade, where the glacier pours over a sharp declivity, and is shattered into massive blocks separated by deep, blue fissures. Fortunately, the day had been warm enough to loosen the ice crystals so as to admit of hollows being dug in the rotten portions of the blocks, thus enabling me to pick my way with far less difficulty than I had anticipated.

Night drew near before I reached the eastern base of the mountain, and my camp lay many a rugged mile to the north; but ultimate success was assured. It was now only a matter of endurance and ordinary mountain-craft. The sunset was, if possible, yet more beautiful than that of the day previous. The Mono landscape seemed to be fairly saturated with warm, purple light. The peaks marshaled along the summit were in shadow, but through every notch and pass streamed vivid sun-fire, soothing and irradiating their rough, black angles, while companies of small, luminous clouds hovered above them like very angels of light.

Darkness came on, but I found my way by the trends of the canyons and the peaks projected against the sky. All excitement died with the light, and then I was weary. But the joyful sound of the waterfall across the lake was heard at last, and soon the stars were seen reflected in the lake itself. Taking my bearings from these, I discovered the little pine thicket in which my nest was, and then I had a rest such as only a mountaineer may enjoy. Afterward, I made a sunrise fire, went down to the lake, dashed water on my head, and dipped a cupful for tea. The revival brought about by bread and tea was as complete as the exhaustion from excessive enjoyment and toil had been. Then I crept beneath the pine tassels to bed. The wind was frosty and the fire burned low, but my sleep was none the less sound, and the evening constellations had swept far to the west before I awoke.

After warming and resting in the sunshine, I sauntered home—that is, back to the Tuolumne camp—bearing away toward a cluster of peaks that hold the fountain snows of one of the north tributaries of Rush Creek. Here I discovered a group of beautiful glacier lakes, nestled together in a grand amphitheater. Toward evening, I crossed the divide separating the Mono waters from those of the Tuolumne, and entered the glacier basin that now holds the fountain snows of the stream that forms the upper Tuolumne cascades. This stream I traced down through its many dells and gorges, meadows and bogs, reaching the brink of the main Tuolumne at dusk.

A loud whoop for the artists was answered again and again. Their campfire came in sight, and half an hour afterward I was with them. They seemed unreasonably glad to see me. I had been absent only three days; nevertheless, they had already been weighing chances as to whether I would ever return, and trying to decide whether they should wait longer or begin to seek their way back to the lowlands. Now their curious troubles were over. They packed their precious sketches, and next morning we set out homeward bound, and in two days entered the Yosemite Valley from the north by way of Indian Canyon.

II THE PHOTOGRAPHS

ENTRANCE TO THE YOSEMITE VALLEY

THE Yosemite Valley has two approaches, each with its own inspiring view. Valley View, on the road from Merced, is sheer enchantment, with the colorful Merced River lighting up the array of meadow, forest, and imposing cliffs and peaks surrounding the valley. Tunnel View, on the road from Fresno, bursts into sight as one leaves the Wawona tunnel through the Yosemite cliff; it is the greatest cathedral on earth. The granite pillars of this cathedral—all cliffs, peaks, or domes from three to five thousand feet high, rising steeply from the valley floor—are names to conjure with: El Capitan, Clouds Rest, Half Dome, Sentinel Dome, Sentinel Rock, Cathedral Rocks.

From the Introduction

1   Tunnel View, Peaks and Clouds

To know and feel the best that nature has to offer demands scrutiny as well as love. I watched this scene for about an hour one autumn morning. Gloomy gray clouds dominated the mountains, shifting to reveal relatively colorless and formless sections of mountain wall and valley floor from time to time, but with no special visual or spiritual significance. Suddenly a parting of the clouds revealed the great forms, and, at the decisive moment, El Capitan, Half Dome, Sentinel Rock, Cathedral Rocks, and the forested valley all co-operated in one grand annunciation—light out of darkness, form out of chaos, joy out of gloom.

2 · *Tunnel View, Dark Sunset*

Few visions are as moving as a dramatic sky of sunset clouds, or as challenging. Frequent shifts in light, color, and form create problems of photographic exposure and composition, and also problems of mood. This picture represents a moment of transition from threatening, stormy darkness to a pretty, warmly sprinkled sunset sky—the moment of maximum meaning for me.

3   Tunnel View, Winter Sunset

Every sunset which I witness inspires me with the desire to go to a west as distant and fair.... We dream all night of those mountain-ridges on the horizon ... which were last gilded by his rays.

(THOREAU)

Gloomy winter often provides a perfect setting for glorious sunset color. Lucky the viewer who finds his patience rewarded, as here one December evening, with a vision of alpenglow on El Capitan.

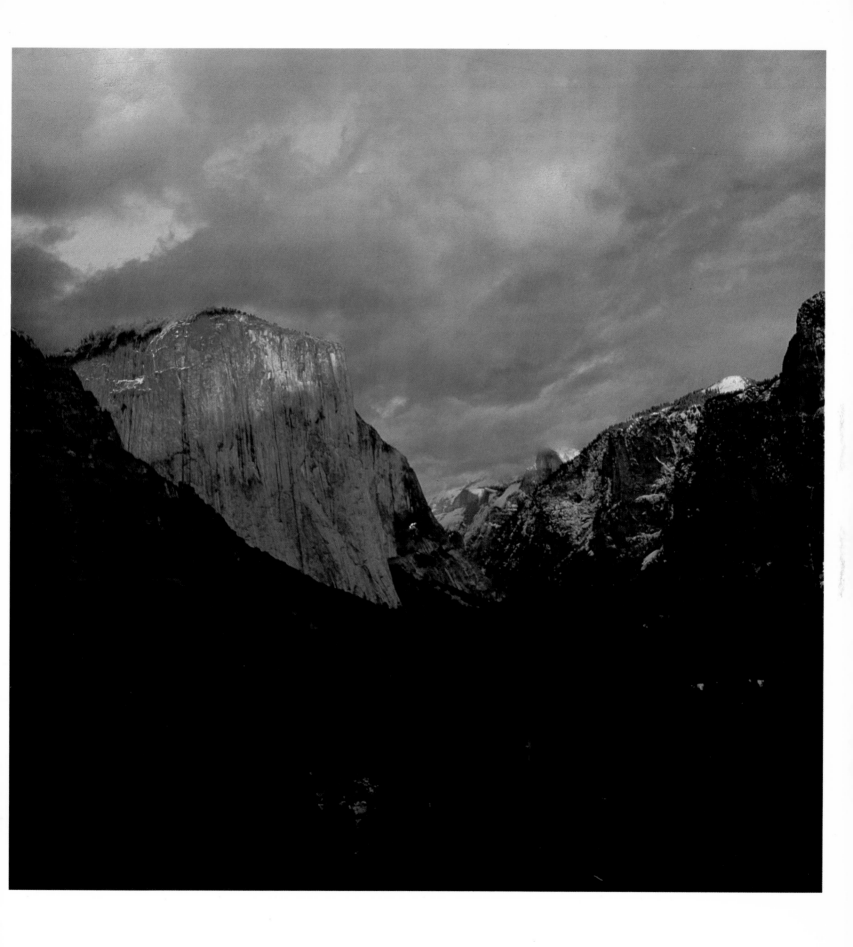

4   Tunnel View, Autumn Sunset

The heavens declare the glory of God.   (Psalm 19)

Autumn, the season of warming color, is the sensuous delight of all who love nature. Every once in a while the sky becomes a riot of color, and the photographer goes wild with a succession of glorious scenes, each uniquely beautiful.

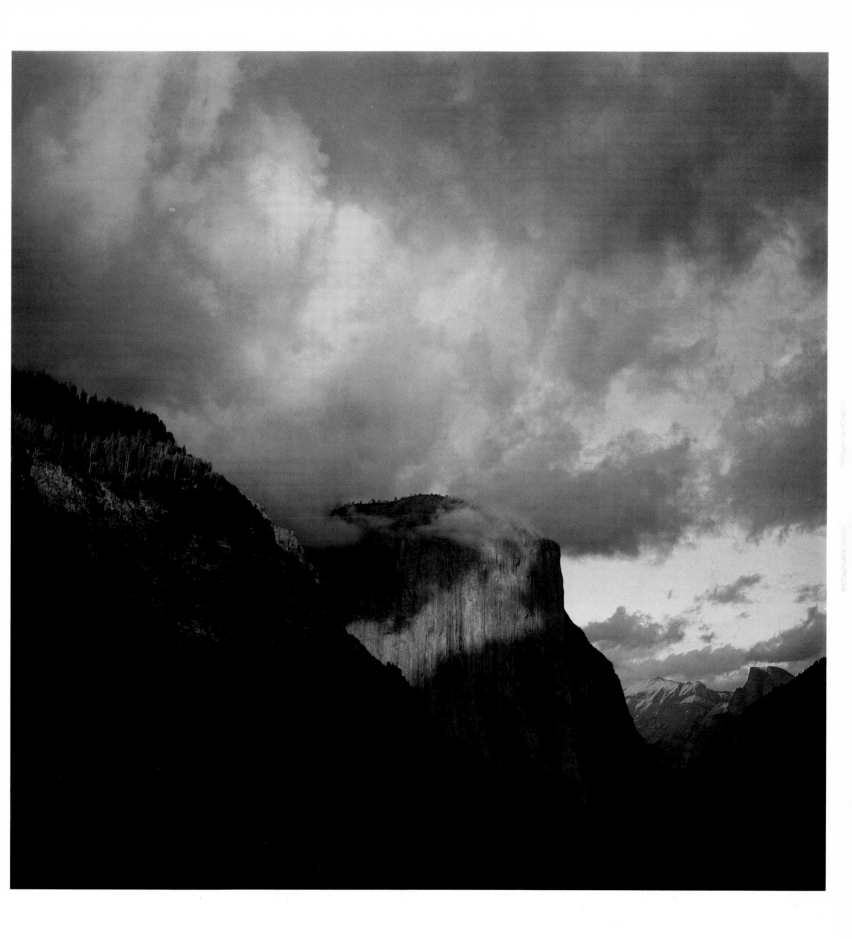

5 Valley View, Pre-Sunrise

The morning steals upon the
night, melting darkness.
(SHAKESPEARE, The Tempest)

Valley View, the entrance to the valley on the road from Merced, offers the Merced River as a foreground for Yosemite's trees and cliffs, and as a very effective reflector of early morning light, especially in the spring. This picture was taken before sunrise, and before any glow of red or gold appeared on the horizon.

ENTRANCE TO THE YOSEMITE VALLEY

6   *Valley View, Pre-Sunrise Colors*

See how the morning opes her golden
gates, And takes her farewell of the
glorious sun!   (SHAKESPEARE, King Henry VI, Part III)

Here the golden pre-sunrise glow in the sky, which would be lost after sunrise, is reflected with deep saturation in the Merced River, as the backlighted forms of El Capitan (left) and Cathedral Rocks (right) are clearly outlined.

44   ENTRANCE TO THE YOSEMITE VALLEY

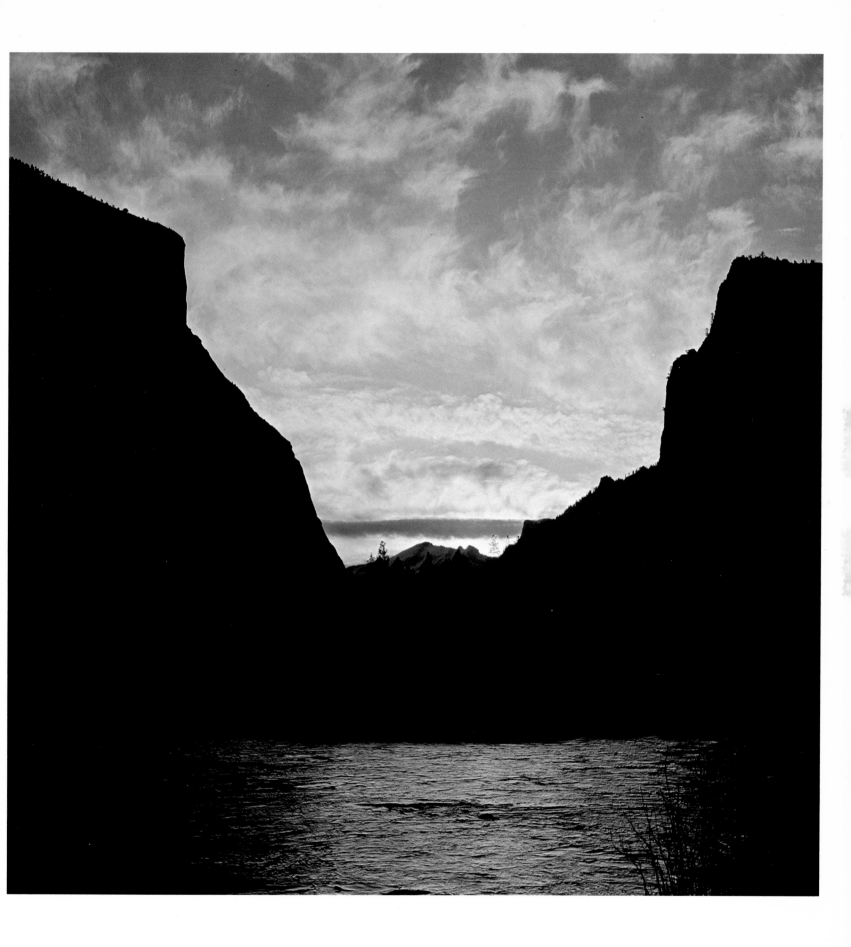

7 Valley View, Bright

> There can be no very black
> melancholy to him who lives in the
> midst of nature and has his senses
> still.   (THOREAU)

This picture was envisioned by me about a month before I took it. At that time, I wasn't satisfied with either the colors (they weren't warm enough, it was too early in the autumn) or the shadows (they were obscuring the riverbank, for I was about ten minutes too late). With the co-operation of Mother Nature when I returned on my next trip, I got my color and my shadows and a picture of Valley View in bright sunshine.

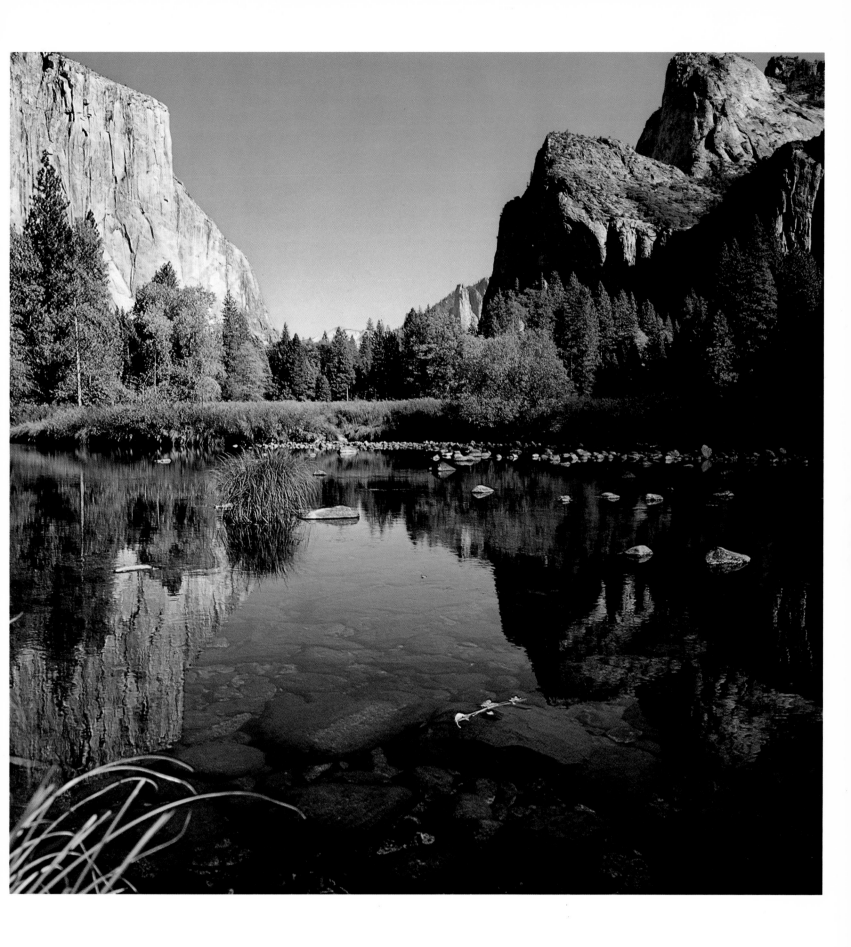

8 Valley View, Post-Sunset

This is a delicious evening, when
the whole body is one sense,
and imbibes delight through every pore.
(THOREAU)

Some of the most beautiful and incredible color effects take place after sunset, as the sky shifts from red-orange-yellow to blue to lavender to purple to black. Exposure is a serious photographic problem—what is required is a good exposure meter, some experience, and efficacious prayer.

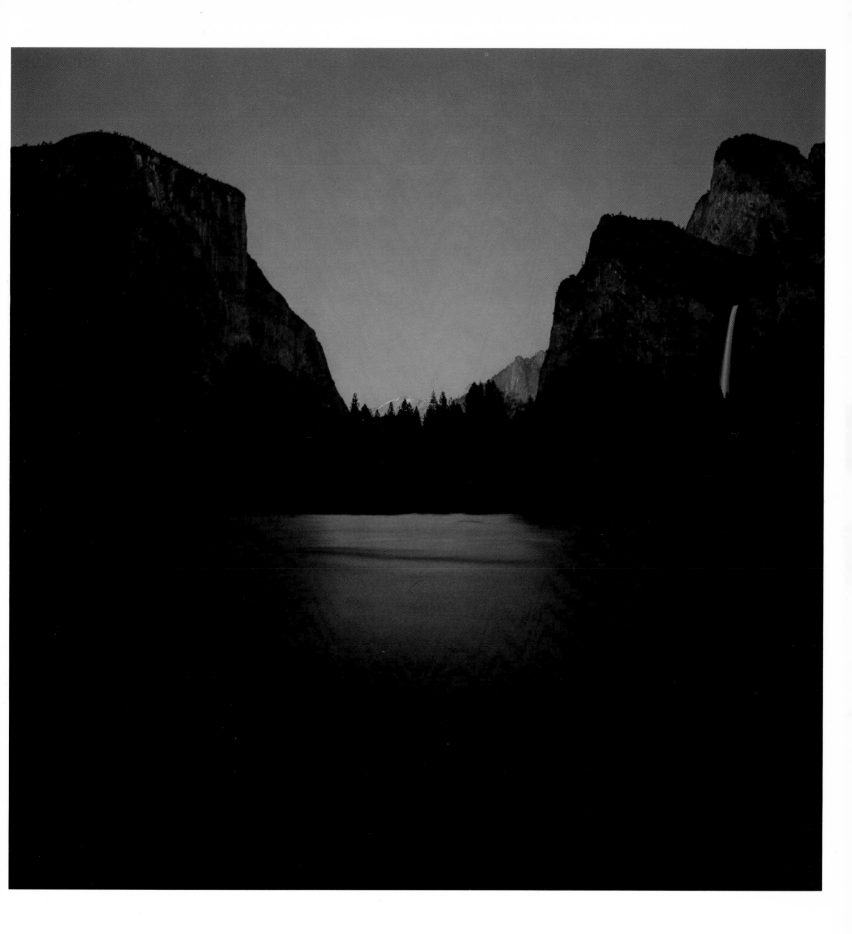

THE GREAT ROCKS

THE central theme that I find in nature is its infinite variety of beauty—in form, in color, in light, in texture, in mood, and in reflection—not only in nature as a whole, or in every great scene, but even in an individual object: a mountain, a peak, a cliff, a rock.

To me, Half Dome is not a static, inorganic object: it is alive with vibrant significance, constantly changing in every aspect of its appearance and mood with the time of the day, the season of the year, and the position of the viewer, but also with every minuscule change in the tone and color of the light.

The same scene, at different times, can be cold or warm, harsh or gentle, boisterous or soothing, dramatic or mystical. . . . In any event, I feel that all the emotions of man can be shared with nature in a mystical union.

From the Introduction

9 El Capitan, Massive

The sun ariseth in his majesty;
Who doth the world so gloriously behold,
That cedar-tops and hills seem burnish'd gold.
(SHAKESPEARE, Venus and Adonis)

El Capitan is "a plain, severely simple, glacier-sculpted face of granite, the end of one of the most compact and enduring of the mountain ridges, unrivaled in . . . flawless strength" (Muir) and rising 3564 feet from the valley floor. In this picture, taken from El Capitan meadow, a telephoto lens was used to create a fresh image of a familiar form glowing in early-morning sunlight.

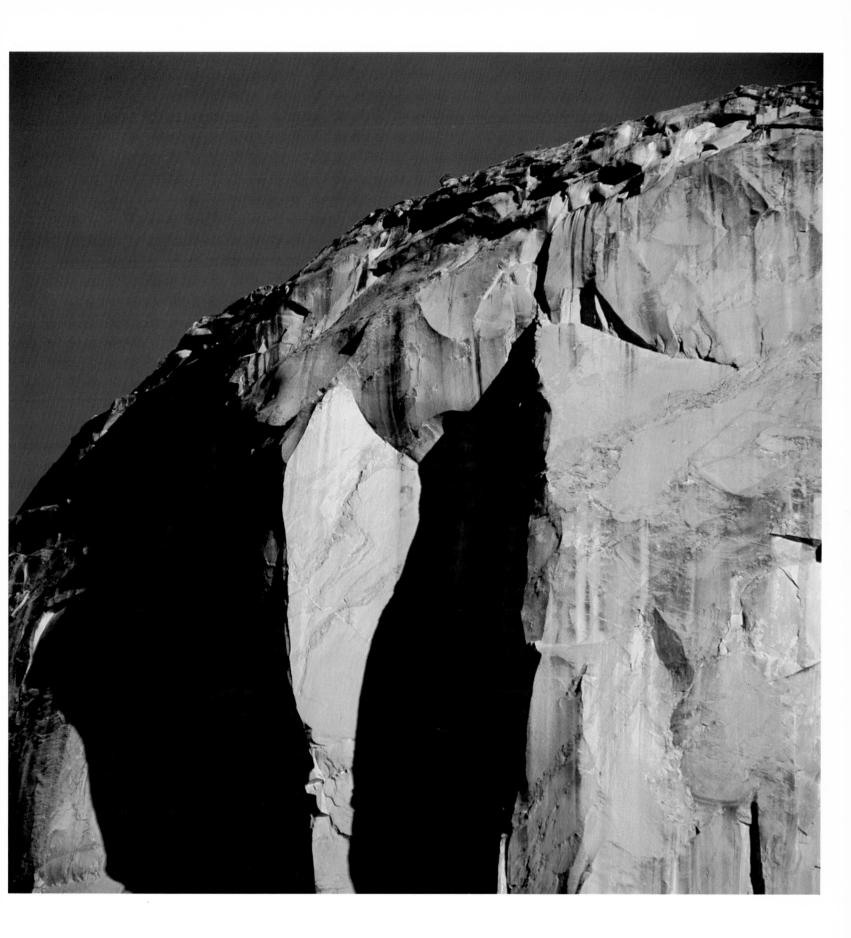

10   El Capitan, Pretty

When proud-pied April, dress'd in all his trim,
Hath put a spirit of youth in every thing. . . .
                    (SHAKESPEARE, Sonnet XCVIII)

The most popular view of El Capitan, from the south road just across the Merced River, is called El Capitan View. This picture was taken one bright May morning in a favorable interlude between the dullnesses of too much and too little shadow. Despite its popularity, this viewpoint is often uncrowded at the height of the season, especially in the early morning, and may serve as a retreat for meditation.

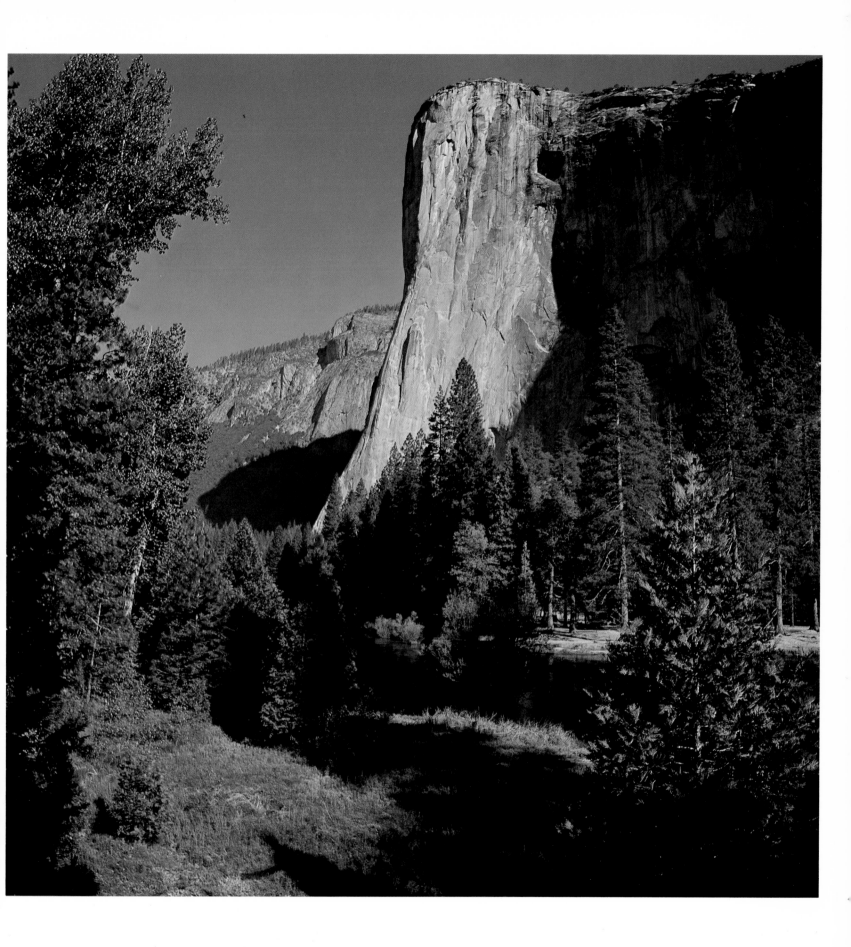

11   El Capitan, Storm

Here is this vast, savage, howling mother of ours, Nature,
lying all around with such beauty. . . . (THOREAU)

This picture, also from El Capitan View, was taken during the brewing of a winter storm, in a moment of maximum illumination of the cliff. It seemed unlikely that any picture could be taken that would express anything but darkness and rather formless gloom. But a momentary blessing from the sun gave meaning and beauty to the scene.

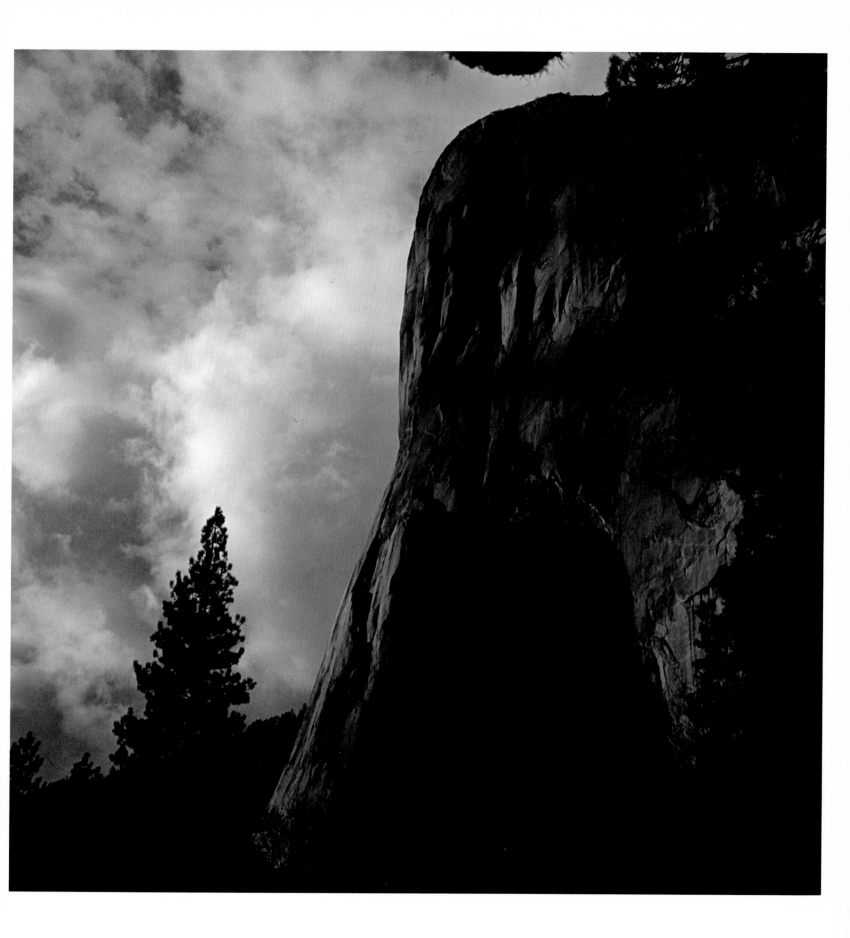

12   *El Capitan, Lyric, Cool*

This picture was taken from the bank of the Merced River, near the south road, about a mile east of El Capitan View, on a cool winter day, when smiling nature suggested a lyric view of El Capitan harmoniously blended with the serene Merced River and its gleaming bank of snow.

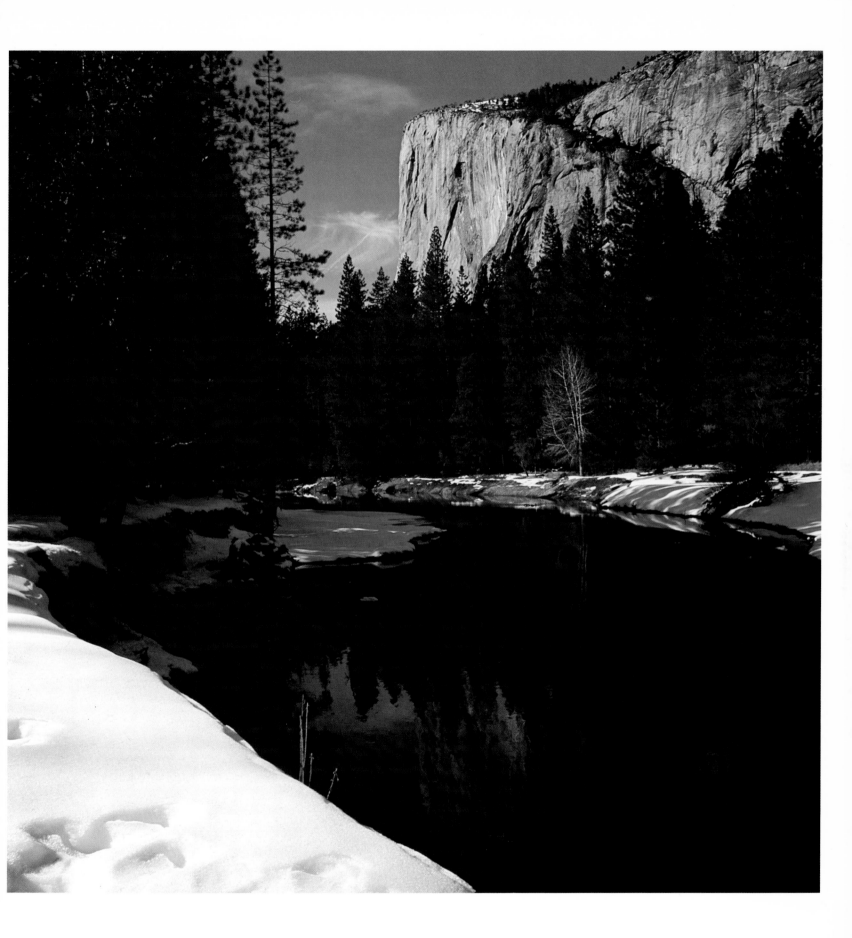

13 *El Capitan, Shoulder, Sunset*

El Capitan, massive mountain ridge, has many aspects, and one of the most interesting views may be seen from the entrance to the El Capitan Picnic Area, where its curved shoulder is prominently displayed, especially in late afternoon in December, when this picture was taken with a telephoto lens.

14   *El Capitan and El Capitan Fall*

Waterfalls, five hundred to one or two thousand feet high, are so subordinated to the mighty cliffs over which they pour, that they seem like wisps of smoke, gentle as floating clouds, though their voices fill the valley and make the rocks tremble.   (MUIR)

One spring afternoon as I looked for El Capitan Fall flowing from the right shoulder of El Capitan, I was startled by a silver shine on the face of the cliff, which proved to be El Capitan Fall being blown skyward by the wind.

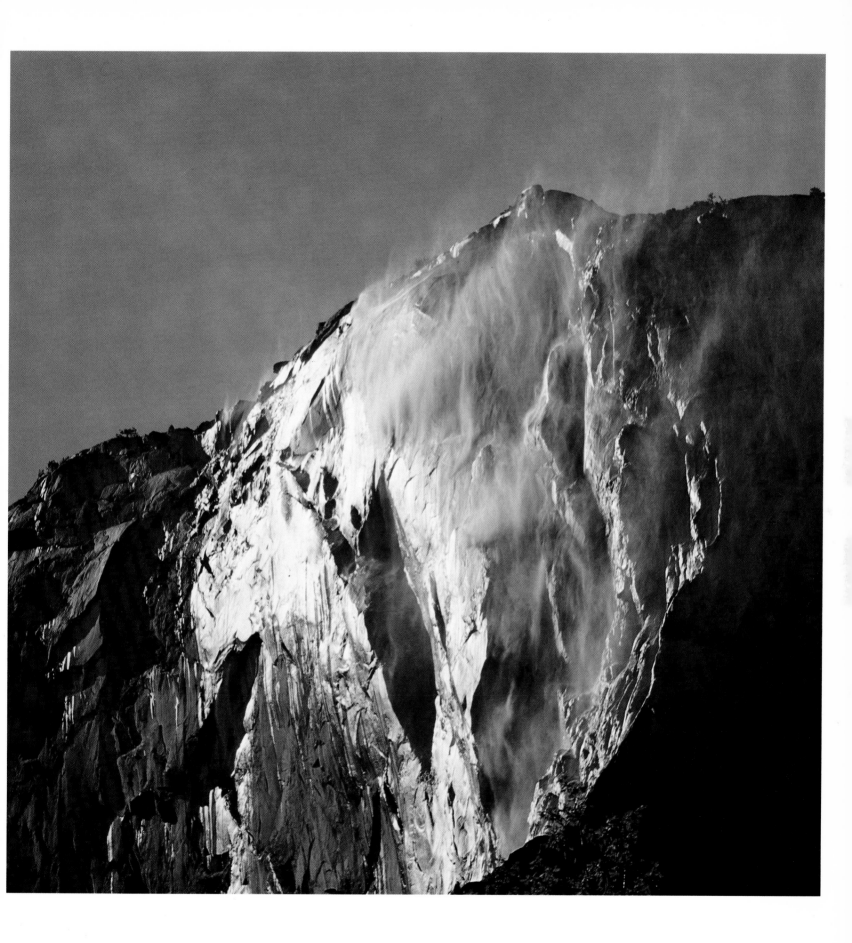

15   Half Dome, Peak, from Mirror Lake

I will lift up mine eyes unto the hills,
from whence cometh my help.   (Psalm 121)

To the left of the great steep cliff of Half Dome and just below the great dome itself is a peak. Ordinarily, the peak merely dresses up the great dome and face, which dominate the view. But, seen from Mirror Lake with a telephoto lens, midafternoon in October, this peak itself becomes a stupendous, classic form with a beauty all its own.

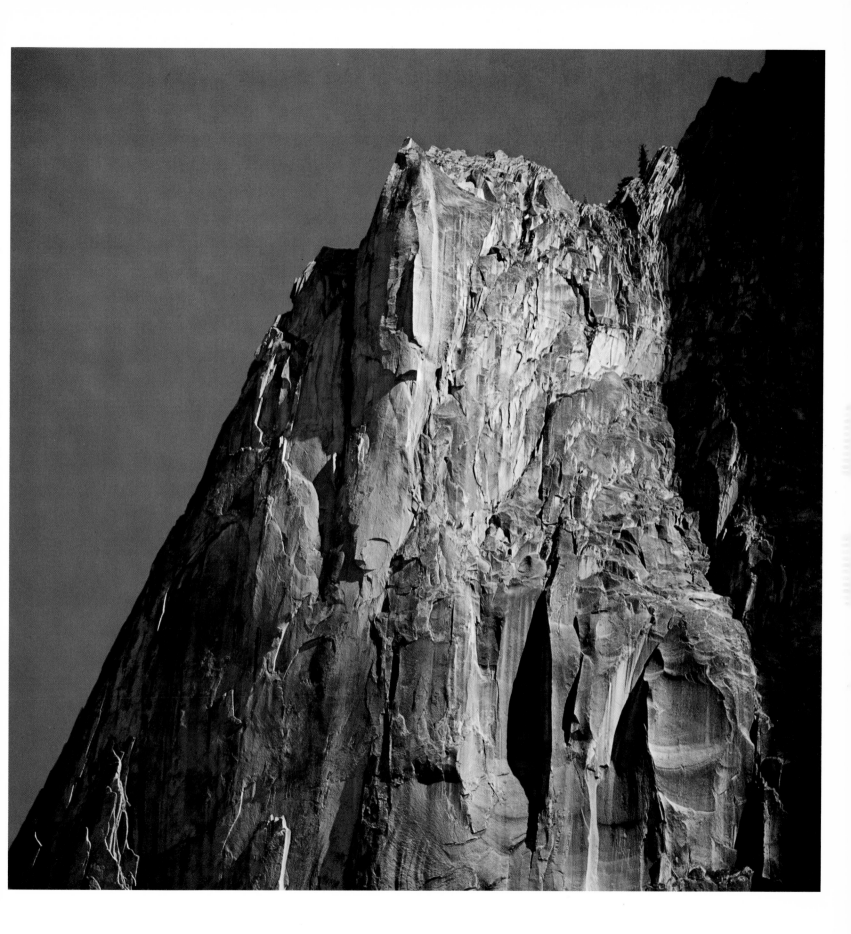

16   Half Dome from Rocky Point Picnic Area

Against the red throb of its sunset-heart
I laid my own to beat,
And share commingling heat.
(FRANCIS THOMPSON, The Hound of Heaven)

The majesty of Half Dome (8842 feet high) is sometimes clearly displayed even when most of the sheer face of the cliff is concealed by intervening mountain walls. This picture was taken from the Rocky Point Picnic Area, on the south side of the Merced River, one sunset in autumn when many beautiful scenes succeeded one another as the sunset colors deepened.

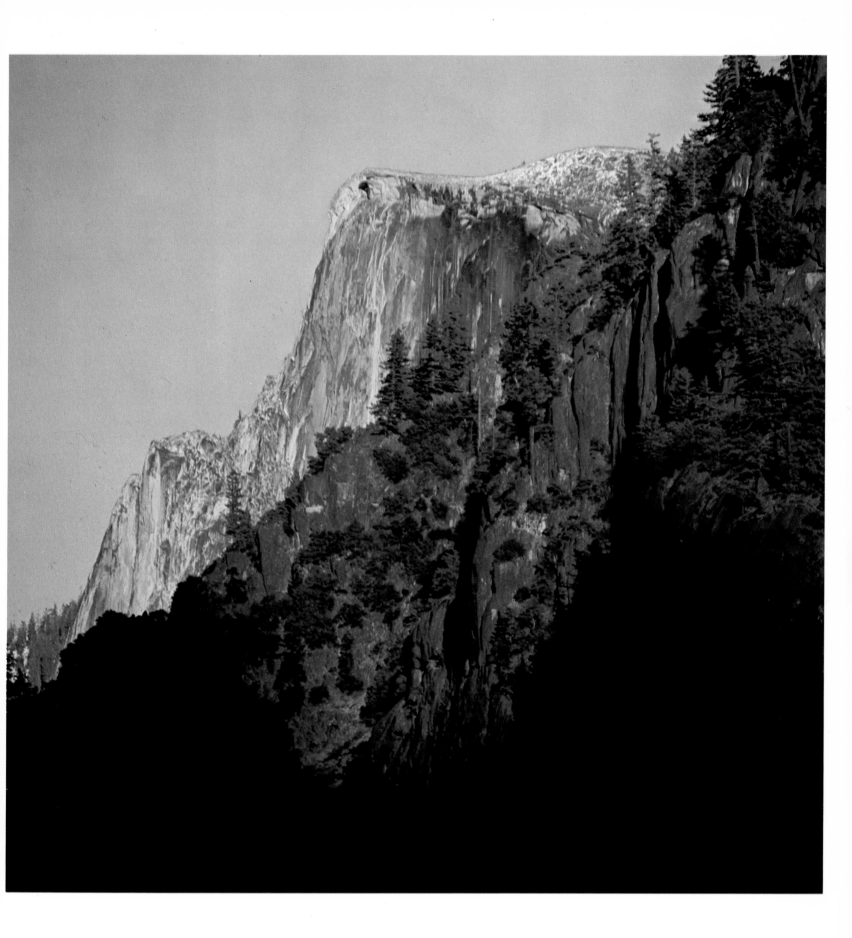

17 *Half Dome from a Point near the Chapel*

We need the tonic of wildness. . . . We can never have enough of nature. We must be refreshed by the sight of inexhaustible vigor, vast and titanic features.   (THOREAU)

The south road, near the Chapel, just before Sentinel Bridge, provides a viewpoint for the sheer face of Half Dome and the sweeping curves of the dome, especially at sunset, when this picture was taken. This is another picture that I dreamt of before I took it. I first envisioned it one sunset when the sun was almost gone, shining only on the very top of the cliff, with a deep, dull red. It seemed to me that if I had been there ten minutes earlier there would have been a glorious view. A month later, I was waiting for it at the right time.

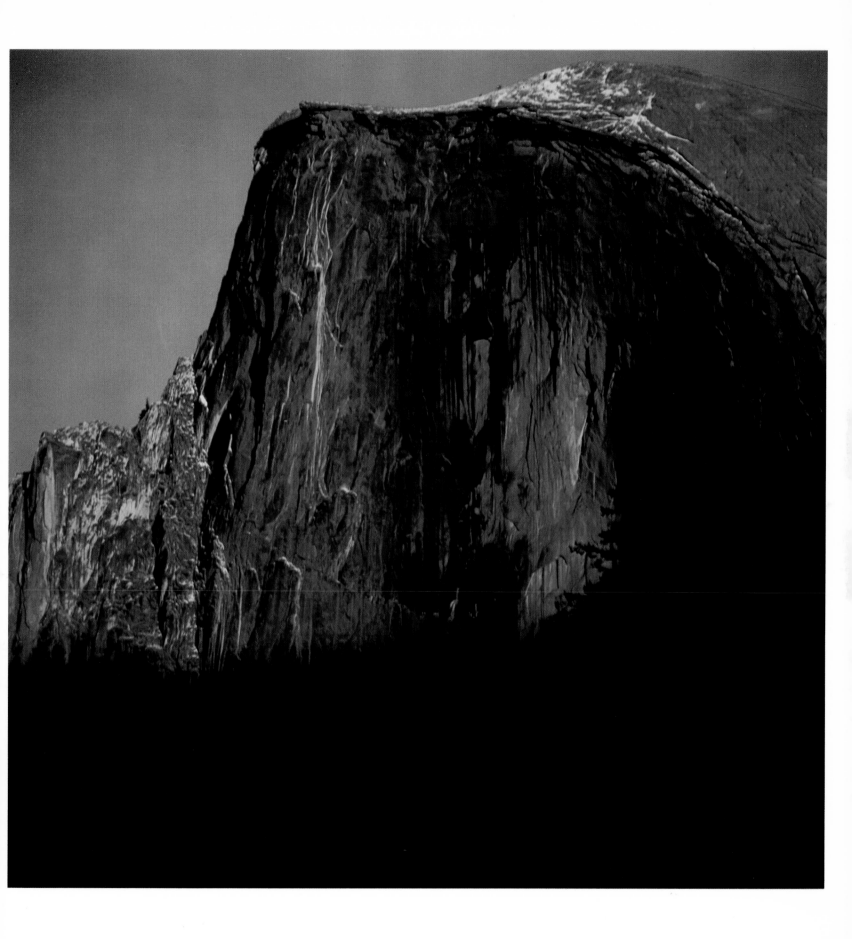

18   *North Dome from Happy Isles*

And this our life exempt from public haunt
Finds tongues in trees, books in the running brooks,
Sermons in stones and good in every thing.
                              (SHAKESPEARE, As You Like It)

One of the favorite views of North Dome (3571 feet above the valley floor) is from the bridge over the Merced River at Happy Isles. This picture was taken shortly after a winter snowstorm, when the storm clouds had not yet fully lifted from North Dome and the snow was still fresh on the rocks and leaves in the foreground.

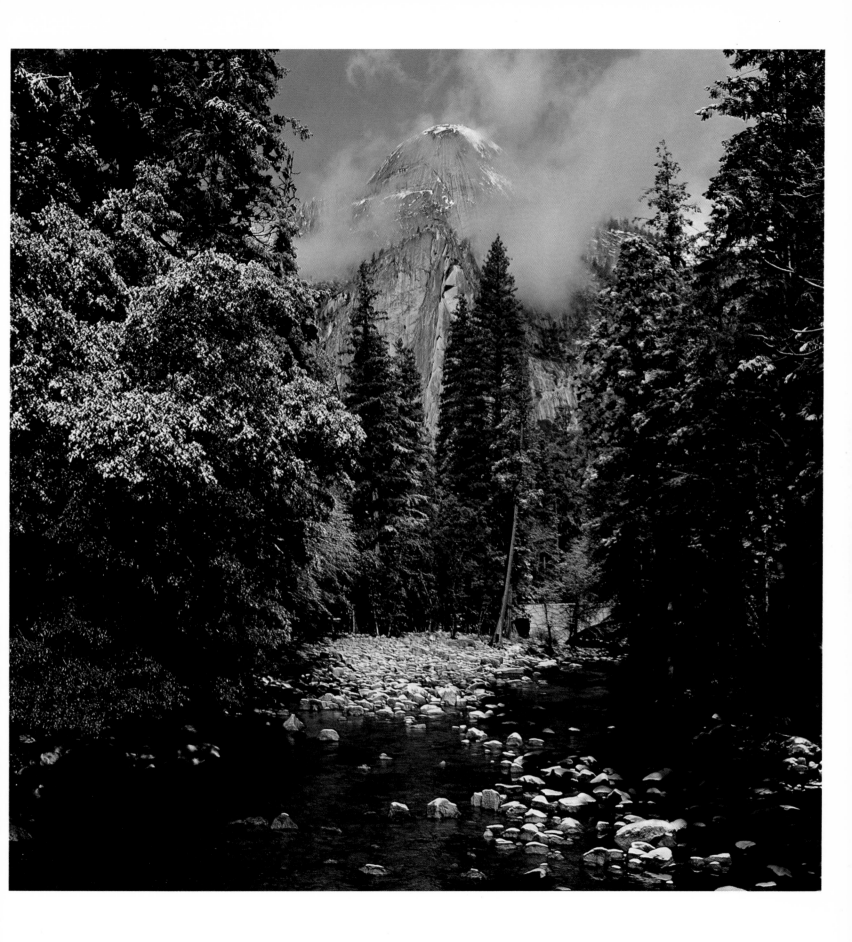

19   Sentinel Rock, Sunset

One day the sun shall shine more brightly than ever he has done . . . and light up our whole lives with a great awakening light . . . warm and serene and golden.   (THOREAU)

There is nothing inorganic . . . earth is . . . living poetry.
(THOREAU)

Of the many aspects of Sentinel Rock, this view from the Rocky Point Picnic Area is my favorite. It illustrates for me, vividly, the feeling I share with Thoreau, that mountains are vibrant with life and spirit.

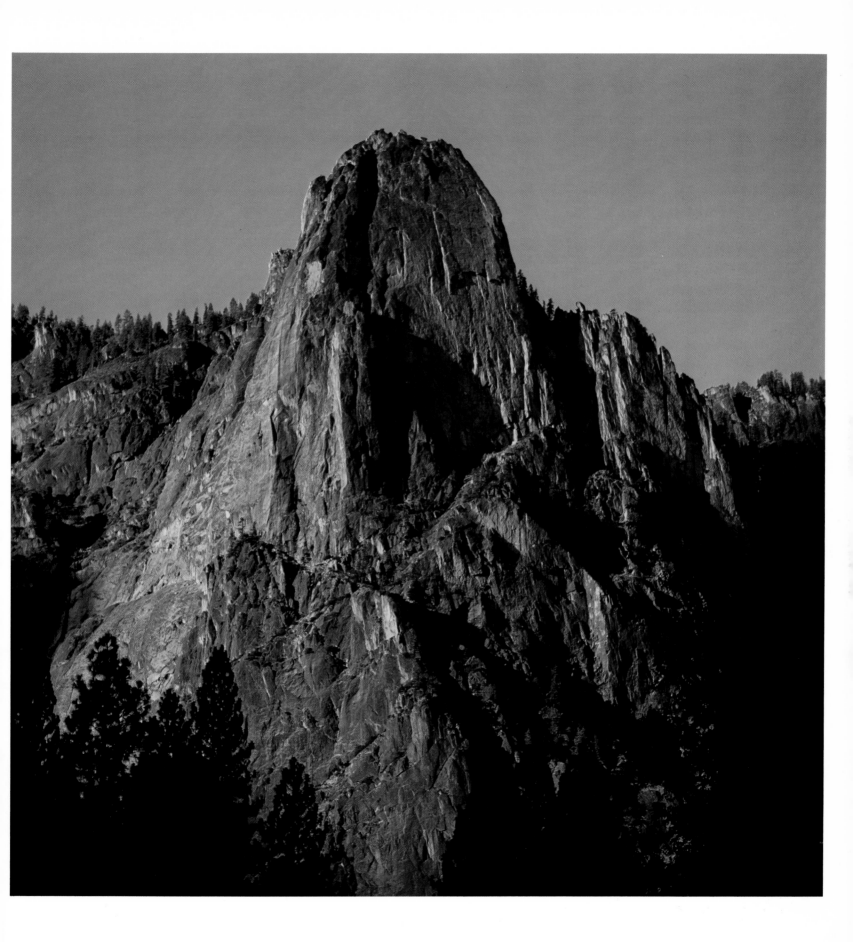

20 Half Dome and North Dome, Reflections

There was a time when meadow, grove, and stream,
The earth, and every common sight,
To me did seem
Apparel'd in celestial light,
The glory and the freshness of a dream.

(WORDSWORTH, Ode on Intimations of Immortality)

In this picture, Half Dome and North Dome are reflected in a temporary spring pond (a residue of melted snow) in Leidig Meadow. Part of the necessary equipment of the Yosemite photographer in early spring, very often, is a pair of waterproof boots as he wades through and stands in fields flooded with the melt of winter snow.

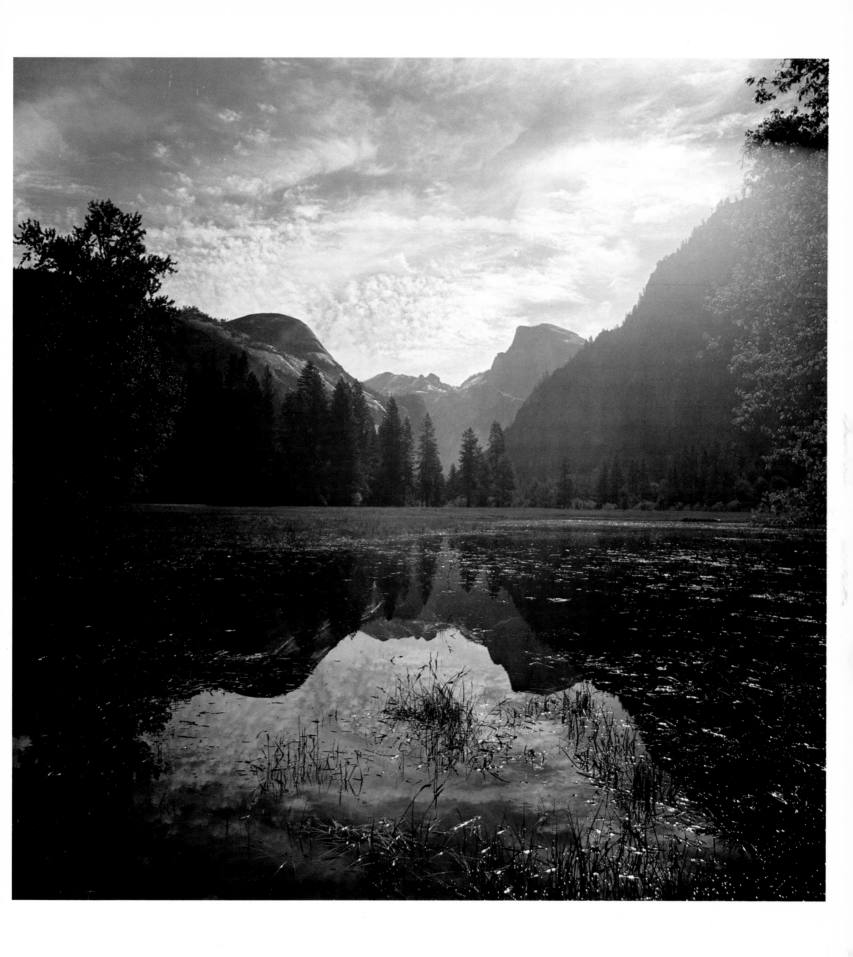

21   *Lost Arrow from Yosemite Lodge*

Magnificent
The morning rose, in memorable pomp,
Glorious as e'er I had beheld. . . .
The solid mountains shone, bright as the clouds,
Grain-tinctured, drenched in empyrean light.
(WORDSWORTH, The Prelude)

Lost Arrow, a spire of granite several hundred feet high, arises from the 2700-foot cliff to the east of Yosemite Falls. The view in this picture may be seen from the Yosemite Lodge grounds just south of the north road, on an appropriate winter morning shortly after sunrise.

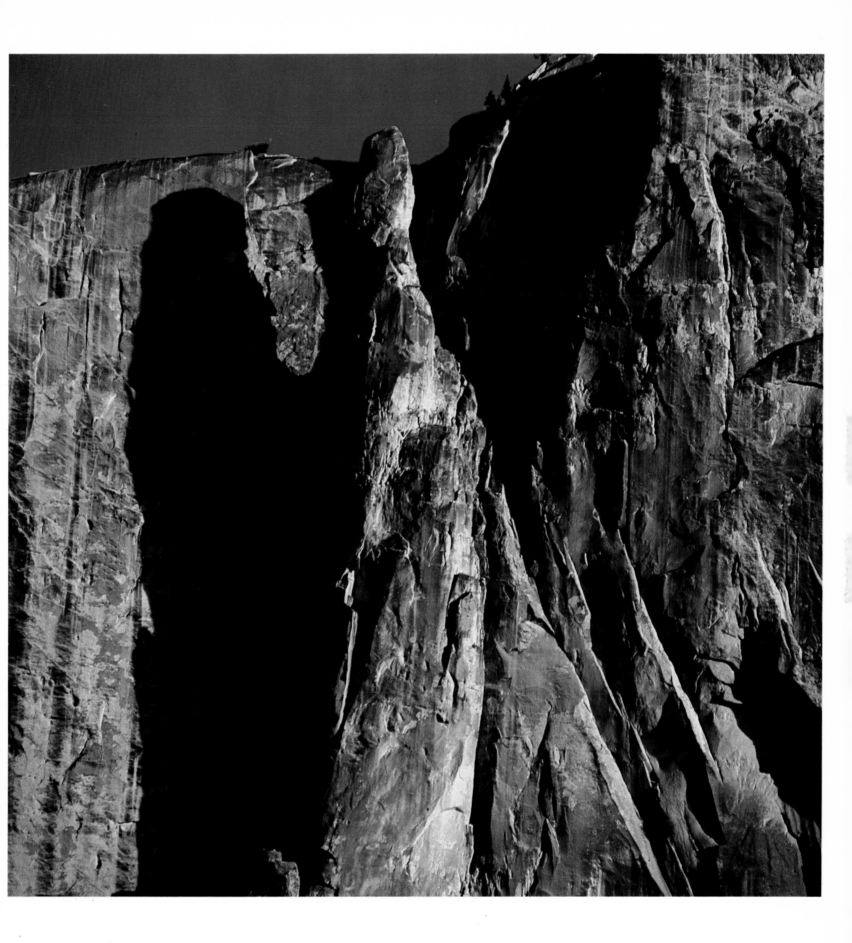

22 *Profile Cliffs from El Capitan Meadow*

In . . . the new world, nature has not only outlined her works on a larger scale, but has painted the whole picture with brighter and more costly colors. . . . The heavens of America appear infinitely higher, the sky is bluer, the air is fresher, the cold is intenser. (THOREAU)

This view of Profile Cliffs, rising 3500 feet above the valley floor on its south wall, between Cathedral Rocks and Sentinel Rock, may be seen from El Capitan meadow. Taft Point, at the edge of the cliff to the right, may be reached by a short, easy hike from the road to Glacier Point, and provides a thrilling view of the valley 3500 feet below.

23   *Three Brothers from the Merced River*

Almost immediately opposite the Sentinel are the Three Brothers, an immense mountain mass with three gables fronting the Valley, one above another. . . . They were named for three brothers, sons of old Tenaya, the Yosemite chief, captured here during the Indian War, at the time of the discovery of the Valley in 1851.

(MUIR)

Between El Capitan and Yosemite Falls, on the north wall of the valley, the Three Brothers, a massive trisected cliff, rises almost 3800 feet above the valley floor, presenting an extreme variety of appearances as one moves about the valley. This picture of them as a classically composed unity was taken from the Merced River bank, south side, just below El Capitan View, on a late afternoon in early autumn.

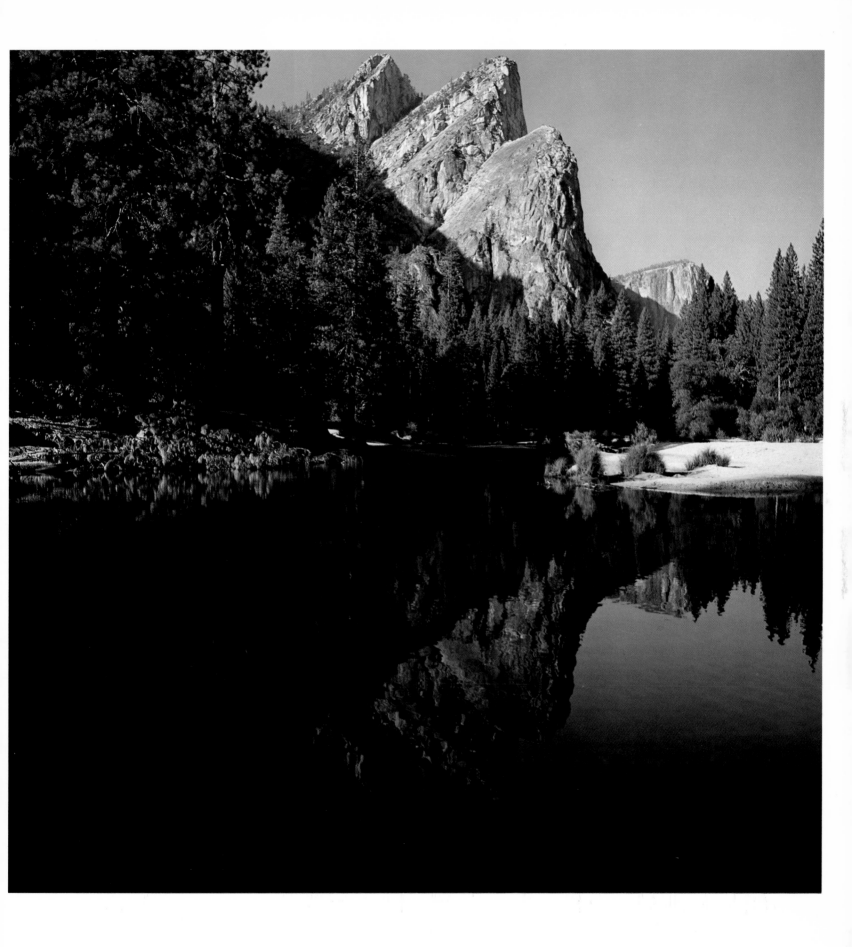

24 Middle Brother, Peak, Sharp

Each of the Three Brothers has its own special interest in addition to the beauty that all three display as a group. One of my favorite views, shown in this picture, is of the peak of the Middle Brother, rising 3000 feet above the valley floor, a luminous twisting thrust of ice-carved granite, as seen from the Rocky Point Picnic Area.

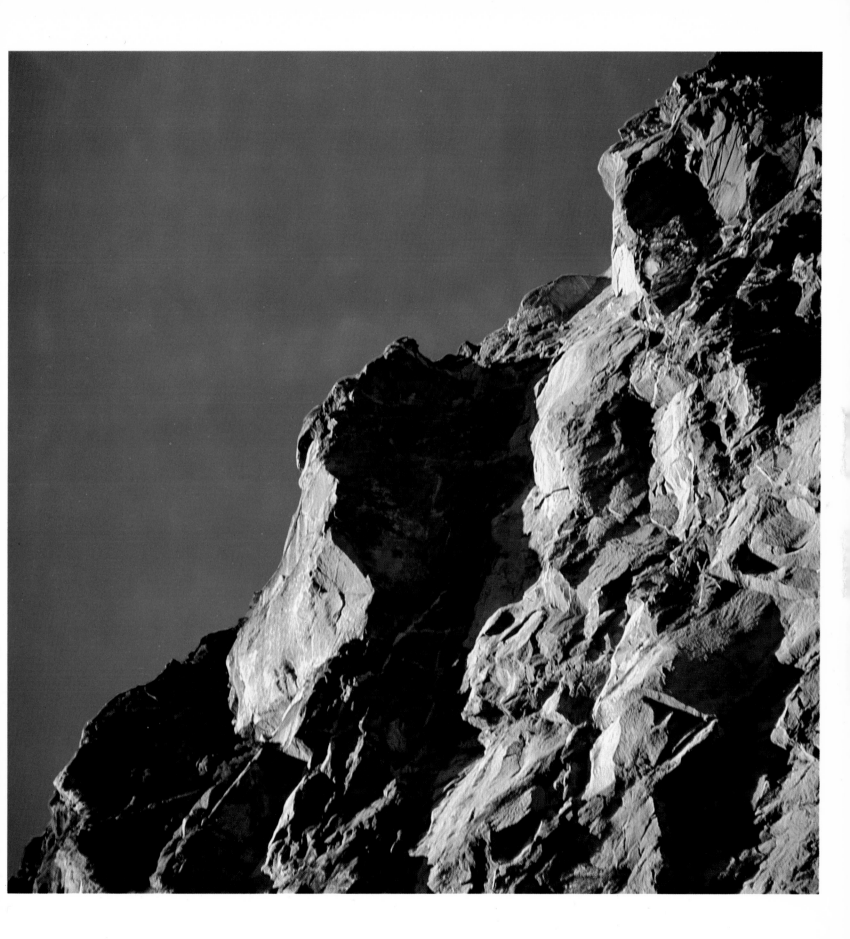

25 Middle Brother, Peak, Mystical

The clouds breaking away a little, we had a glorious wild view.
(THOREAU)

Taking this picture was a memorable experience. It was a rainy spring morning, with gray clouds obscuring all the great valley views, and with the barest suggestion of a possible lifting of the clouds. It seemed to me unlikely that the clouds would lift sufficiently to provide a meaningful panoramic view, but I hoped there would be some local clearing that would offer photographic possibilities. I envisioned the peak of Middle Brother, seen from the Rocky Point Picnic Area, as a remote but fantastically beautiful and moving experience, if there should be a fortuitous local cloud-clearing at that spot. Shielding myself under the branches of a tree from the intermittent rain, I waited. After being discouraged by many cloud liftings that fitfully revealed too little of the great form, I was finally rewarded.

26   *Royal Arches, Washington Column, and North Dome*

It required a separate intention of the eye, a more free and abstracted vision, to see the reflected trees in the sky, than to see the river bottom merely; and so there were manifold visions in the direction of every object.   (THOREAU)

One of the most popular of all Yosemite views is of the great Royal Arches cliff (about 1250 feet above the valley floor) as buttressed by Washington Column on the right (rising 1952 feet) and topped by North Dome (rising 3571 feet). This picture was taken from the Merced River just before Stoneman Bridge, which is shown here.

I remember being very disappointed when I first viewed this scene: the river was lower than I expected, and I was looking at sand rather than water. But I felt that a great scene was there if I could only find the right spot—which I finally did, standing in the river with my tripod set firmly on the sand of the river bed.

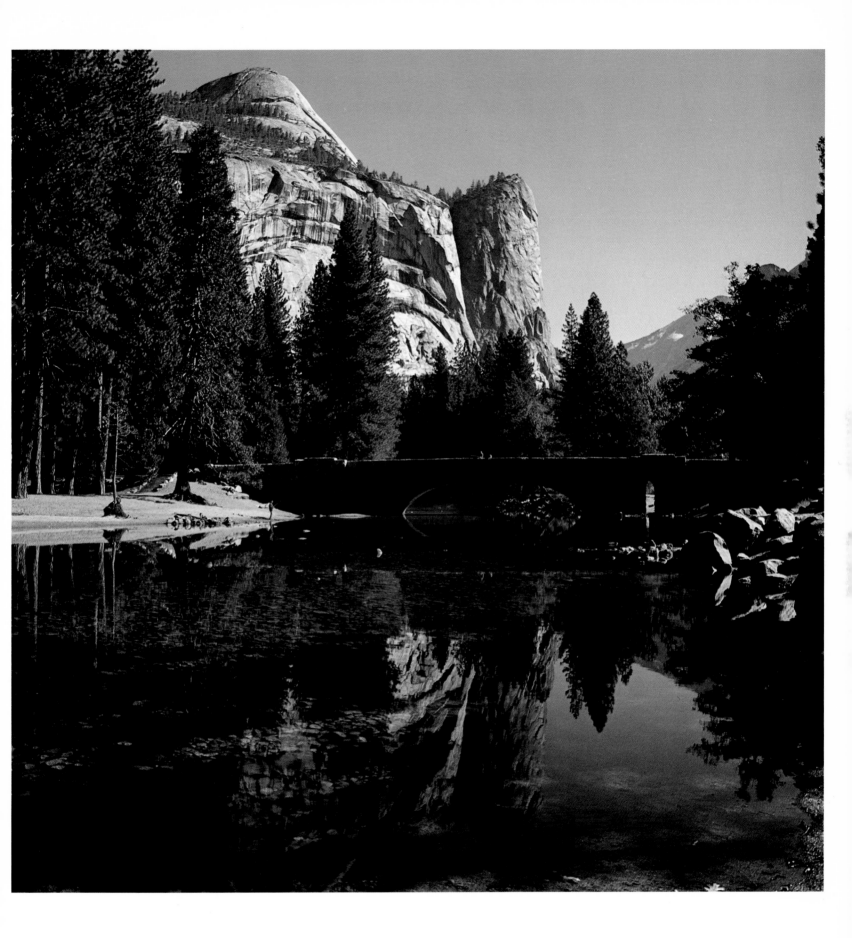

27 Royal Arches, Washington Column, and North Dome

When seen from the south road near Camp Curry on a late afternoon in autumn, Royal Arches, Washington Column, and North Dome seem to be posing for their individual portraits in harmonious unity—the sweeping curves of Royal Arches, the bold thrust of Washington Column, and the classic arc of North Dome all blazing in splendor.

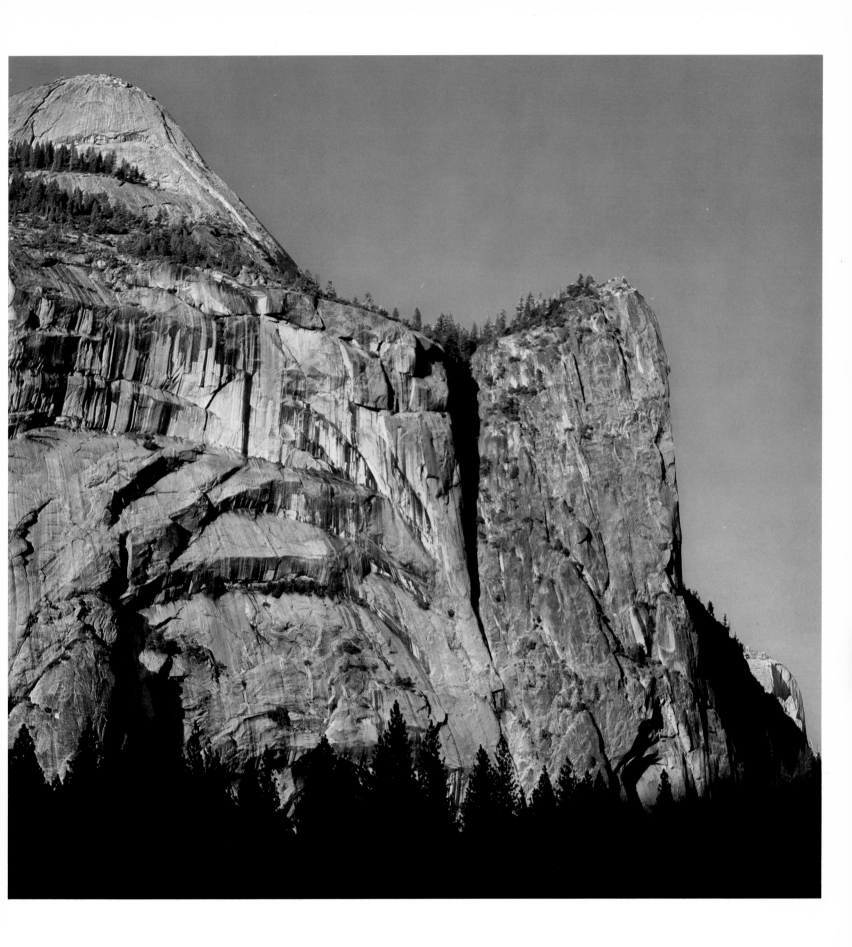

28   Glacier Point Cliff

This picture was an unexpected bonus. I had been searching for a special view of the Royal Arches, Washington Column, and North Dome cliff from the Merced River near Stoneman Bridge one spring morning and was walking away disappointed when I looked up and found this view waiting for me, stark and magnificent.

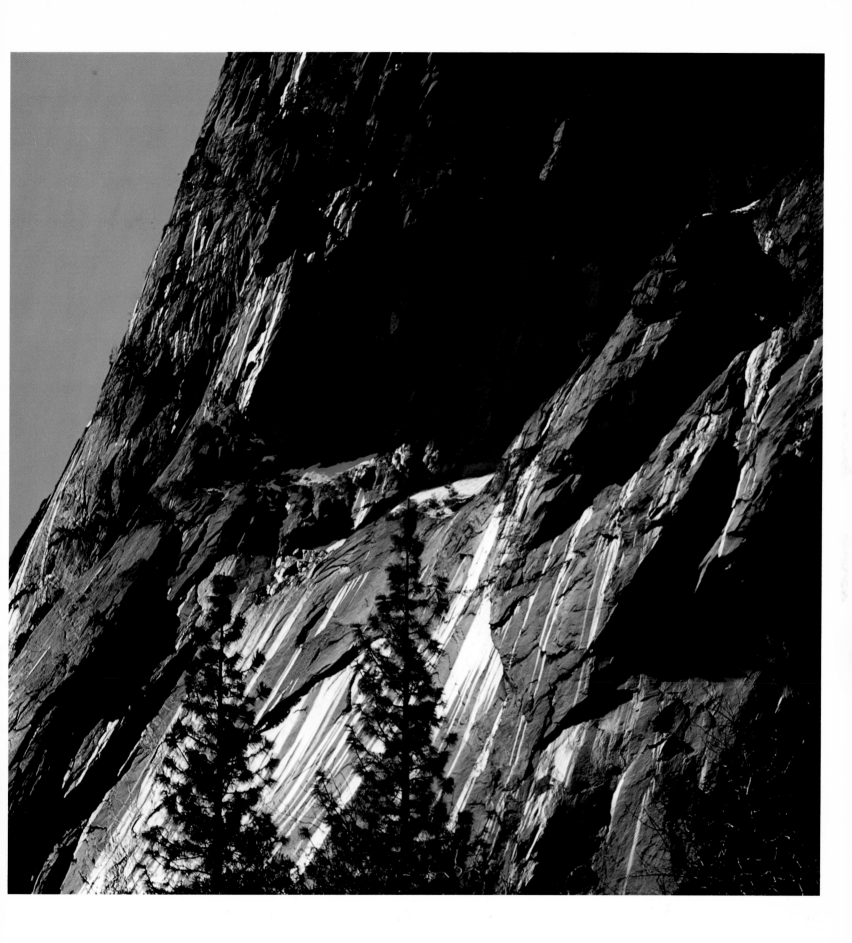

29 *Valley Sunset*

Really to see the sun rise or go down every day . . .
would preserve us sane forever. (THOREAU)

This view was another unexpected delight. I had turned away from Sentinel Bridge, disappointed in the dullness of the light on Half Dome, when, to the west, I saw all sorts of strange colors and shapes in the sunset sky. Rushing to a vantage point on the south road just west of Sentinel Bridge, I found an appealing combination.

THE FALLS

Yosemite Falls, the most popular of all the falls, is a symphony of flowing form. From the wild leap of the Upper Fall (1430 feet) to the tumultuous, rock-gouging, churning Middle Cascade (675 feet) and the classic smashing climax of the Lower Fall (320 feet), it pours forth an ode to joyous abandon.

Vernal Fall (317 feet) is a vision of loveliness in form and color. Sliding smoothly over the lip of a great, dark cliff, it crashes into giant rocks below, generating a spray of heavenly rainbows, when the light is right, that seem to envelop the viewer on the Mist Trail in an unearthly bliss.

Nevada Fall (594 feet) is a display of the fury of water in motion, as it plunges through a narrow channel of rock that thrusts it forth in violent bursts of vaulting form and shifting light.

From the Introduction

30   Yosemite Falls, Winter

The morn, in russet mantle clad
(SHAKESPEARE, Hamlet)

The beauty of Yosemite Falls varies from season to season, as well as from day to day and hour to hour. But even within any one season there are many different kinds of beauty displayed. Winter in Yosemite often finds the falls coldly brilliant, but, as this view shows, also warmly glowing. This picture was taken from the north road, just east of Yosemite Creek, shortly after sunrise.

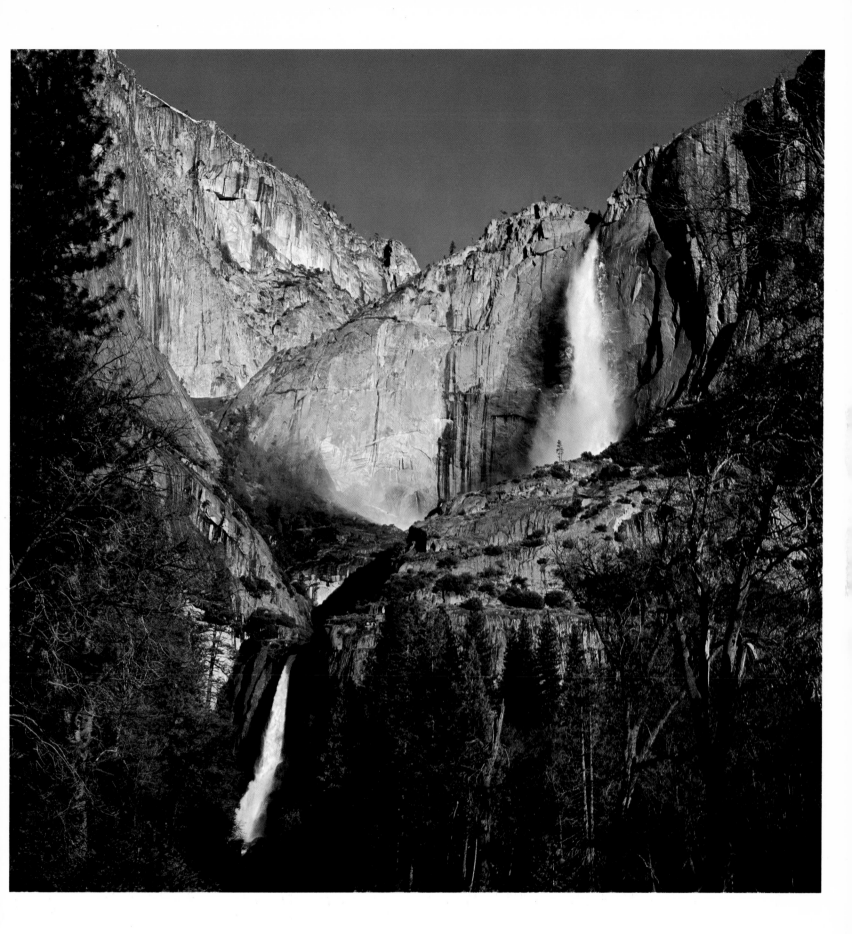

31 Lower Yosemite Fall

One of the most popular and most thrilling views of Yosemite Falls is from the base of Lower Yosemite Fall, which is easily reached by a short walk of a few hundred yards from the parking lot across the north road opposite Yosemite Lodge. It is most impressive in the spring as the enduring rock seems to embrace the tumultuous flowing waters. The extraordinary combination of power and beauty at this spot makes it a special favorite of lovers of waterfalls. I have known a devotee of this view who spent hours at a time at this spot, enthralled by the joyous song and the boisterous dance of the water.

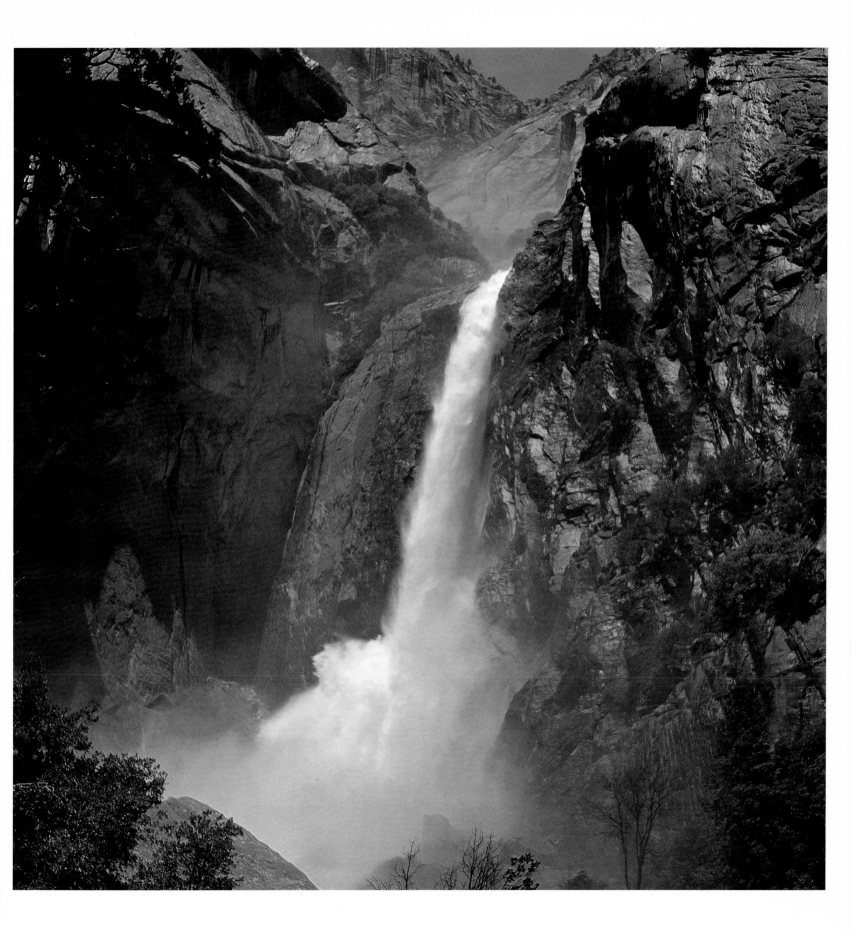

32 Upper Yosemite Fall, Rainbow

Amid the spray and foam and fine-ground mist ever rising from the various falls and cataracts there is an affluence and variety of iris bows scarcely known to visitors who stay only a day or two. Both day and night, winter and summer, this divine light may be seen wherever water is falling, dancing, singing; telling the heart-peace of Nature amid the wildest displays of her power.   (MUIR)

This picture of Upper Yosemite Fall illuminated by a rainbow was taken from Yosemite Village early one autumn morning as I watched with almost hypnotic fascination the dazzling flow of seemingly infinite combinations of rainbow color and swirling foam.

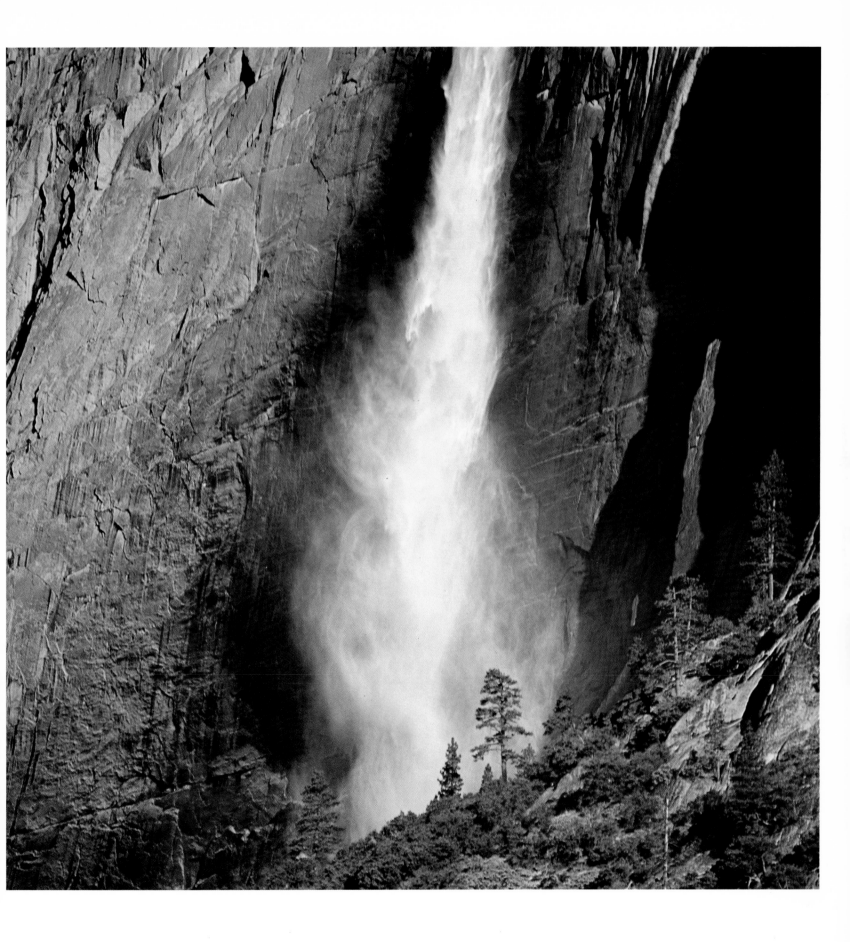

33   *Upper Yosemite Fall Mist, Rainbow*

Sunbeams play with spray and mist in rainbow colors.
(MUIR)

The mist at the base of Upper Yosemite Fall spreads out for hundreds of feet in all directions, providing an opportunity for the first warm rays of deep winter sunshine to create a rhapsody of lovely color, as in this picture. Of all the seasons of the year, perhaps winter is when warmth of color is most deeply appreciated.

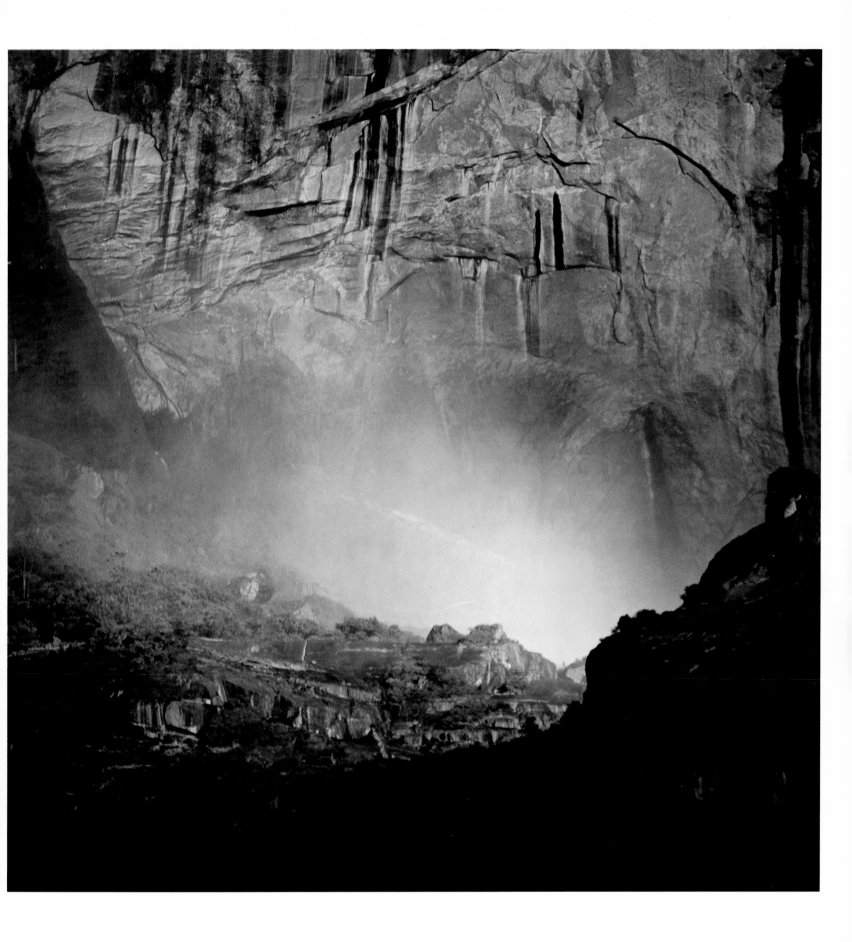

34   *Vernal Fall from Lady Franklin Rock*

Vernal Fall may be seen from Washburn Point or Glacier Point without any hiking strain, the viewpoints being close to the road. Both viewpoints reveal spectacular mountain scenes. But to get the feel of Vernal, my favorite as the loveliest of all the great falls of Yosemite, one needs to hike. Perhaps the best view of Vernal Fall that is close and yet panoramic may be had from Lady Franklin Rock, on the trail from Happy Isles, from which this picture was taken one spring morning.

35   *Vernal Fall from the Mist Trail, Blue*

My own favorite view of Vernal Fall is from a spot on the Mist Trail a few hundred yards past and a couple of hundred feet above Lady Franklin Rock. To reach this spot, one climbs through a drenching mist. Rarely, it is so heavy that one can safely ascend the rocky trail only on hands and knees. Usually, it is less intimidating and provides merely an exhilarating soaking. Just above the mist, my favorite view appears. This particular scene, on a cloudy day, first displayed nothing but a barely visible flow of dull water, in dull surroundings. Then, as my eyes adjusted to the dim light, the form and color challenged my attention.

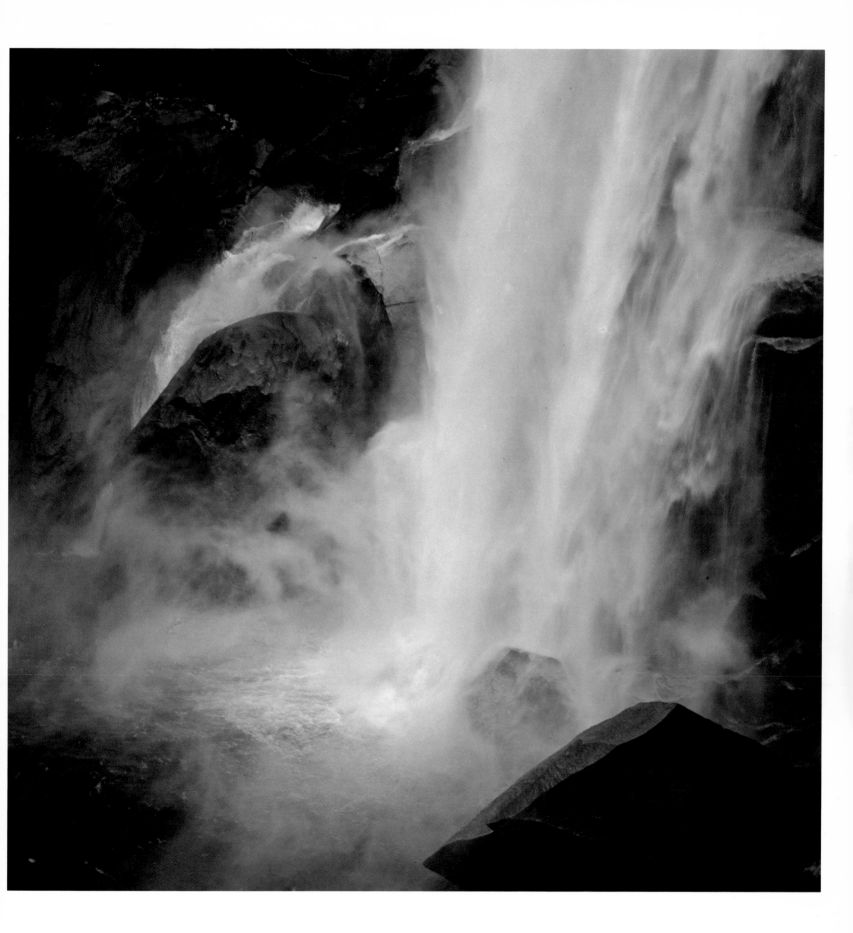

36   *Vernal Fall from the Mist Trail, Beige*

My favorite view of Vernal Fall, as described on the preceding page, here displays the fall with warm, gentle, luminous tones that linger lovingly in my memory.

37   *Vernal Fall from the Mist Trail, Rainbow*

The enchantment of Vernal Fall is, perhaps, best experienced in a rainbow scene, lush with verdant beauty and drenched with joyous light. The most ethereally beautiful experience of my life occurred one spring morning on the Mist Trail, when the rainbow mist of Vernal Fall seemed to envelop me in a kaleidoscopic paradise.

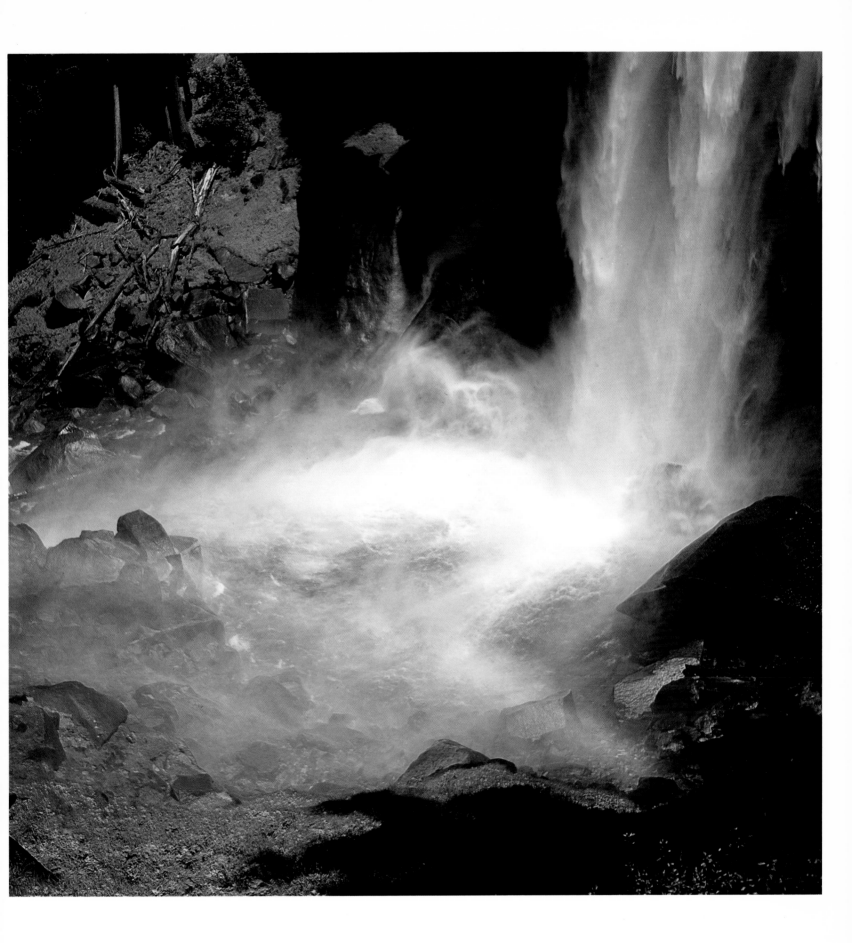

38   Nevada Fall from the Zig-Zag Trail

Nevada Fall, just above Vernal Fall, like Vernal may be seen in beauty and with ease from Washburn Point or Glacier Point. Also like Vernal, however, it is best seen from a trail. The most dramatic view of Nevada Fall may be seen from the Zig-Zag Trail, which is a continuation of the Mist Trail for a couple of miles and a few hundred feet in altitude. From this trail, from which this picture was taken, one gains the single most furiously powerful waterfall view in Yosemite, as the churning, leaping water thunders past.

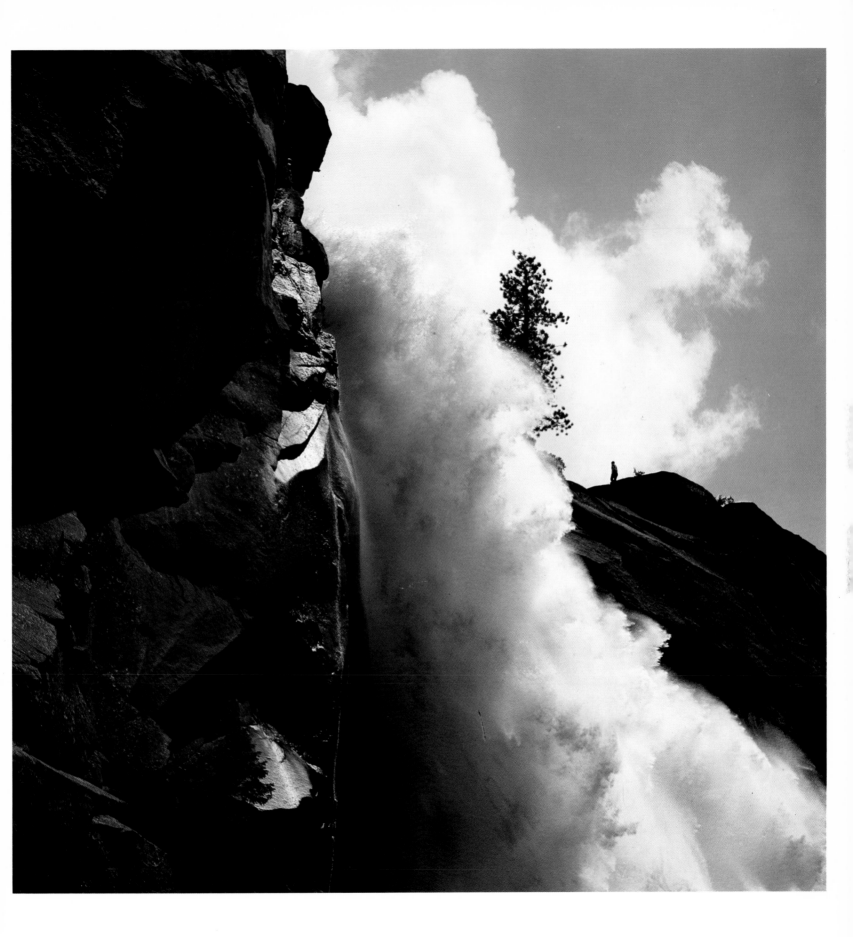

THE RIVER

Among the great rivers of the West, the Merced would seem to have no special excellence, except for the stunning waterfalls and cascades it generates. It is simply another beautiful, clear Sierra stream, smoothly winding its way through meadow, forest, and cliff. However, as it reflects the colors of meadow, forest, cliff, and sky, and boldly mirrors the great forms, adding its own various moods to those about it, the Merced enhances the glories of Yosemite.

Among the many Yosemite streams is Tenaya Creek, famous for its Mirror Lake, which reflects serene images of Mount Watkins, Clouds Rest, and Half Dome.

From the Introduction

39   Happy Isles

The brooks sing carols and glees to the spring.
(THOREAU)

Perhaps the most popular view of the Merced River is from Happy Isles, where the Merced flows around some small wooded islands and reunites in one merry flow just before the bridge. The whirling dance of the Merced River at Happy Isles may be captured from many viewpoints, such as this one, where the trees seem to be flowing with the water.

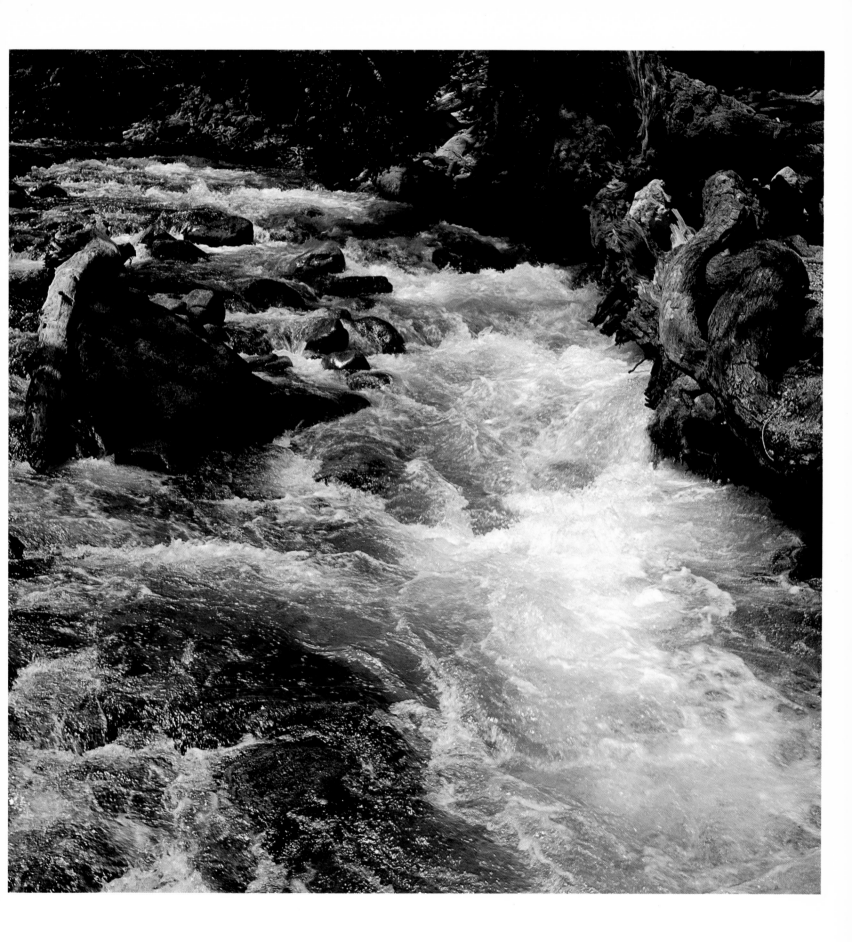

40   Mirror Lake

Tenaya Creek, threading its way from the High Country to the Yosemite Valley through Tenaya Canyon, with Mt. Watkins (8500 feet) on the south and Clouds Rest (9926 feet) and Half Dome (8842 feet) on the north, pauses at Mirror Lake just before it flows into the Merced River. Here the beauty of Yosemite, especially Mt. Watkins, is strikingly displayed in crystal sharpness on the shining surface of the lake. The most popular time for a view of Mirror Lake is sunrise.

41   Merced River, Winter

Its surface is lit up here and there with a fine-grained silvery sparkle which makes the river appear something celestial.   (THOREAU)

In winter, the Merced River often displays a serene, cool brilliance, as in this view with Sentinel Rock (rising 3000 feet) in the background. The picture was taken from the river near the south road, about a half mile west of El Capitan View. The valley as a whole was shaded from the low winter sun, which accentuated the illumination of the view.

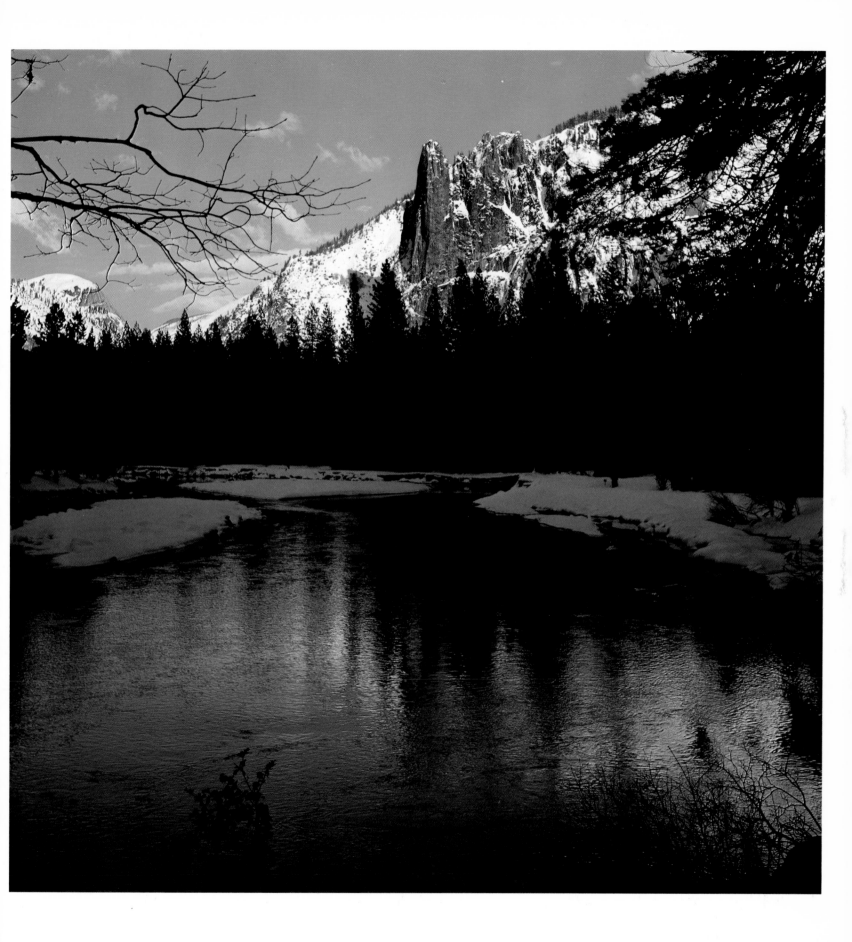

42   Merced River, Autumn

So we saunter toward the Holy Land, till one day the sun shall shine more brightly than ever he has done, shall perchance shine into our minds and hearts, and light up our whole lives with a great awakening light, as warm and serene and golden as on a bank-side in autumn.   (THOREAU)

I stumbled upon this view one late-October morning as I was searching for autumn color along the Merced River. To me, it represents the warming heart of that season.

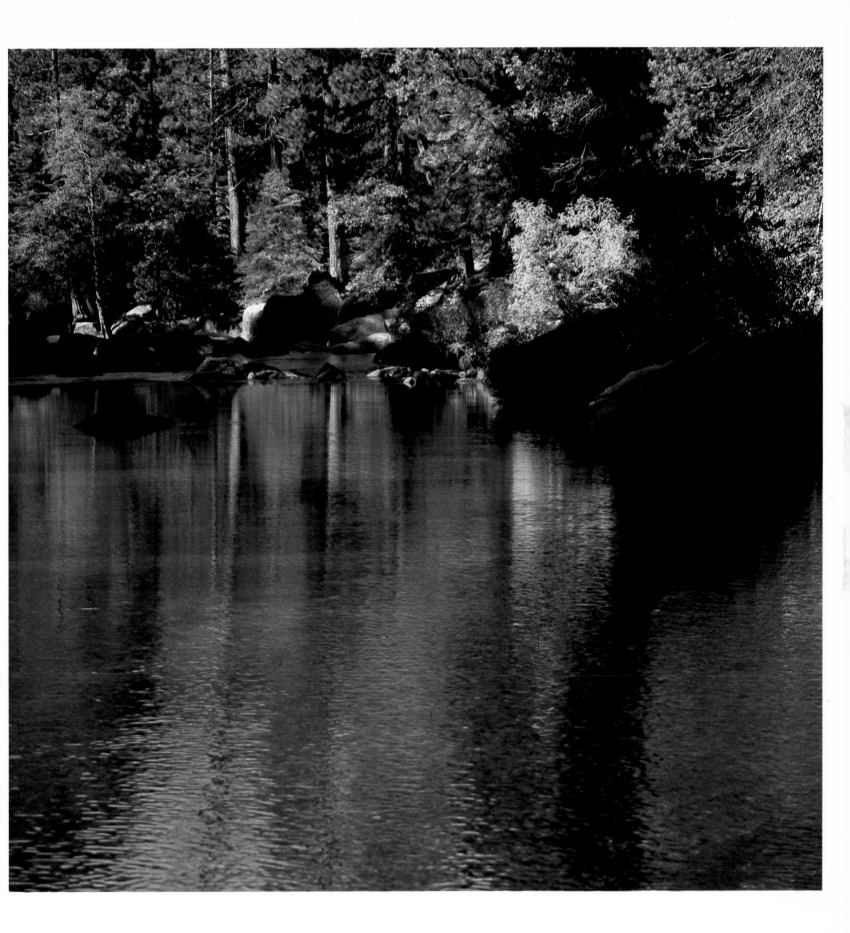

43   Merced River, Abstract

The shallowest still water is unfathomable. Wherever the trees and skies are reflected there is more than Atlantic depth, and no danger of fancy running aground.   (THOREAU)

Reflections in the river are a springboard for the imagination, and the quick succession of infinitely various forms and colors leads the mind to lose itself in enchanting visions.

THE TREES

T HE trees of Yosemite are varied in their beauty—the massive Sequoias, the tall pines and firs, the broad-leafed oaks, maples, and cottonwoods, among many others.

From the Introduction

44   Sequoia Tree "Grizzly Giant," Mariposa Grove

*The Big Tree (Sequoia gigantea) is nature's forest masterpiece, and, as far as I know, the greatest of living things. It belongs to an ancient stock, as its remains in the old rocks show, and has a strange air of other days about it, a thorobred look inherited from the long ago, the auld lang syne of trees. Once the genus was common, and with many species flourished in the now desolate Arctic regions, in the interior of North America, and in Europe; but in long eventful wanderings from climate to climate only two species have survived the hardships they had to encounter, the **gigantea** and **sempervirens**: the former now restricted to the western slopes of the Sierra, the other to the Coast Mountains, and both to California, excepting a few groves of redwood which extend into Oregon. The Pacific coast in general is the paradise of conifers. Here nearly all of them are giants, and display a beauty and magnificence unknown elsewhere. The climate is mild, the ground never freezes, and moisture and sunshine abound all the year. Nevertheless, it is not easy to account for the colossal size of the sequoias. The largest are about three hundred feet high, and thirty feet in diameter. Who, of all the dwellers of the plains and prairies and fertile forests of roundheaded oak and maple, hickory and elm, ever dreamed that earth could bear such growths?—and so old, thousands of them still living had already counted their years by tens of centuries when Columbus set sail from Spain, and were in the vigor of youth or middle age when the star led the Chaldean sages to the infant Saviour's cradle. As far as man is concerned, they are the same yesterday, today, and forever, emblems of permanence.* (MUIR)

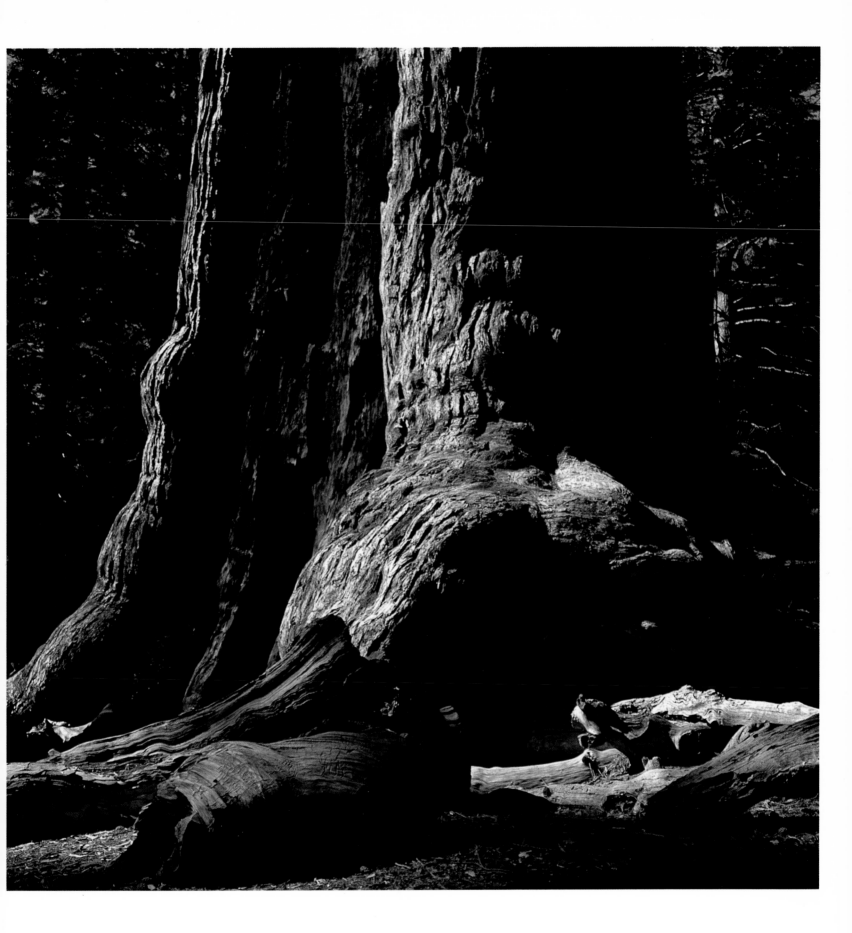

45　Ponderosa Pine Tree, Bark

The Yellow Pine, as it is commonly called, because of its superior powers of enduring variations of climate and soil, has a more extensive range than any other conifer growing on the Sierra. On the western slope it is first met at an elevation of about 2000 feet, and extends nearly to the upper limit of the timber line.

Where there is plenty of free sunshine and other conditions are favorable, it presents . . . a symmetrical spire, formed of a straight round trunk, clad with innumerable branches that are divided over and over again. About one half of the trunk is commonly branchless, but where it grows at all close, three fourths or more become naked; the tree presenting then a more slender and elegant shaft than any other tree in the woods. The bark is mostly arranged in massive plates, some of them measuring four or five feet in length by eighteen inches in width, with a thickness of three or four inches, forming a quite marked and distinguishing feature. The needles are of a fine, warm, yellow-green color, six to eight inches long, firm and elastic, and crowded in handsome, radiant tassels on the upturning ends of the branches. The cones are about three or four inches long, and two and a half wide, growing in close, sessile clusters among the leaves.

The species attains its noblest form in filled-up lake basins, especially in those of the older yosemites, and so prominent a part does it form of their groves that it may well be called the Yosemite Pine. Ripe specimens favorably situated are almost always 200 feet or more in height, and the branches clothe the trunk nearly to the ground.　(MUIR)

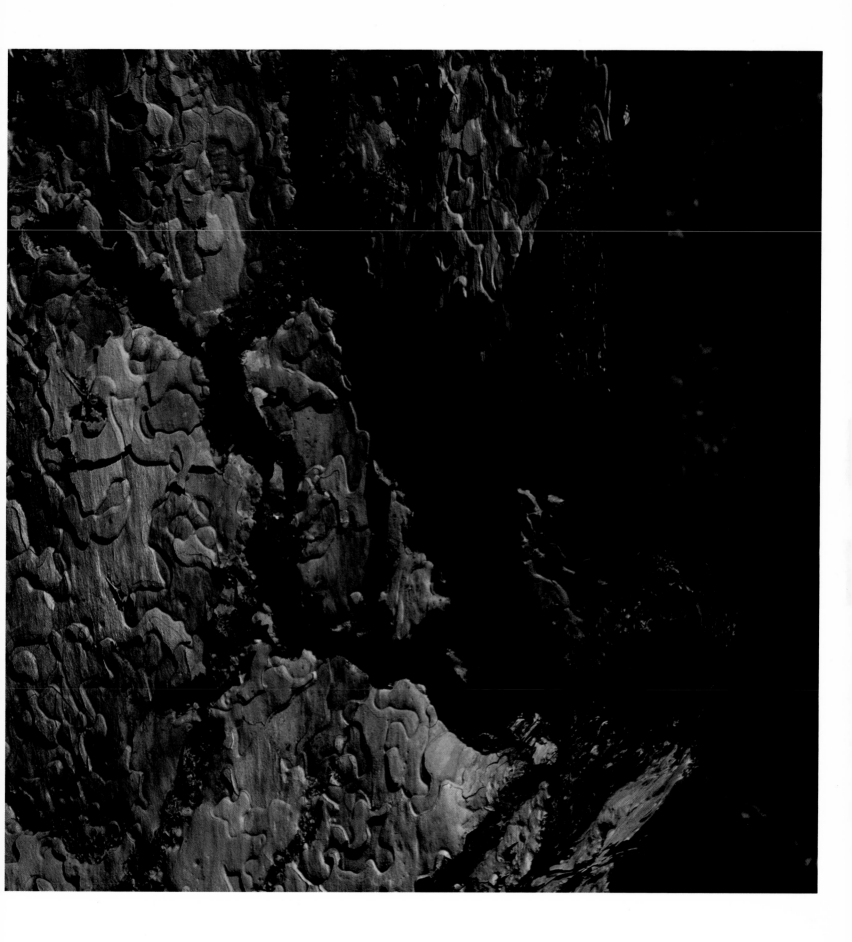

46   Incense Cedar Tree at Valley View

The Incense Cedar is another of the giants quite generally distributed throughout this portion of the forest, without exclusively occupying any considerable area, or even making extensive groves. It ascends to about 5000 feet on the warmer hillsides, and reaches the climate most congenial to it at about from 3000 to 4000 feet, growing vigorously at this elevation on all kinds of soil, and in particular it is capable of enduring more moisture about its roots than any of its companions, excepting only the Sequoia.

The largest specimens are about 150 feet high, and seven feet in diameter. The bark is brown, or a singularly rich tone very attractive to artists, and the foliage is tinted with a warmer yellow than that of any other evergreen in the woods. Casting your eye over the general forest from some ridge-top, the color alone of its spiry summits is sufficient to identify it in any company.   (MUIR)

Sunrise at Valley View is one of Yosemite's most beautiful scenes, with the golden glow of the sky on the Merced River lighting up the valley behind it. But if one turns one's back on this glorious view, in the first few minutes after sunrise, there is displayed the glowing trunk of a mature incense cedar as it greets the first rays of the morning sun.

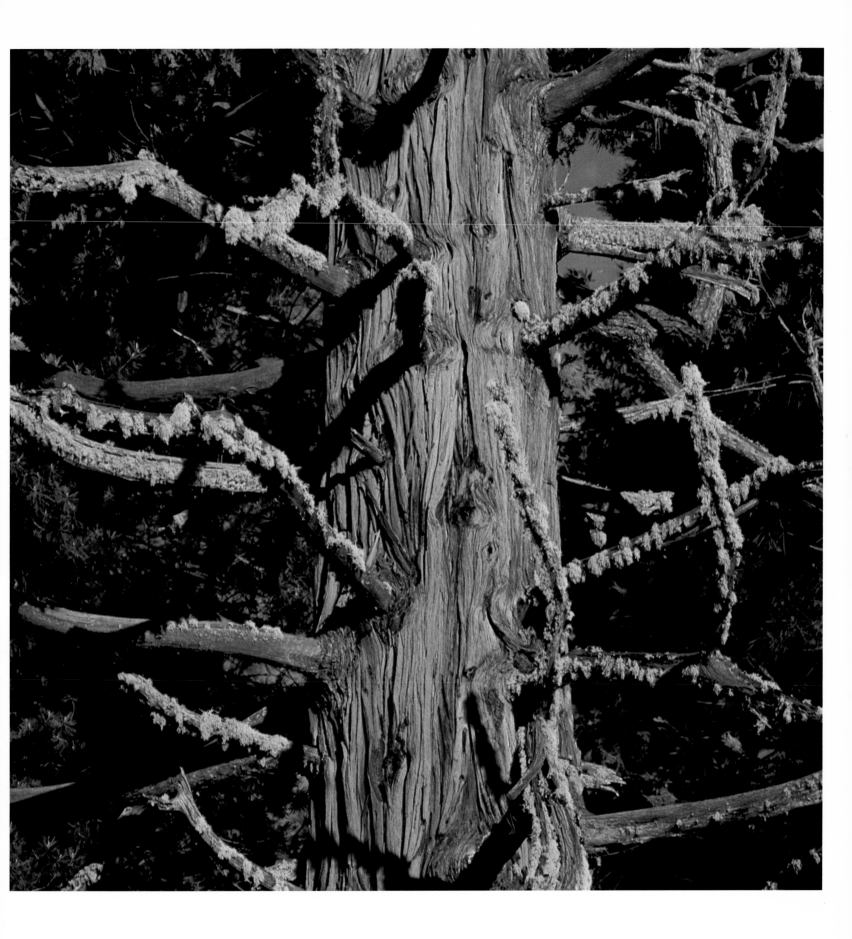

47   Cottonwood Tree and Merced River

October is the month for painted leaves. Their rich glow now flashes round the world. As fruits and leaves and the day itself acquire a bright tint just before they fall, so the year nears its setting. October is its sunset sky; November the later twilight.   (THOREAU)

One of my favorite viewpoints in the valley is the Rocky Point Picnic Area. Here may be viewed a sweeping panorama of the eastern half of the valley—from the great cliff of the Three Brothers to Yosemite Falls to Royal Arches, Washington Column, and North Dome, to Clouds Rest, Half Dome, and Sentinel Rock—all calling for a wide-angle lens to capture their sweep as they pose behind the Merced River. In addition, however, some of my favorite intimate scenes are also displayed here, and, at times, autumn decorates the river view, as here, with indescribably beautiful tones of color and light.

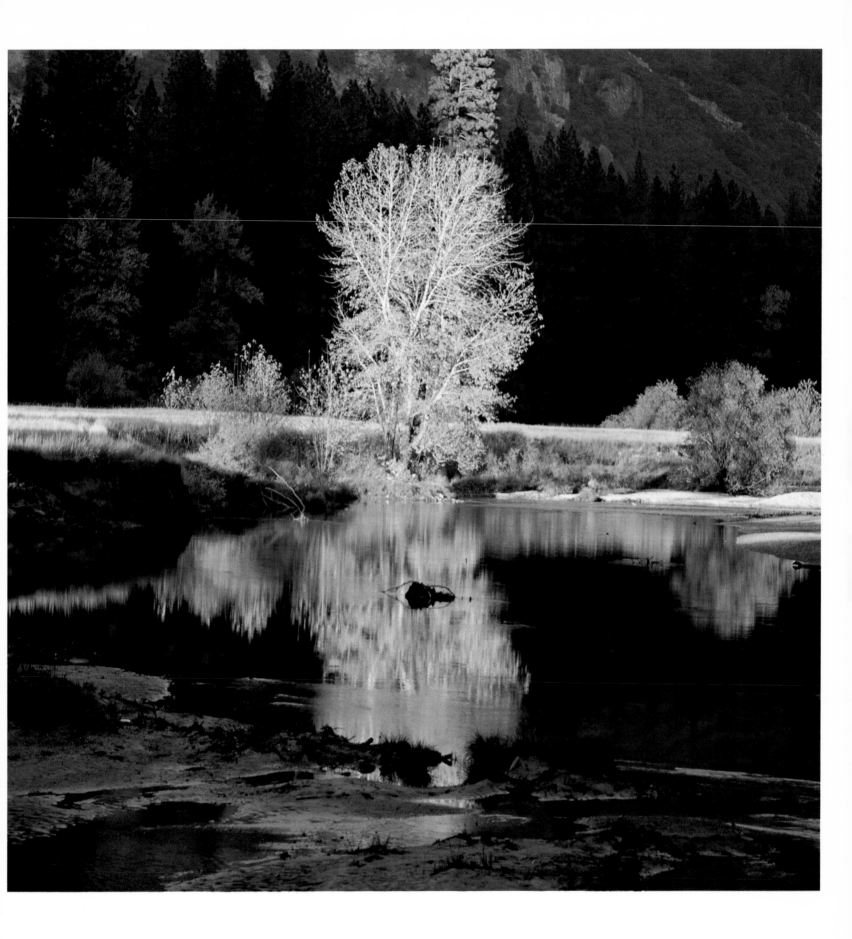

HALF DOME FROM SENTINEL BRIDGE

M<small>UIR</small> called Half Dome "the most beautiful and most sublime of all the wonderful Yosemite rocks," and I have been fascinated by its various essences and appearances. From Mirror Lake it is an overpowering mass; from Glacier Point it is a soaring, proud dome; from Sentinel Bridge it is majestic and serene.

Capturing the moods of Half Dome from Sentinel Bridge has been one of my favorite preoccupations. From scores of pictures I have chosen four to illustrate the moods of Half Dome as seen in the four seasons.

From the Introduction

48   *Half Dome from Sentinel Bridge, Spring Morning*

Now the wide upper portion of the Valley is displayed to our view, with the finely modeled North Dome, the Royal Arches and Washington Column on our left; Glacier Point, with its massive magnificent sculpture on the right; and in the middle, directly in front, looms Tissiack or Half Dome, the most beautiful and sublime of all the wonderful Yosemite rocks, rising in serene majesty from flowery groves and meadows to a height of 4750 feet.   (M<small>UIR</small>)

It is glorious to behold the ribbon of water sparkling in the sun, the bare face of the pond full of glee and youth.   (T<small>HOREAU</small>)

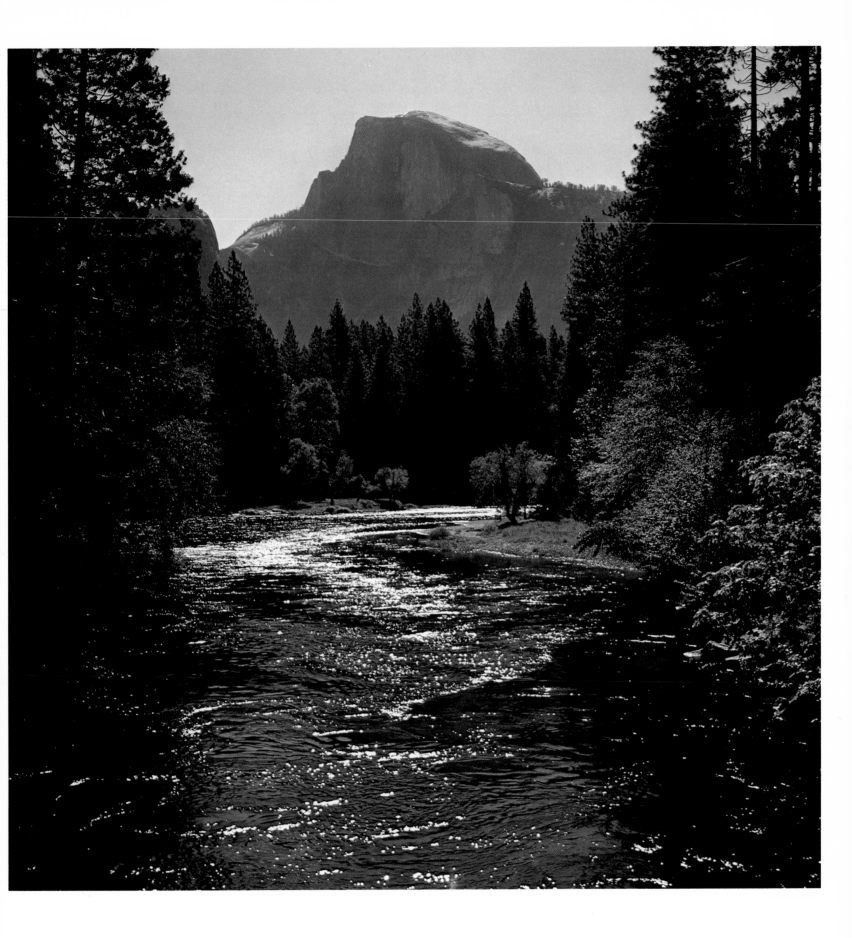

49 *Half Dome from Sentinel Bridge, Autumn Afternoon*

During these blessed color-days no cloud darkens the sky, the winds are gentle, and the landscape rests, hushed everywhere, and indescribably impressive.   (MUIR)

Half Dome, from Sentinel Bridge, enriching and being enriched by the Merced River and the trees of Yosemite, is a fantastically varied scene, displaying to optimum advantage the beauties of nature and summoning up the myriad moods of man.

In springtime, shortly after sunrise, as in the preceding picture, the heart leaps with the exhilarating promise of glorious life ahead. And early on an afternoon in autumn, rich with light and color, the promise seems realized.

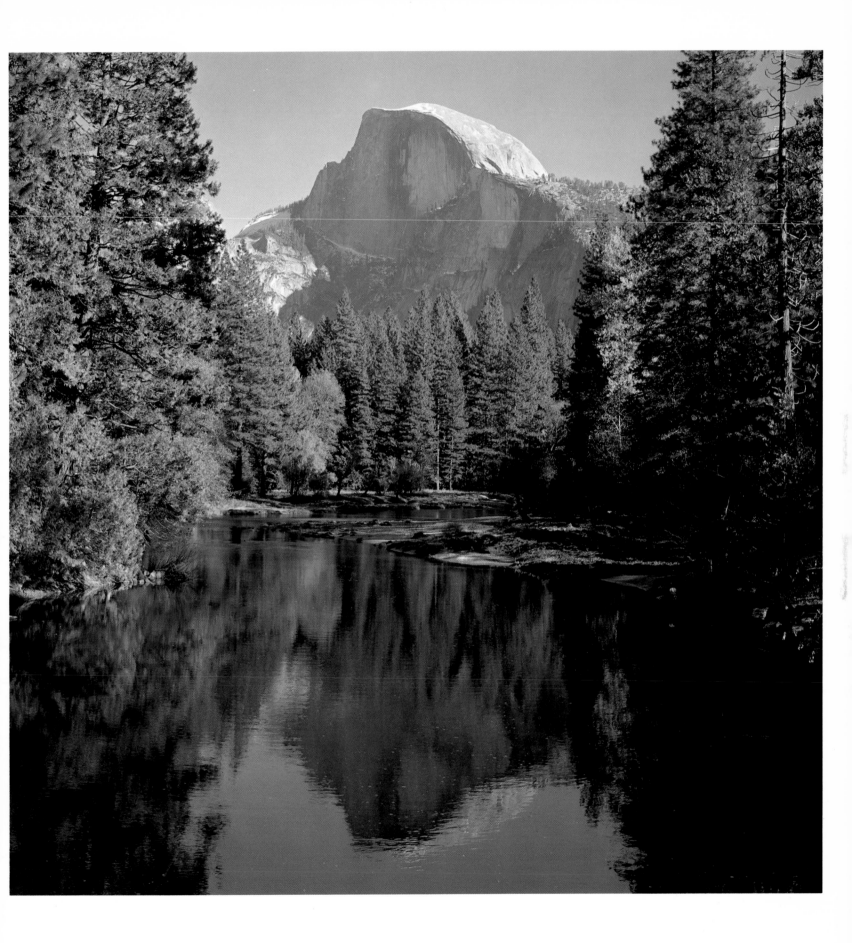

50 *Half Dome from Sentinel Bridge, Summer Evening*

Soft stillness and the night
Become the touches of sweet harmony.

(SHAKESPEARE, The Merchant of Venice)

Taking pictures after the sun goes down isn't easy, but, if you are persistent, or lucky, the results may be thrilling. The easy way is usually not the best way. As Spinoza said, "All things noble are as difficult as they are rare."

This picture was taken at 9 o'clock on a summer evening, when, "flushed by the purple light of . . . evening" (Muir) the velvety Merced River seemed to cast a spell over Half Dome and the world.

132   HALF DOME FROM SENTINEL BRIDGE

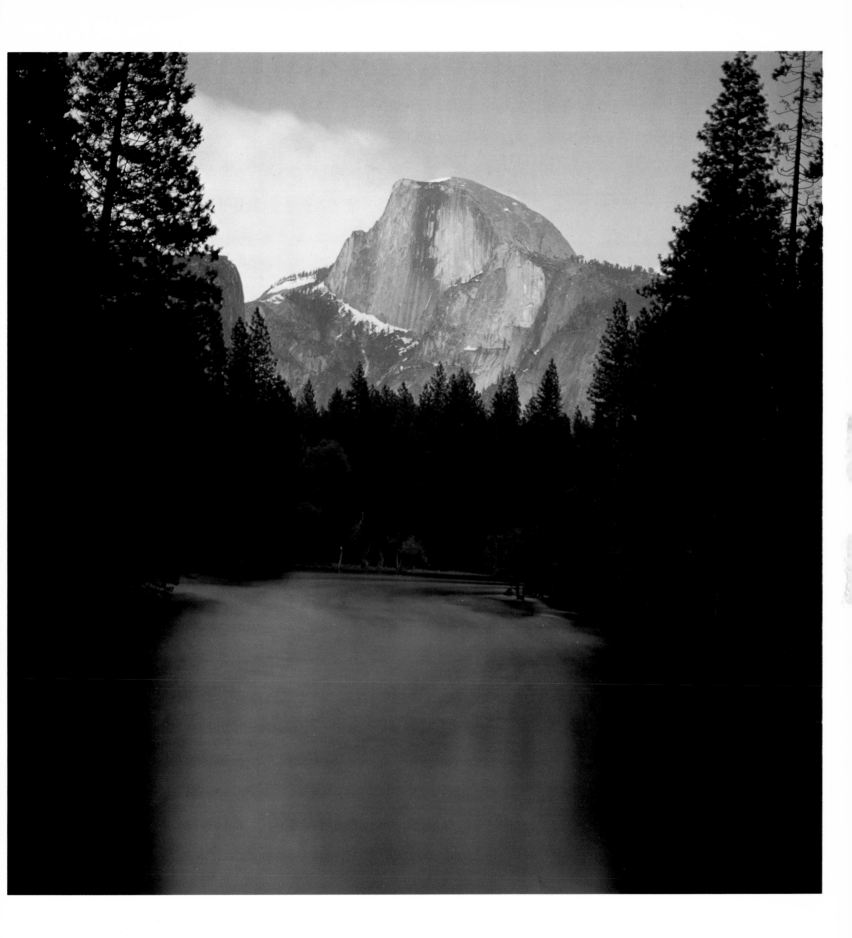

51　Half Dome from Sentinel Bridge, Winter Sunset

The rocky summits, split and rent,
Formed turret, dome or battlement,
Nor were these earth-born castles bare,
Nor lacked they many a banner fair;
So wondrous wild, the whole might seem
The scenery of a fairy dream.

(SIR WALTER SCOTT, The Lady of the Lake)

There are times when a view before me seems so unusual that I shake my head, not in disbelief but to readjust my vision, to reassure myself that my fantastic vision is based on reality. This winter sunset of Half Dome, majestically yet softly rising from lavender clouds, provided such an experience.

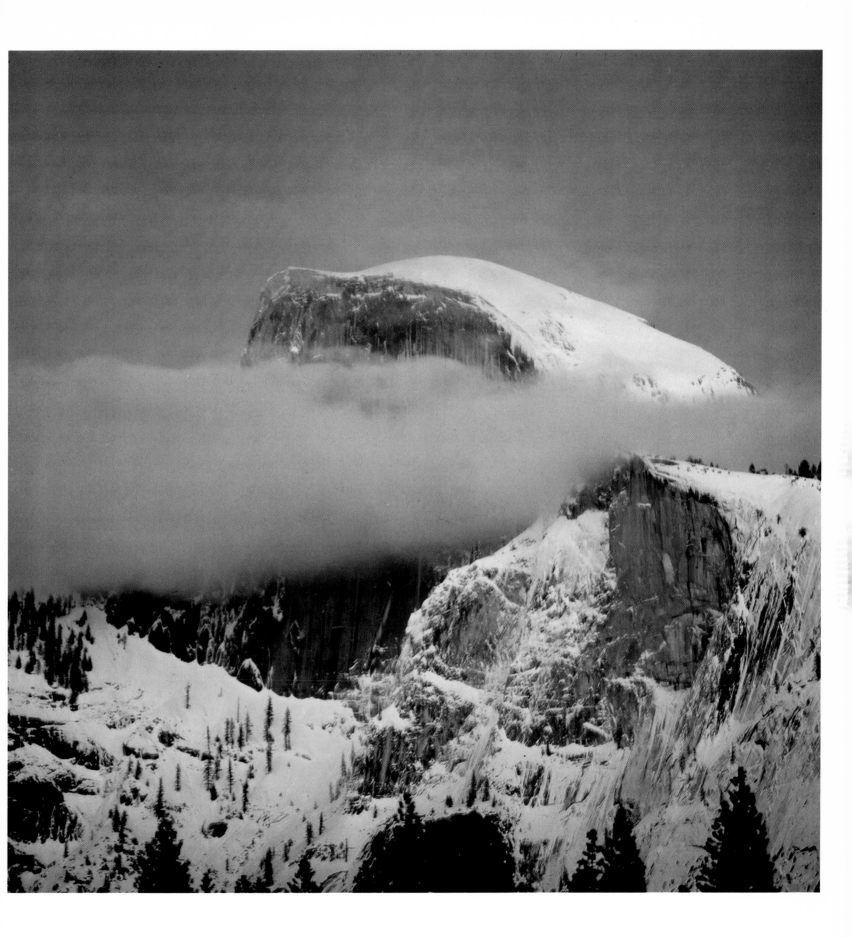

THE HIGH COUNTRY

Outside the valley, the great favorite of Yosemite lovers is the High Country, roughly the region over 7000 feet high. There are a few famous High Country scenes—among them the views of the Sierra peaks and domes from Glacier Point and Sentinel Dome. But, more than individual scenes of great beauty, the High Country offers a different world, in which the air is cleaner, the sky is bluer, the light is more dazzling, and nature is alive with challenge.

From the Introduction

52   Mt. Dana and Mt. Gibbs, Tuolumne Meadows

There are two roads leading to the High Country—to the north the Tioga Road, which leads to the Tioga Pass exit from Yosemite, and the road to Glacier Point, which ends there. Perhaps the most celebrated region in the High Country to the north is Tuolumne Meadows, about 8600 feet high, a summer headquarters for campers and hikers, and a Sierra jewel, which is about 43 miles from the valley. In the spring, before the winter snows have fully melted, but while the snow melt is flooding the meadow, spectacular scenes present themselves. In this picture are Mt. Dana, left (over 13,000 feet), Mt. Gibbs, center (almost 12,800 feet), and Mammoth Mountain, right (over 12,100 feet), spread out and reflected in the flooded Tuolumne River.

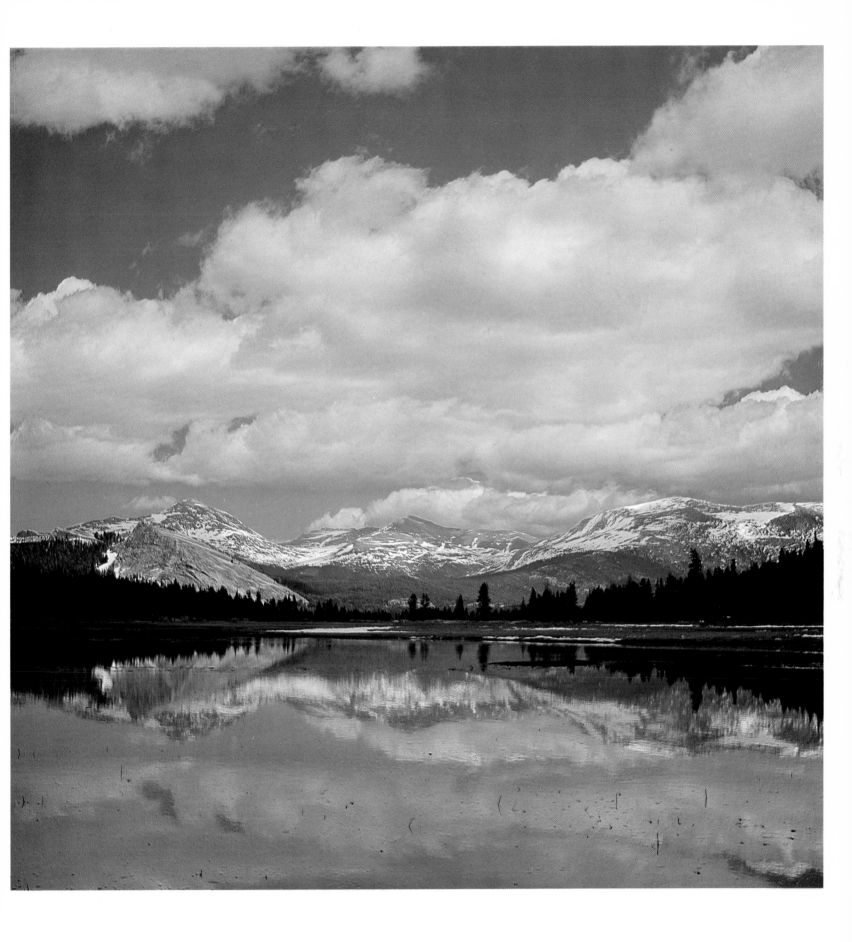

53   *Mt. Dana and Mt. Gibbs, Near Tioga Pass*

Mt. Dana and Mt. Gibbs may be seen not only from Tuolumne Meadows but from many other viewpoints along the Tioga Road. My favorite view of them is from the bank of the Tuolumne River, about a mile west of Tioga Pass. Here, over 9000 feet high, they display their beauty to best panoramic advantage, sometimes dramatically, as in a storm, and sometimes, as in this picture, serenely.

54 Half Dome from Tioga Road

How glorious a greeting the sun gives the mountains! To behold this alone is worth the pains of any excursion a thousand times over. The highest peaks burned like islands in a sea of liquid shade. Then the lower peaks and spires caught the glow. (MUIR)

One of the most spectacular viewpoints along the Tioga Road is Olmsted Point, about 8500 feet high, and about thirty-five miles from the valley. From this spot, as in this picture, Half Dome may be viewed from an unfamiliar aspect, but with all its familiar majesty, as it rises from waves of glacially rounded rock.

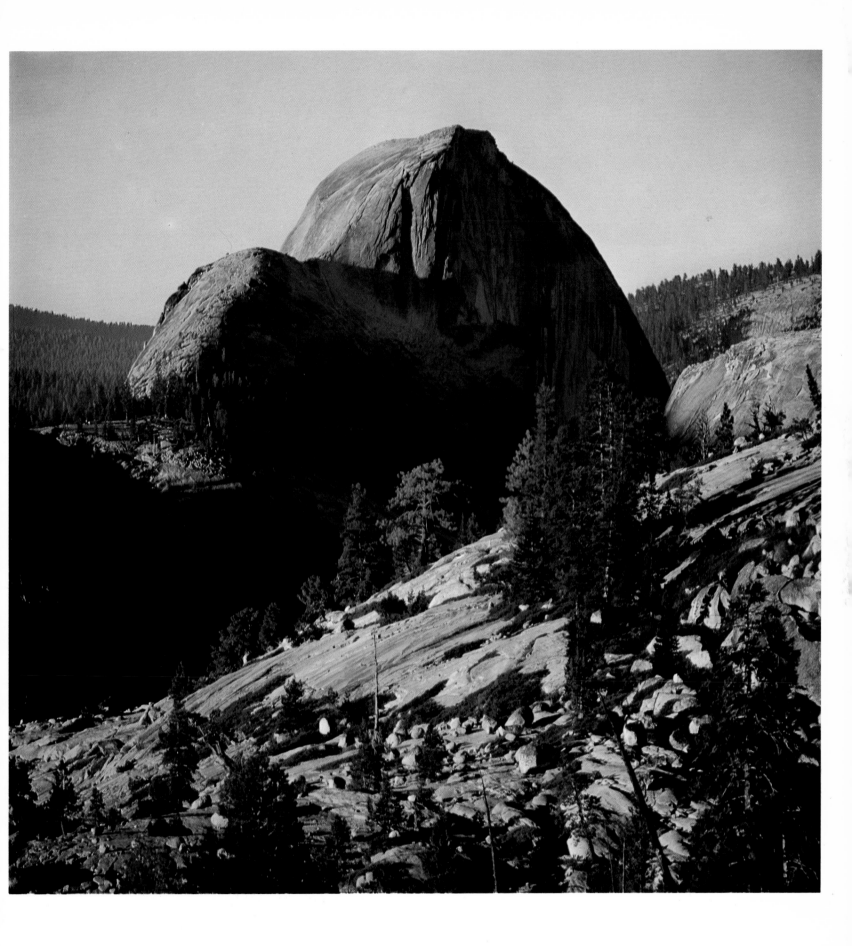

55   *Tenaya Lake, Spring, Winter Snow*

The sinking sound of melting snow is heard in all hills,
and the ice dissolves apace in the ponds.   (THOREAU)

From Olmsted Point there is a beautiful view of Tenaya Lake (almost 8100 feet high), which is justly famous as one of the jewels of the Sierra. About four miles past Olmsted Point you may stand on the shores of Tenaya Lake and capture the beauty of the lake itself and the surrounding mountains. This picture, with Polly Dome at the left and the base of Tenaya Peak at the right, was taken in late spring with the melting winter snow still covering most of the lake.

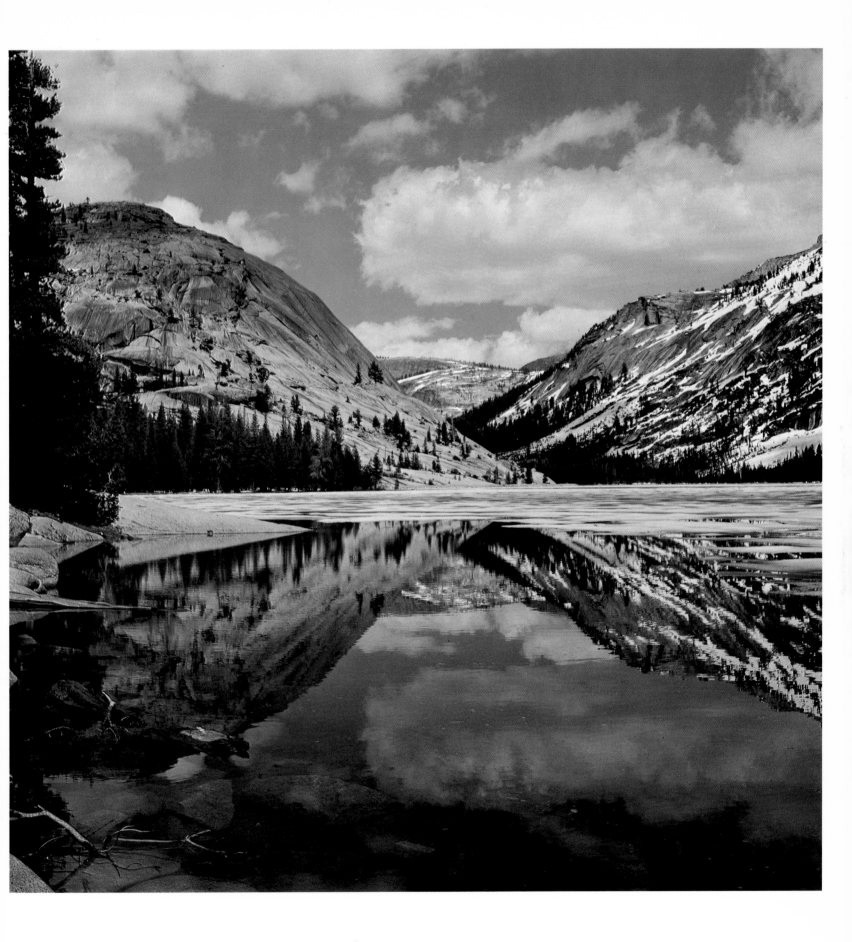

56   *Polly Dome, Tenaya Lake*

The High Country often presents an imposing view of waves of rounded, glacially smoothed rock seeming to flow earthward from the sky. One of the finest examples is Polly Dome (9786 feet), on the shore of Tenaya Lake. Its bold and gleaming curves of rock are vividly displayed in the late-afternoon sun of autumn, as seen in this picture from Olmsted Point.

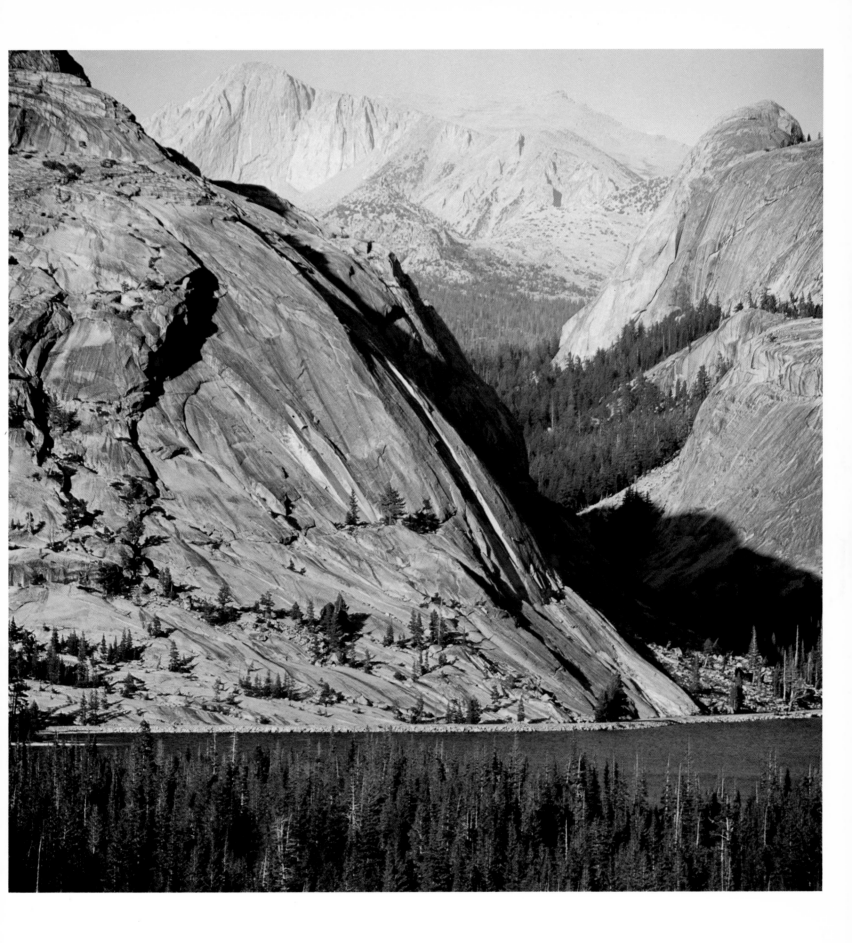

57   Jeffrey Pine Tree, Sentinel Dome

The Jeffrey [pine] . . . climbs storm-swept ridges, and wanders out among the volcanoes of the Great Basin. Whether exposed to extremes of heat or cold, it is dwarfed like every other tree, and becomes all knots and angles. . . . Old specimens . . . may sometimes be found clinging to rifted rocks at an elevation of seven or eight thousand feet. (MUIR)

The road to Glacier Point passes a relatively easy one-mile trail to Sentinel Dome (about 8122 feet). Here the view of the Sierra peaks and domes is in many respects similar to the more famous view from Glacier Point, although the unobstructed 360-degree view inspires an even greater feeling of being out of the world. In addition, as a world-famous symbol of struggle, courage, and beauty, growing out of the rock at the very top of Sentinel Dome is the Jeffrey pine shown in the picture.

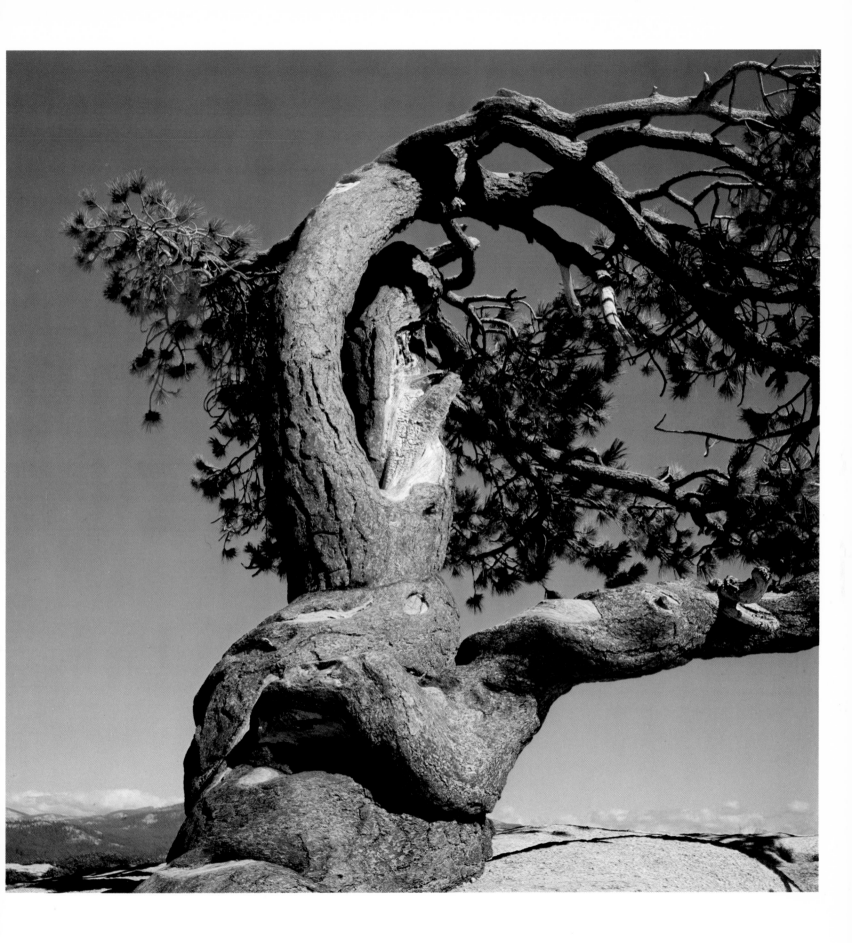

58   View from Glacier Point

To one who has been long in city pent,
　　'Tis very sweet to look into the fair
　　And open face of heaven—to breathe a prayer
　　Full in the smile of the blue firmament.
                                                    (KEATS, Sonnet)

From Glacier Point you look down 3000 feet over the edge of its sheer face to the meadows and groves and innumerable yellow pine spires, with the meandering river sparkling and spangling through the midst of them. Across the Valley a great telling view is presented of the Royal Arches, North Dome, Indian Canyon, Three Brothers and El Capitan, with the dome-paved basin of Yosemite Creek and Mount Hoffmann in the background. To the eastward, the Half Dome close beside you looking higher and more wonderful than ever; southeastward the Starr King, girdled with silver firs, and the spacious garden-like basin of the Illilouette and its deeply sculptured fountain-peaks, called "The Merced Group"; and beyond all, marshaled along the eastern horizon, the icy summits on the axis of the range and broad swaths of forests growing on ancient moraines, while the Nevada, Vernal and Yosemite falls are not only full in sight but are distinctly heard as if one were standing beside them in their spray.   (MUIR)

59   *Glacier Point, Sunset, Half Dome*

The sun begins to gild the western sky
(SHAKESPEARE, The Two Gentlemen of Verona)

A forest ranger once told me, as we were viewing the Sierra panorama from Glacier Point (7214 feet), that he had been in every national park in the United States and western Canada and felt that the most spectacular view he had ever experienced was that from Glacier Point. Some of the greatest visual thrills of my life have been sunsets at Glacier Point in which Half Dome, as in this picture, shines in warming color.

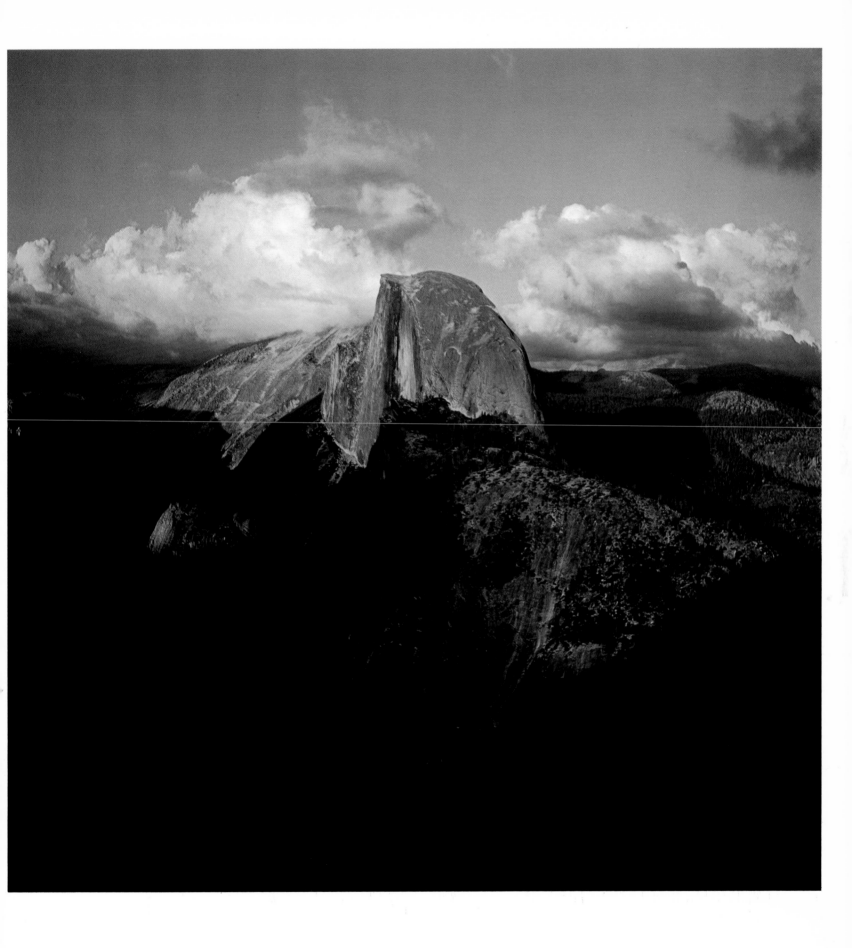

60 Glacier Point, Sunset, Mt. Starr King

With floods of the yellow gold of the gorgeous, indolent, sinking sun,
   burning, expanding the air. . . .
                    (WALT WHITMAN, When Lilacs Last in the Dooryard Bloomed)

Although Half Dome is the star of the famous Sierra array, there are times when the splendor of sunset illuminates and dramatizes a peak such as Mt. Starr King (over 9000 feet) with its final blazing touch, as in this view, which I almost didn't see. I had been watching the light on Half Dome intently, as it shifted from bright to deep to dull, and thought that beauty had gone to rest for the day, until the flame in the corner of my eye drew my attention to Mt. Starr King.

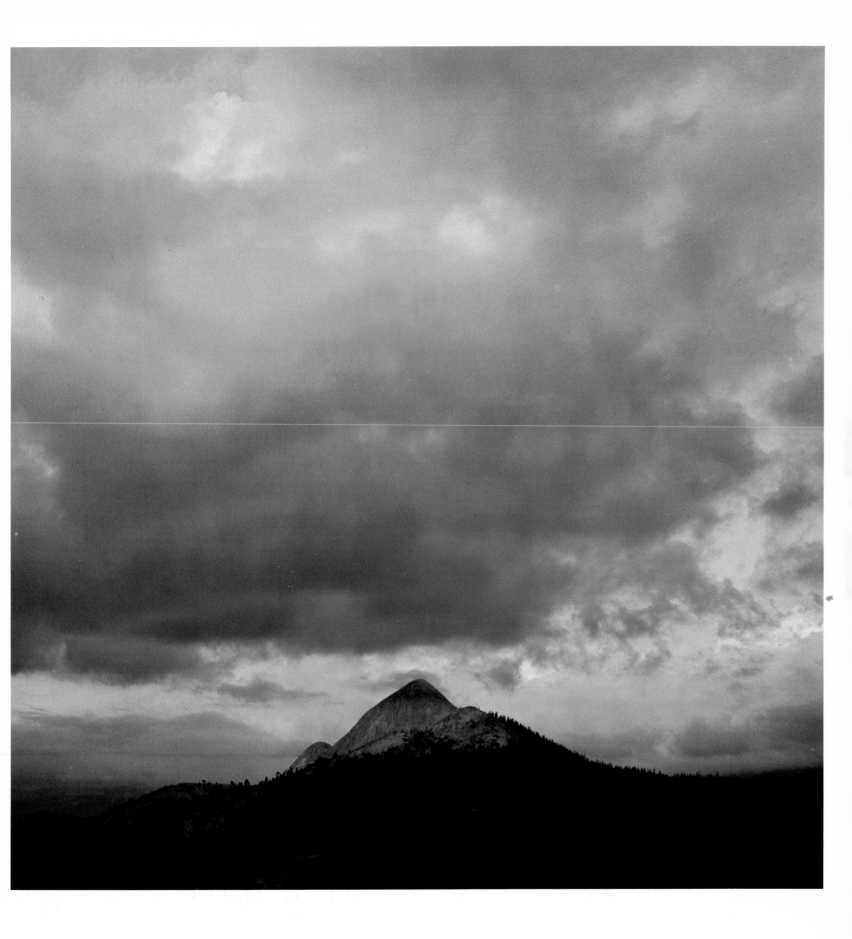

III APPENDIXES

Appendix A: A Guide to Yosemite National Park   157

        B: Camping Accommodations in the National Parks   175

        C: Addresses of the National Parks   181

        D: Camping Accommodations in the National Monuments   183

        E: Glossary of Geologist's and Naturalist's Terms   187

        F: Selected Bibliography   197

        G: John Muir, Ecological Prophet   203

APPENDIX A

A Guide to Yosemite National Park*

Sierra Wonderland

Located high on the western flank of the Sierra Nevada is Yosemite National Park, a 1200-square-mile wonderland of granite domes, foamy waterfalls, and lofty giant sequoias. Here is some of the world's most spectacular and accessible glaciated scenery, and here is Yosemite Valley, an incomparable ice-carved trough that is world famous for its rugged grandeur. Although it represents only seven square miles of the Park's total area, Nature has been generous to Yosemite Valley. Its broad, level floor contains wooded groves and meadows flanked by sheer granite walls that, in places, tower more than four thousand feet above the level, stream-watered valley floor. At various points along the rim, water tumbles from hanging valleys, thereby producing waterfalls of unusual height and beauty. Elsewhere, the valley walls have been sculptured into a host of interesting shapes including bulbous domes, slender spires, and graceful arches.

Since 1855, when the first tourist party rode horses into Yosemite Valley, tens of millions of visitors have succumbed to the magic splendor of its rocks and waters. It is probable that the early visitors, like those of today, wondered how nature could bestow such lavish beauty on so small an area and what natural agents could have shaped the valley walls into such an unusual array of geometrical forms.

Behind the Scenery

The geologic story of Yosemite is much like that of Kings Canyon and Sequoia national parks, which lie to the southeast. All three parks lie across the heart of the Sierra Nevada in east-central California, and all are distinguished by similar granite mountains, steep-walled chasms, and magnificent forests. The development of the Sierra Nevada and the early geologic history of the Yosemite-Kings Canyon-Sequoia region have already been discussed elsewhere, so let us now direct our attention to Yosemite Valley and the way in which it was formed.

*From *A Guide to the National Parks,* William H. Matthews III, Doubleday & Company, Inc., 1968.

A Valley Is Born

The sculptured walls of Yosemite Valley pay silent tribute to the geologic efficiency of natural forces, for ice, running water, and the agents of weathering have played key roles in shaping this unusual gorge. But equally important is the character of the bedrock, for in places the granitic rocks are riddled with fractures that render them more susceptible to weathering and facilitate glacial erosion. Other exposures consist of massive, unfractured granites which have more effectively withstood the onslaught of weather and ice.

. . . the rocks of the Sierra Nevada date far back into the geologic past, but the valley itself was carved within relatively recent geologic time. During early Tertiary time, perhaps during the Eocene or Oligocene epoch, the area now occupied by the Sierra Nevada began to acquire its characteristic slant to the southwest. It was then that the Merced River (which now flows along the valley floor) came into existence and began to flow southwestward to empty into the ancient sea that then occupied most of the Great Valley of California. Throughout early Miocene time the Merced meandered sluggishly through the area, gradually developing a wide, level valley floor.

During later Tertiary time, the Sierra region was subjected to renewed uplift, which further steepened the western slope and raised the eastern margin several thousand feet. So strong were these movements that a series of great faults developed along the eastern border, causing the land beyond to subside or remain stable. Thus the Sierra Nevada was eventually produced into a massive, tilted fault-block mountain range similar to the Teton Range in Grand Teton National Park. . . . The further steepening of the block accelerated the flow of the Merced River, thereby increasing its entrenching, or down-cutting, ability. This enabled the rejuvenated stream to carve a new inner gorge on the old valley floor. Throughout Pliocene time the Sierra Block remained relatively stable, but the Merced continued to deepen its gorge until it eventually produced a sharply incised valley more than one thousand feet deep.

What appears to have been the final elevation of the Sierra Block occurred about two million years ago, near the end of the Pliocene Epoch, and culminated in a series of uplifts that raised the Sierra Nevada to its present height of more than fourteen thousand feet. Concurrently the eastern lowlands such as Owens Valley were depressed or remained stable, thereby producing the impressive rocky face that marks the eastern Sierra escarpment today. . . . Once more the Merced experienced renewed vigor, as it plunged down the steepened southwestern slope, and once more it incised the granitic valley floor, this time to a depth of fifteen hundred feet.

Ice—The Master Sculptor

But this early valley was not the Yosemite that we see today. With the advent of the Ice Age, great thicknesses of snow began to accumulate in the wintry heights of the High Sierra. At the heads of the deeper valleys the snow became compacted into dense masses of glacial ice; it was then that the powerful glaciers began their slow, relentless descent into the stream-cut valleys. . . . Geologic evidence indicates that Yosemite underwent not one but at least three distinct periods of glaciation. Each of these *glacial stages* lasted for thousands of years and each was followed by a warmer (but equally long) *interglacial stage* during which time the ice melted and receded.

GLACIATION IN THE VALLEYS. The first two ice advances were by far the most prolonged and erosive. During this time, ice filled the valley from rim to rim, and Glacier Point, which now looms thirty-two hundred feet above the valley floor, was covered by five hundred feet of ice. Only the more lofty prominences, such as El Capitan, Half Dome, Eagle Peak, and Sentinel Dome, were not overridden; their towering summits appeared as ice-surrounded rock "islands" called *nunataks.* (Nunataks are present today in certain parts of the great ice sheets of the Arctic and Antarctic.) The first two glaciers reached as far southwest as El Portal; here, at an elevation of two thousand feet above sea level, the climate was warmer and the glaciers began to melt.

During the first two glacial invasions, a great tongue of ice (called a *trunk glacier*) was formed by two smaller glaciers which entered Yosemite Valley from the upper Merced and Tenaya canyons. As the trunk glacier moved slowly down the valley, the twisting, river-cut, V-shaped inner gorge was gradually transformed into a slightly sinuous, U-shaped glacial trough, and it was deepened as much as two thousand feet. The smaller tributary valleys, such as those of Yosemite and Bridalveil creeks, contained only small bodies of ice and were not eroded downward into the Yosemite Valley. When the ice receded, these were left as hanging valleys . . . from which drop the waterfalls that we see in the Park today.

Although most of the ice erosion was caused by the Yosemite Glacier, other ice streams which flowed from Little Yosemite Valley and Tenaya Canyon also were effective agents of erosion. Their ability to erode was greatly facilitated by the highly fractured bedrock over which they passed. These vertical fractures, or *joints,* divide the granite into natural blocks that may become frozen into the base of the glacier. As the glaciers moved downslope, some of these blocks were pulled from the valley floor—a process known as *glacial quarrying* or *plucking*—and transported downstream by the flowing ice. Thus, the Tenaya Glacier, which moved parallel to one set of joints, was able to erode a canyon with a gently sloping floor. But the glacier that flowed into Merced Canyon from Little Yosemite Valley moved at an angle across the trend of the joints. Here the ice excavated with varying degrees of efficiency: in places, it removed large blocks from the fractured granite; elsewhere it could only scour and polish the massive, unfractured rock. This *selective quarrying* resulted in the formation of a glaciated valley whose floor rises in a series of irregular steplike benches literally forming a giant stairway. Parts of this long *glacial stairway* are now occupied by Nevada and Vernal falls. . . .

The third and final glacial invasion filled the valley to only one third of its depth, and the ice extended but a short distance below El Capitan. There the glacier began to melt, depositing its load of glacial debris in a series of arcuate, moundlike, *recessional moraines* . . . , each of which represents a temporary decrease in the rate of glacial retreat. One of these glacier-deposited ridges, the El Capitan Bridge moraine, near Bridalveil Fall, formed a natural dam that impounded the melt water from the last glacier. This lake—called Ancient Lake Yosemite—occupied a basin scooped from the valley floor by the old Yosemite Glacier and is believed to have extended to the head of the valley, a distance of about five and a half miles. But like most lakes, Ancient Lake Yosemite lasted only a short time, geologically speaking; it soon became filled with sediment deposited by the many post-glacial streams that emptied into it. Thus Yosemite Valley was eventually filled with thousands of feet of silt, sand, and gravel, which form the broad, level valley floor that we see today.

GLACIATION IN THE HIGH SIERRA. Although the visitor usually sees the evidence of glaciation that has taken place in the valleys, the effects of the Ice Age are even more obvious in the higher elevations of the Park. Here the glacial scenery assumes an entirely different aspect, for in these areas the glaciers were not confined between narrow valley walls; rather, the broad, rolling topography permitted the ice to overrun the region and to cover most of the land surface. In Tuolumne Basin, the area now occupied by beautiful **Tuolumne Meadows . . . ,** a broad ice sheet four and a half miles wide spread out over the landscape. So thick was this glacier that many of the mountain peaks in the area were overridden by an ice mass more than fourteen hundred feet thick; even mighty **Fairview Dome . . . ,** which now rises twelve hundred feet above the surrounding meadows, was buried beneath eight hundred feet of ice.

Today we see Tuolumne Meadows as a lovely mountain garden; the Tuolumne River lazily meanders over its grassy surface, and in places large granite domes project above the basin floor. Mountain meadows such as Tuolumne and Big Meadow appear to be of glacial origin, for they are believed to have formed from the filling of shallow, interconnected glacial lakes.

High-country glaciation also affected some of the High Sierra domes; certain of these are distinctly asymmetrical, gently sloping on their *upstream* sides (the direction from which the ice flowed) and very steep-sided *downstream.* . . . Unlike most of Yosemite's domes—which have been formed primarily by exfoliation . . . —these domes assumed their rounded shape as glaciers passed over them. Some of these, for example **Fairview Dome** . . . and **Lembert Dome,** appear to be leaning in the opposite direction from which the ice came. But they did not always have this appearance; as the ice passed over them, great blocks of granite were quarried from their downstream faces to leave steep cliffs. The upstream sides resisted the removal of large blocks, but the rock-studded bottoms of the glaciers scoured their surfaces into gentler, more streamlined slopes.

When the glaciers receded, the ice-quarried granite blocks were dropped where the ice melted. . . . Some of these boulders, called *glacial erratics,* consist of rock types that are completely foreign to the area in which they now rest, thus indicating that they were picked up elsewhere and carried many miles downstream.

As the glaciers ground over the bedrock, they produced a smooth, rather lustrous surface called *glacial polish.* . . . Although evident at various localities throughout the Park, glacial polish is especially well developed on the upstream flanks of **Fairview, Lembert,** and **Pothole domes.** The latter dome, a low, easily climbed feature located just north of where the Tioga Road enters Tuolumne Meadows, is a good place to get a close look at glacial polish. Although these mirrorlike surfaces have been weathered away in most places, it may still be found in irregular patches, especially under glacial erratics that have protected the underlying bedrock from the elements. Ice-polished rock surfaces are also common on the shores of **Tenaya Lake** and in **Tenaya Canyon.** Interestingly enough, the Indians, noticing the abundance of glacial polish in this area, referred to the body of water now called Tenaya Lake as Py-we-ak, "the lake of shining rocks."

Many glacially polished rock surfaces contain rounded cavities called *weather pits.* . . . Although somewhat similar to potholes (which are produced by running water), these pits are the results of strongly localized weathering. Look for weather pits on **Glacier Point, Pothole Dome,** and other areas throughout the Park.

Most of Yosemite's glacial ice melted thousands of years ago, but a few small glaciers and ice-fields can still be seen in well-protected valleys on the flanks of the higher mountains. The largest of these is **Lyell Glacier,** an ice mass about a half mile long and a mile in width; it lies near the summit of 13,114-foot Mount Lyell, the highest point within the Park. Nearby **McClure Glacier** measures about a half mile in length and clings to the side of Mount Maclure (13,005 feet in elevation). Although not within Park boundaries, **Dana Glacier,** a smaller body of ice, is situated in a shaded cirque north of the 13,053-foot summit of Mount Dana, which is located about ten miles northeast of Lyell and McClure glaciers. But as interesting as they are, these small ice bodies are quite insignificant when compared to the massive Pleistocene glaciers that shaped the face of the High Sierra.

Shaping of the Landscape

Most visitors to Yosemite soon notice the irregular but distinctive outline of the valley rim: bold cliffs, angular spires, massive pillars, and rounded domes rise abruptly above the broad valley floor, sharply accentuating the valley's rock-ribbed walls. Hopefully, the more inquisitive visitor will wonder how and why these fantastic rock structures evolved. Why, for example, do the walls exhibit such an incredible variety of rock structure? And how could such dissimilar geometric forms as, say, a dome and a pinnacle develop side by side from a seemingly homogeneous rock mass? Finally, what combination of geologic processes joined forces to produce so many varied and diverse landforms in such a small area?

To answer the above questions we must carefully examine Yosemite's rocks, for in the final analysis it is the structure and composition of the rock as well as the erosive agent that determines what forms shall be developed.

CLIFFS, PINNACLES, AND PILLARS. To the casual observer, Yosemite's landforms appear to have all been shaped from exactly the same kind of rock. But the rocks are not identical; in fact, approximately twelve different types of granitic rocks have been identified in the Yosemite area. Despite the fact that these are all granitelike rocks, they vary greatly in color, texture, and durability, and these variations played an important role in determining how the rocks react to various erosional processes.

For example, some of the rocks consist of massive, unfractured granite; such rock is highly resistant to erosion and has resisted destruction by ice or weathering. The majestic **El Capitan,** a vast monolith whose almost vertical cliff face rises three thousand feet above the valley floor, is a classic example of the type of landform developed in unjointed granite. Rock of this type is most resistant to erosion—it can even withstand the rigors of glaciation. Thus, **Mt. Broderick** and **Liberty Cap** were only rounded and polished by the glaciers, whereas similar bodies composed of fractured granite were completely demolished as the ice moved over them. But, in general, most of Yosemite's rocks have undergone varying degrees of jointing, and this has facilitated their destruction. Some have split readily along rather widely spaced vertical joints; these rocks have given rise to most of the perpendicular walls and smooth cliffs that characterize the valley. The cliff face of **Half Dome** . . . is a good example of structures controlled by this kind of jointing. In addition, the main cliff at **Glacier Point,** the precipice of **Upper Yosemite Fall,** and the sheer cliffs adjacent to **Ribbon Fall** are also associated with this type of rock. Elsewhere, rocks containing more closely spaced vertical joints have been sculptured into angular, multifaced structures such as obelisks, columns, and monuments. **Washington Column,** a massive natural pillar seventeen hundred feet tall, and **Sentinel Rock,** a colossal obelisk with a flat front and sharp, splintered crest, exemplify structures originating in this type of rock.

Other rock forms have developed in rocks containing sets of master joints trending in several different directions. These include **Cathedral Rocks,** whose three summits loom 1650, 2590, and 2680 feet, respectively, above the valley floor . . . , and the **Three Brothers,** an asymmetrical, gabled structure whose slanting "roofs" have formed along westward-sloping joint planes. In some places the rocks are crosscut with a bewildering array of intricate intersecting joints; such formations have given rise to some finely carved, castlelike columnar structures.

But not all the landforms have developed from joints. A few prominent landmarks on the valley rim are composed of granite intrusions that have been injected into the surrounding rocks.

DOMES AND ARCHES. Yosemite possesses a variety of scenic wonders, but none are as distinctive as the massive granite domes that dot its spectacular landscape. Because of the region's icy past, it was originally thought that all these helmet-shaped monoliths were upheaval domes or that they had been rounded and polished by overriding glaciers. It is now known, however, that the Sierra Nevada was never completely ice-covered; instead, the glaciers were local in extent and the higher elevations were never buried by ice. For example, such well-rounded features as **Half Dome** and **Sentinel Dome** could not possibly have been shaped by ice, for their summits were never subjected to glaciation. Moreover, one of the world's most perfectly formed granite domes—Stone Mountain, near Atlanta, Georgia—is located several hundred miles beyond the known southern limits of the Pleistocene glaciers.

But if the domes were not formed by glaciation, how were they formed? Geologic field studies indicate that their smooth, rounded surfaces were produced by *exfoliation,* a special type of weathering in which curved sheets or plates of rocks (called *shells*) are stripped from a larger rock mass. . . . You will notice that the surface of every dome is covered with these curving shells, or *spalls* as they are also called. Closer observation reveals that these great sheets of granite are arranged in concentric layers—like the rings of an onion. One should not, however, think of the domes as huge "rock onions." Unlike onions, their concentric shells are confined to the exterior of the dome. The interior is composed of solid rock.

As weathering progresses, the outer spalls—which range in thickness from a few inches to tens of feet—become loosened and drop off, exposing a fresh rock surface to the elements. In time, this too will become separated and fall away; thus, as exfoliation proceeds, successive spalls are removed and the angularities of the original rock are replaced by smooth curves. . . .

That the domes were produced by exfoliation rather than glaciation has been conclusively established, but the process by which the massive, stony slabs are peeled from the parent rock is still not clearly understood. Most geologists agree that exfoliation is a type of *sheeting,* a form of rock rupture similar to jointing. Sheeting develops along fractures that have slightly curved surfaces and lie essentially parallel to the topographic surface, and although the rupture separating each sheet can be seen at the surface, visible sheeting disappears with depth. However, invisible zones of weakness parallel to the sheeting are still present in the rock.

The effects of exfoliation are clearly observable, but its cause is not so obvious. We are not sure, for example, of the origin of the expansive stresses that produce sheeting fractures. It has been suggested that expansion was caused by *hydration* as water combined chemically with the minerals in the granite thus causing it to swell. There is also evidence to indicate that external solar heating may cause the rock to expand. Still another theory proposes that sheeting fractures develop from tension cracks produced during the cooling and crystallization of the rock. Research indicates, however, that solar heating, hydration, and crystallization are not in themselves capable of generating sufficient stress to produce exfoliation. The most accepted belief is that the ruptures develop due to release of stress as the overlying rocks are stripped away by erosion. As confining pressures are relieved, the underlying rock mass gradually swells, producing expansion fractures that lie approximately parallel to the exposed surface. These partings mark off the slabs, which, upon being exposed to weathering, will eventually disintegrate and drop off the dome.

Sheeting is best developed in granitelike rocks such as those exposed in the core of the Sierra Nevada and is strikingly illustrated by the scaly granite domes of Kings Canyon, Sequoia, and Yosemite national parks. For example, such famous Yosemite features as **Half Dome** and **Sentinel Dome** were produced by exfoliation, and similar exfoliation domes are common throughout the Park. Half Dome, which might be considered Yosemite's "trademark," is by far the most unusual dome in the Park . . . , if not in the world. Visitors commonly ask: "What happened to the other half of Half Dome?" The answer to this question is simple: "It was never there." Contrary to earlier belief, the "missing half" of the dome was not sheared off by an ancient glacier. Neither the Tenaya Glacier nor the normal agents of erosion could have effectively done away with this much rock material during the amount of time involved. Instead, the stark, precipitous front of Half Dome was developed relatively rapidly as the result of sheeting along a master set of vertical joints. As exfoliation proceeded, great slabs of rock were displaced in a plane parallel to the set of joints, thereby producing zones of weakness that rendered the rocks more susceptible to the processes of glacial erosion. Thus, as these rocky scales dropped away or were plucked from the dome by glaciers, the familiar sheer face of this famous monolith was gradually developed. The smoothly rounded back of Half Dome evolved more slowly; it appears to be the product of exfoliation along convex fractures whose planes lie essentially parallel to the gently curving surface of the dome.

Sentinel Dome is easily accessible and is a good place for a closer look at the effects of exfoliation. It is reached by a spur road off the Glacier Point Road near Washburn Point, and by means of a short but steep scramble you can reach its 8,122-foot summit. The concentric shell structure of Sentinel Dome can readily be observed, and its surface is covered with exfoliation spalls which range from six inches to several feet in thickness. In addition, the various Park roads pass by and over a number of other exfoliation domes. Note especially the great slabs that litter the surface of **Turtleback Dome;** you will see these on the south side of Wawona Road about one half mile west of Wawona Tunnel.

But not all of Yosemite's domes are the exclusive products of exfoliation; as noted earlier . . . , some have been shaped by glaciers. Two of these, **Liberty Cap** and **Mt. Broderick,** were sculptured by the Merced Glacier. Their curving backs and smooth summits were ground and polished as the ice moved downslope; their steep, craggy fronts face in the direction of ice flow and were subjected to the quarrying action of the glacier. Asymmetrical, ice-hewn landforms of this type are called *roches moutonnés,* a term that literally means "sheep rocks." They were so named because when viewed from a distance their rounded, polished forms are somewhat reminiscent of the backs of grazing sheep. Domes such as Liberty Cap and Mount Broderick are composed of massive, unyielding granite and have successfully withstood demolition by the Merced Glacier.

Among the more remarkable geological features seen in Yosemite are the unusual *arches* which sometimes develop in exfoliating granite. Consisting of a series of vaulted, sculptured arcs recessed one within another, these graceful structures are formed by the collapse of the lower portions of exfoliation spalls; the remaining portion of each spall tends to assume the shape of an arch. Although imperfectly formed arches can be seen on a number of domes and cliff faces, the **Royal Arches** are a classic example of this type of weathering phenomenon. Located on the north wall near the head of Yosemite Valley, these arches are carved on the face of a slanting cliff that rises fifteen hundred feet above the valley floor. The arches are of gigantic proportions—the largest has a span of eighteen hundred feet and its underside looms one thousand feet above the base of the cliff. The massive shells which frame the arches range from ten to eighty feet thick, but they join to form a ponderous sheet two hundred feet thick near the top of the main arch. Glacial erosion must also have played an important part in the sculpture of the arches, for during the last stage of glaciation the Yosemite Glacier probably quarried away the lower portions of the shells which had previously been loosened by sheeting.

The Waterfalls

Yosemite's waterfalls, like its cliffs and domes, reflect the influence of rock structure on the scenery. This is especially true in the development of Yosemite's spectacular free-leaping waterfalls, for these plunge from hanging valleys and are associated with sheer cliff faces developed along vertical or steeply inclined master joints. . . . The waters of such falls pour over sheer precipices and, whipped by the wind, fall gracefully downward to pound the rocks below. An alcove—the product of the action of exfoliation by hydration—is eventually produced at the base of the falls.

Yosemite's waterfalls are noted for their height. For example, **Upper Yosemite Fall** plummets 1430 feet—a height equal to nine Niagara Falls piled one on top of the other. After hitting the base of the Upper Fall, the water cascades and falls an additional 675 feet before pitching over the lip of **Lower Yosemite Fall** to descend yet another 320 feet. The combined distance of the Upper and Lower Yosemite falls plus the intermediate cascades is 2425 feet, a drop that makes Yosemite Falls one of the highest waterfalls in existence. Other examples of free-leaping waterfalls include **Bridalveil Fall,** with an untrammeled vertical descent of 620 feet, and **Illilouette Fall,** which drops 370 feet from the hanging valley of Illilouette Creek.

Ribbon Fall, the highest in Yosemite, pours over the north rim of Yosemite Valley almost directly opposite Bridalveil Fall. Here the waters of Ribbon Creek drop a sheer 1612 feet, a distance greater than the height of the Empire State Building.

Not all of Yosemite's waterfalls are associated with hanging valleys. **Vernal** and **Nevada falls** tumble down "steps" of the giant stairway carved by the Merced Glacier. . . . In this part of the canyon, the Merced River drops two thousand feet in a distance of one and a half miles. In the lower part of this stretch the river descends in series of tumultuous cascades and rapids, but in its upper reaches the river makes a more rapid descent via Vernal and Nevada falls. **Nevada Fall,** at the upper step, drops 594 feet, and, one half mile downstream, **Vernal Fall** has a drop of 320 feet, a height almost twice that of Niagara Falls.

To see the waterfalls in full splendor, visit Yosemite early in the season; they are at their fullest in May and June, while the winter snows are melting, but their volume decreases rapidly during July. Although a few falls run all year, in dry years some have no visible water after the middle of August.

Plants and Animals of Yosemite National Park

As in most of the mountain national parks, the majority of Yosemite's plants and animals are confined to definite life belts that are related to climate and altitude. There are five life zones in Yosemite National Park and they range from two thousand feet above sea level at Arch Rock to 13,114 feet on Mount Lyell, the highest point in the Park. Each of these zones supports its own characteristic assemblage of plants and animals, and it is interesting to watch the fauna and flora change as you ascend to the higher elevations in the Park. The change is more noticeable in the vegetation, for certain of the animals migrate from one zone to the next according to the season. Plants characteristic of the warmer, drier slopes, the Upper Sonoran Zone, at about two thousand feet above sea level, are brushy plants such as the buckthorn and manzanita, with an occasional stand of redbud and Digger pine. Animals that occupy this zone include California mule deer, gray fox, ringtail, the scrub jay, and the thrasher.

At four thousand feet Yosemite Valley is in the *Transition Zone,* which ranges from thirty-five hundred to about sixty-five hundred feet elevation. Living here are ponderosa pine, incense cedar, white fir, and canyon live-oak and black oak. California mule deer, gray and Douglas squirrel, and the chipmunk are common mammals. Steller's jay is the bird that you are most likely to see in this zone.

Coniferous trees increase with altitude and predominate in the *Canadian Zone,* which begins at about six thousand feet. Prominent in the extensive evergreen forests are California red fir, Jeffrey, sugar, lodgepole, and western white pines. Animals that may be seen include the golden-mantled ground squirrel, Townsend's solitaire, blue grouse, western bluebird, western tanager, mountain quail, and fox sparrow.

Still higher is the *Hudsonian Zone,* which is encountered between eight thousand and ten thousand feet above sea level. This life belt supports a fauna and a flora that resemble those of the Hudson Bay area of Canada. Lodgepole pine and mountain hemlock are the most common trees; Belding's ground squirrel, marmot, Clark's nutcracker, white-crowned sparrow, and the mountain bluebird also live here.

Above about eleven thousand feet lies the treeless, barren *Arctic-Alpine Zone.* Life is sparse here; trees are stunted and deformed by wind and weather and few animals can withstand the rigors of this inhospitable area.

The Big Trees

Worthy of special note are the famous giant sequoia trees of **Mariposa Grove,** in the extreme southern part of the Park. . . . These huge trees, like those of Sequoia National Park . . . , are among the oldest and largest living things on earth. The largest tree in the grove is the **Grizzly Giant** . . . , with a base diameter of 30 feet, girth of 94.2 feet, and a height of 200 feet. Although it is not possible to determine the exact age of this monstrous tree, its size and gnarled appearance suggest that it is almost three thousand years old. The Grizzly Giant is the largest and oldest tree in Mariposa Grove, but the best-known and most photographed sequoia was **Wawona Tunnel Tree,** through whose trunk passed the Mariposa Grove Road until the tree was toppled by winter storms a few years ago. The tunnel was cut in 1881 and was 8 feet wide, 10 feet high, and 26 feet long; the tree stood 234 feet high and had a base diameter of $27\frac{1}{2}$ feet. Other interesting trees to be seen here include the **California Tree,** which also has a tunnel in it, and the 286-foot-high **Columbia Tree,** which is the tallest in the grove. In addition to Mariposa Grove, giant sequoias grow in **Merced** and **Tuolumne groves,** southeast of Big Oak Flat Entrance, in the western part of the Park.

What to Do and See at Yosemite National Park

One of Yosemite's more pleasant features is that you can enjoy many of its attractions without having to leave your automobile, or by walking only a very short distance. And this park has something for everyone. Unlike most national parks, Yosemite has tennis courts, golf courses, and a swimming pool; and in season you can hike, ride a horse, or rent a bicycle. Most of the visitor activity is confined to Yosemite Valley, for this eight-square-mile area is the "heart" of the Park. But minutes away from the crowded valley floor is the back country, whose wilderness areas are the goal of the hiker, the camper, the fisherman, and the lover of nature. Another feature of Yosemite National Park is its especially well-developed and diversified naturalist program. And this is as it should be, for Yosemite was the first national park in which naturalist programs were offered.

VISITOR CENTER MUSEUMS. As in all national parks, your visit will be more enjoyable and you will understand more of what you see if you start your visit at one of the museums. The best place to start here is in the Yosemite **Visitors Center,** at Yosemite Village. There are educational exhibits which will explain the geology of the Park and the geologic history of the Sierra Nevada. In addition, there are exhibits that will acquaint you with Yosemite's plants and animals and provide interesting information about the Indians and early human history in the area. Of special interest is the **Indian Circle,** located behind the museum; during the summer there are daily explanations of how the Indians hunted, cooked, dressed, and lived. You can also see Indian basketry demonstrations here during the summer.

Yosemite Visitors Center is the headquarters for all interpretive programs in the Park, and a schedule of such activities is usually posted. Here, too, there is a book counter where you can purchase books and maps treating subjects of interest to Park visitors.

Near the upper end of Yosemite Valley is **Happy Isles,** the meeting place of Yosemite's **Junior**

Ranger Program. First started in 1930, this is a program of conservation education for students in grades three through eight. Classes are held in appropriate natural surroundings, and natural history, human history, Indian lore, and conservation topics are presented by well-trained ranger-naturalists; class sessions are supplemented by nature walks, demonstrations, and campfire programs. Those students who attend for five days and complete their work will receive the coveted Junior Ranger Patch. However, those who cannot participate for this length of time may still earn a notebook and certificate for the number of days attended. Students in grades seven and up are designated **Senior Rangers** and are provided a special program of hiking activities. There is a very nominal charge for materials used during each morning session, but campfire programs are free. Many of the High Sierra trails begin at Happy Isles, and a display of back-country information can be seen at **Happy Isles Nature Center.**

The **Mariposa Grove Museum** is situated in the "Big Trees" area in the southern end of the Park. Housed in a replica of a log cabin somewhat like the one which occupied this site more than a hundred years ago, the exhibits here deal primarily with the giant sequoias. During the summer, there are daily talks by ranger-naturalists.

The **Pioneer Yosemite History Center** at Wawona is devoted exclusively to telling the story of Yosemite's early settlers in the age of the horse. Located nearby is the reconstructed covered bridge over the South Fork of the Merced River; this is the only covered bridge in the entire national park system. Completely furnished historic cabins and an excellent collection of stagecoaches can be seen here. At El Portal, on the highway from Merced, is the **Pioneer Yosemite Transportation Center.** Its theme of the age of steam and early gasoline vehicles is supported by a number of interesting old vehicles.

CAMPFIRE PROGRAMS. At regularly scheduled times, ranger-naturalists give illustrated talks on various aspects of the Park at informal outdoor programs. These are held nightly (except Sunday) in Yosemite Valley at **Camps 7 and 14, Camp Curry,** and **Yosemite Lodge;** and several nights a week at the **Ahwahnee Hotel, Wawona, Glacier Point, Tuolumne Meadows,** and at **Bridal-veil Creek, Crane Flat,** and **White Wolf campgrounds.** The weekly program, showing schedules and subjects, is posted on campground bulletin boards and at the museums and visitor centers.

A highlight of any evening at Yosemite is the famous **Firefall.** This spectacle, which can be seen every night during the summer, originates at Glacier Point, more than thirty-two hundred feet above the valley. The fire is made of red fir bark, which is allowed to burn down to glowing embers. After a signal from Camp Curry, in the valley below, the embers are pushed over the precipice and cascade down the cliff.

NATURE WALKS. Ranger-naturalists conduct leisurely guided walks through the valley and to important scenic points in the **Glacier Point, Tuolumne Meadows,** and **Wawona areas;** other walks originate in certain of the campgrounds. Longer, more strenuous hikes are also regularly conducted for the more seasoned hiker. Times and destinations of these trips are posted on bulletin boards throughout the Park.

SELF-GUIDING TRAILS. The **Inspiration Point Self-guiding Nature Trail,** which begins at Tunnel View on Wawona Road, leads to Inspiration Point, about fifteen hundred feet above the valley floor. The distance covered by this rather long, strenuous trail is about three miles (round trip) and average hiking time is approximately three hours. Along this path you will see the effects of altitude on the plants and animals of the Park . . . , for the trail starts in the Transition Zone, which ranges from about thirty-five hundred to six thousand feet elevation, and ends near the Canadian Zone. The view from the upper part of the trail is magnificent and you can see classic examples of jointing, exfoliation, domes, and arches.

The **Pioneer Cemetery,** located across the street and west of the Yosemite Visitor Center, is perhaps the most unique self-guiding "trail" in any national park. In this cemetery are the graves of some of the pioneers who contributed to the early growth and development of Yosemite National Park.

MOTOR DRIVES. As mentioned earlier, many of the Park's feature attractions can be seen from your car as you drive over excellent hard-surfaced roads. Your drive will be more interesting if you purchase a pamphlet such as *Self-guiding Auto Tours in Yosemite National Park,* by Richard P. Ditton and Donald E. McHenry, which can be ordered from Yosemite Natural History Association, Box 545, Yosemite National Park, California 95389. By following the text in the guide and watching your speedometer, you can locate road markers which indicate various points of interest along the Park roads.

The **Yosemite Valley Drive** is the ideal tour to give you the feel of the Park in a very short time. As you enter the valley from the west and approach **Valley View,** you get the first glimpse of what has been called the "Incomparable Valley." Continuing eastward, 1612-foot **Ribbon Fall** . . . is seen on your left, and graceful **Bridalveil Fall** (620 feet) plunges over the south rim to your right. Next comes your first view of **El Capitan,** . . . which juts 3604 feet above the valley floor. This imposing mass of rock is believed to be one of the world's largest exposed granite monoliths. . . . After passing El Capitan you will notice the gabled summits of the **Three Brothers** . . . ; the tallest "brother," **Eagle Peak,** has an elevation of 7779 feet and is the highest point on the north rim. On the south wall, **Sentinel Rock** . . . stands three thousand feet tall and broods over the valley like a stony, medieval watchtower.

Shortly after passing **Yosemite Lodge,** a trail from the parking area on your left will take you to the foot of **Yosemite Falls,** one of the world's tallest waterfalls. . . . After driving through **Yosemite Village,** site of **Park Headquarters, Yosemite Visitors Center, Pioneer Cemetery,** the post office, hospital, and various concession facilities, you will note the luxurious **Ahwahnee Hotel** on your left. Soon you see the Yosemite's "trademark," world-renowned **Half Dome,** a sheer-faced semidome which rises forty-eight hundred feet above the upper end of the valley. Follow the road to the left in order to pass by the **Royal Arches** . . . , **North Dome,** and **Washington Column** . . . on your left. Beautiful **Mirror Lake,** in whose waters can be seen the reflection of **Mt. Watkins,** is at the end of the road. You also get a good view of **Basket Dome** from here.

On the return trip, follow the south (left-hand) fork of the road to **Happy Isles Nature Center. . . .** Stop here long enough to visit the displays about Yosemite's wilderness. About one half mile farther is **Camp Curry;** its rustic accommodations are among the most popular in the Park, and a gift shop, cafeteria, and swimming pool are but a few of the facilities available here. Looking north from Camp Curry there is a fine view of the vaulted front of the **Royal Arches, Washington Column,** which is more than three times taller than the Washington Monument, and the bulbous, **North Dome,** 3571 feet above the valley floor, which rises above both. Turning your eyes to the south wall and—looking almost straight up—you will see Glacier Point, a massive granite wall that looms 3254 feet skyward. This is the cliff from which the **Firefall** originates, and Camp Curry is a good place to witness this traditional evening display, though across the valley is even better.

LeConte Memorial is less than a half mile down the valley road from Camp Curry, and visitors interested in rock climbing will find this stop a "must." Members of the **Sierra Club,** an outstanding group of conservationist-naturalists, will provide information on mountaineering and exhibits, and publications are also available. The building is, appropriately enough, in keeping with the geologic interest of Yosemite, for the lodge is named after Joseph LeConte, a well-known early geologist.

Sentinel Bridge crosses the Merced River at Old Village, and you may turn right if you want to return to Yosemite Village. But unless you have already toured the south side of the valley, by all means continue your drive along the south bank of the meandering Merced. There are, incidentally, many beautiful picnic areas located along its banks. . . .

Shortly after leaving Old Village the road enters a broad meadow from which you can get a magnificent view of Yosemite Falls on the north wall and **Sentinel Rock** on the south wall. If you are visiting during late spring or early summer you may get to see **Sentinel Fall,** a 2000-foot waterfall formed by the waters of Sentinel Creek. The gap from which the water pours is a good example of a hanging valley. . . .

Continuing down-valley, there is a fine view of **El Capitan** across the river on your right. Graceful **Cathedral Spires** dominate the south-rim skyline. The taller of these granite pinnacles rises about twenty-one hundred feet above the valley floor; the other is approximately nineteen hundred feet tall. Slightly down-valley from Cathedral Spires are the three **Cathedral Rocks. . . .** These massive structures are fitting counterparts to El Capitan, which faces them from across the valley. Although you cannot see them, there are large glacial boulders on the tops of Cathedral Rocks. These erratics are further proof that the Yosemite Glacier once covered portions of the valley rims.

Just before reaching the junction with the road to Valley View, there is a fine view of **Bridalveil Fall** on the left. This completes the tour of the valley floor, and motorists wishing to return to Yosemite Village should take the right fork of the road to California 140 and then turn right.

Time permitting, you may wish to drive on to **Wawona Road,** which leads to **Glacier Point** and **Mariposa Grove.** You should, however, go at least as far as **Tunnel View;** the view from the parking area is superb and clearly emphasizes the glacial origin of Yosemite's landscape. The U-shaped valley profile, the ice-hewn valley walls, and the hanging valley of Bridalveil Creek all bear silent witness to the geologic efficiency of the mighty Yosemite Glacier.

Wawona Road passes through **Wawona Tunnel,** which was constructed in 1933. The tunnel, which took nearly two years to construct, is twenty-eight feet wide, nineteen feet high, and 4233 feet long; it cost $847,500. Wawona Tunnel is an excellent example of the care taken by the National Park Service to preserve an area's natural features. If this section of the road had been blasted out of the side of the valley, the natural landscape would have been irreparably defaced.

As the road leaves the tunnel, it skirts **Turtleback Dome** (where exfoliating granite is beside the road) and continues to **Chinquapin.** As you follow Wawona Road to Chinquapin, watch for changes in vegetation. Chinquapin (elevation 6039 feet) is in the Canadian Zone, and in the intervening 1629 feet the typical Transition Zone ponderosa pine and oak trees are replaced by Jeffrey and sugar pine.

The Glacier Point-Wawona Road junction is located at Chinquapin, and persons wishing to go to **Glacier Point** should turn left (east) here. In the sixteen miles from Chinquapin to Glacier Point, the road passes the **Badger Pass Ski Center,** Yosemite's winter recreation center . . . , and crosses **Bridalveil Creek,** whose waters form Bridalveil Fall. About five miles from the turnoff to **Sentinel Dome** . . . A steep but short path leads to the 8122-foot summit, from which there is an excellent view; this is also a good place to examine exfoliation shells at close range.

Returning to Glacier Point Road, you soon encounter a series of sharp switchbacks by which you drop down to **Washburn Point,** a popular scenic lookout. From here it is less than a mile to **Glacier Point,** which commands an unsurpassed view of the High Sierra. Spread before you is a far-flung panorama of domes, pinnacles, cliffs, and waterfalls. And dominating all in silent majesty is world-renowned **Half Dome,** its 2000-foot sheer face towering 4882 feet above the valley floor.

Glacier Point Lookout, 3254 feet above Yosemite Valley, is but a short distance from the **Glacier Point Hotel.** From here you can look down into the valley, where automobiles are but moving specks and the Merced River resembles a winding thread. Across Yosemite Valley, **Yosemite Falls, Royal Arches, Washington Column, North Dome,** and **Basket Dome** stand out in bold relief. **Half Dome** can be seen to the northeast and eastward; beyond **Nevada** and **Vernal falls** stands **Liberty Cap.** . . . In addition to the splendid view, you will enjoy the geologic exhibits (which explain many of the features that are seen) and the lectures given by the ranger-naturalists.

As mentioned earlier . . . , Glacier Point is the origin of the **Firefall,** which is produced nightly during the summer. If you stay overnight you can watch as the coals are pushed over the precipice to fall almost a thousand feet before being dashed out on a rocky ledge on the cliff face.

Retracing the Glacier Point route to Chinquapin and turning left (south) on Wawona Road (state route 41) will take you to Mariposa Grove and the South Entrance. Along the way you pass through **Wawona,** site of the **Pioneer Yosemite History Center** . . . and a reconstructed covered bridge . . . , both of which are located near the **Wawona Hotel.** However, the highlight of the South Entrance area is the Mariposa Grove of "Big Trees. . . ."

A totally different but equally beautiful part of Yosemite is the famous "High Country." The center of activity in this part of the Park is **Tuolumne Meadows,** located fifty-five miles from and about forty-six hundred feet above Yosemite Valley. Here there are no dance pavilions or swimming pools, for the High Country is the mecca of the outdoorsmen—those who want to hike, ride, camp, and fish.

To reach this part of the Park, take the **Big Oak Flat Road,** which intersects the Merced Highway (California 140) about one mile west of Valley View. This road will take you to **Crane Flat.** If you wish to visit the **Tuolumne Grove** of giant sequoias, inquire at Crane Flat as to access to this area. This stand of sequoias covers about twenty acres, and there are several "tunnel trees" in the grove.

Tioga Road is the road to the High Country. From an elevation of 6192 feet at Crane Flat it climbs to 9945 feet at Tioga Pass, a rise of 3753 feet in about forty-eight miles. **Tuolumne Meadows,** about forty miles from Crane Flat, is an expansive mountain meadow at an elevation of about eighty-six hundred feet. In the summer at Tuolumne, there is a naturalist program, a large campground, and a store, lodge, restaurants, and service station. This is the starting point of many of the High Sierra trails, and concessioner-operated saddle or hiking trips are conducted by the Yosemite Park and Curry Company. If you do not have time to take one of the longer trips, there are many short trails that lead to secluded lakes and granite domes. Many of the High Sierra domes, such as **Fairview Dome** . . . and **Lembert Dome** . . . , are among the best developed in the Park. The road passes near several exfoliating domes and knobs, some of which bear scratches and grooves caused by glacial abrasion. In addition, large glacial erratics can be seen at many places in the vicinity of Tuolumne Meadows. These glacial markings are conclusive evidence that even the High Sierra did not escape the onslaught of the Ice Age glaciers.

Leaving Tuolumne Meadows, the road continues to the **Tioga Pass Entrance Station,** the only eastern entrance to Yosemite, and **Tioga Pass** (elevation 9945 feet), the highest automobile pass in California. From here California 120 drops sharply down the east front of the Sierra to U.S. Highway 395 in the valley below.

HIKING. Although much can be seen from an automobile, those who would *know* Yosemite must take to its trails. Hiking brings you into close contact with nature and you will be surprised to find how many things you notice while hiking that you would not otherwise see. There are more than seven hundred and fifty miles of well-marked trails radiating from Yosemite Valley to all sections of the Park, and there are several camps, lodges, and hotels situated within an easy day's walking distance of each other. Thus, the hiker may travel light, depending upon the lodges and hotels for accommodations, or he may carry his equipment on his back or by pack animal and thereby be totally independent.

Yosemite's trails are numerous and varied, permitting short, easy trips that require only a few hours, and longer, more difficult ones that may last for several weeks. Among the more popular trails that originate in the valley are those to **Vernal Fall** (two miles round trip from Happy Isles to base of the fall) and the longer **Nevada Fall** trail, a round-trip distance of about six and a half miles from Happy Isles to the top of the fall. More demanding are the trails that involve climbs from the valley floor to the valley rim. These include the **Yosemite Falls Trail,** from Camp 4 to the top of the falls (a round trip of almost seven miles) and the trail to **Glacier Point,** a strenuous 9½-mile round trip from the base of Sentinel Rock. These are but a few of the valley trails, for there are dozens of other trails leading from Wawona and Tuolumne Meadows. You can get additional information at the Visitors Center or any ranger station.

A long-time favorite of veteran hikers is the **High Sierra Loop,** a 53-mile round trip from the valley via Tuolumne Meadows. You can "pack in" if you wish, or you may obtain food and lodging at one of the six High Sierra camps, most of which are about ten miles apart on the Loop Trail. One of the longest Sierra trails is the **John Muir Trail,** which covers two hundred and twelve miles of High Country wilderness. Named after John Muir, famous Scottish-born naturalist who wrote extensively on Yosemite Valley and the High Sierra, the trail starts in Yosemite Valley, climbs to Tuolumne Meadows, and ends at Mount Whitney, in Sequoia National Park.

Persons intending to take longer hikes will find the U.S. Geological Survey topographic maps to be most helpful. They can be purchased at Yosemite Visitors Center at any time of the year and at Tuolumne Meadows and Wawona during the summer. But before starting overnight trips, be sure to stop at ranger stations to check trail conditions and obtain camping information and a fire permit.

CAMPING. There are a number of free campgrounds in **Yosemite Valley,** one of which is open all year. In addition, there are others at **Glacier Point, Bridalveil Creek, Wawona, Crane Flat, Hodgdon Meadow, White Wolf, Tuolumne Meadows,** and in other attractive, but less used or more remote parts of the Park. House trailers can be accommodated at most campgrounds, and camper trucks are welcome at all campgrounds; no utility connections are available except at a privately owned trailer park at Wawona. Many campsites have fireplace and table, and all are situated near water and rest rooms. Public showers are located near the campgrounds in Yosemite Valley and Tuolumne Meadows; other facilities such as stores and service stations are also available.

During the summer, camping is limited to ten days and campsites are available on a first-come first-served basis. The latest camping regulations and a list of campground locations can be obtained from Superintendent, Yosemite National Park, California 95389.

Those who do not own camping equipment can rent tents, cots, blankets, and cooking utensils at **Housekeeping Camp** headquarters.

Horseback Riding. During the summer, saddle horses and pack animals may be rented from concessioners at stables in **Yosemite Valley, Tuolumne Meadows, Mather, White Wolf Lodge,** and **Wawona.** Guides are available for extended trips if desired.

Swimming. Unlike most national parks, Yosemite has concessioner-operated swimming pools, at **Camp Curry, Yosemite Lodge,** and **Wawona.** You may also swim in Park streams unless they are used to supply drinking water; these streams will be posted.

BOATING. Boating is permitted only on **Benson, Kibbie, Many Islands, May, Merced, Tenaya, Tilden,** and **Twin Lakes.** Motors are not permitted.

FISHING. The fishing season at Yosemite conforms to state regulations, and a California license is required for persons sixteen years and older. The limit is ten fish but not more than ten pounds and one fish.

Some of the Park's waters are closed to fishing; consult a ranger or check bulletin boards for latest fishing regulations.

WINTER SPORTS. The **Badger Pass Ski Center** . . . , twenty miles from Yosemite Valley on Glacier Point Road, is headquarters for the ski season, which usually lasts from about mid-December to mid-April, depending on the weather. There are ski slopes for most degrees of skill at Badger Pass, and all have T-bar lifts and there is also one chair lift. In addition, there are marked ski trails through the nearby woods; these are maintained by the National Park Service. Ski equipment can be rented and lessons are available. You may also arrange an all-expense ski tour through Yosemite Park and Curry County, Yosemite National Park, California 95389. In the valley, there is an ice-skating rink at Camp Curry; skates and sleds can be rented there.

SPECIAL PROGRAMS. Yosemite has several fine programs for children. In addition to the popular **Junior Ranger Program,** which has already been mentioned . . . , there are **daily burro picnic trips** and the **Kiddie Camp** and **Grizzly Club** at Camp Curry. There are baby-sitters available at Camp Curry in summer and Badger Pass in winter.

PHOTOGRAPHY. Yosemite has been called a photographer's paradise, for the unusual rock formations are as striking in black and white as they are in color. Even the rankest amateur can produce interesting photographs with such outstanding subjects as Yosemite and Bridalveil falls, Sentinel Rock, El Capitan, Royal Arches, and Half Dome.

Because of the distance involved and the high altitude of the Park, a haze filter should be used on long-distance shots. And when photographing the waterfalls, get far enough away to include both the top and the base of the fall.

Tunnel View and Glacier Point are especially good vantage points from which to take pictures, but the entire Park offers unusual photographic opportunities at every turn.

The Firefall can be photographed, but not with flashbulbs. Instead, place your camera on a tripod or other steady support and set the timer for a one- or two-minute time exposure; leave the camera open for another two or three minutes and you may pick up some of the detail of the surrounding cliffs. If your lens is adjustable, set the aperture at f/2.8 or wider.

Yosemite National Park at a Glance

ADDRESS: Superintendent, Box 577, Yosemite National Park, California 95389.

AREA: 760,951 acres.

MAJOR ATTRACTIONS: Mountainous region of unusual beauty; Yosemite and other inspiring gorges with sheer granite cliffs; spectacular waterfalls; three groves of giant sequoias.

SEASON: Year-round.

HOW TO REACH THE PARK: *By Auto*—From the west: California 140 to Arch Park Entrance. From the south: California 41 to South Entrance. From the east: California 120 to Tioga Pass Entrance (Tioga Pass over 9945 feet, trailers at night only, closed winter). *By Train and by Bus*—Merced and Fresno are served by Southern Pacific, and Santa Fe, also Pacific Greyhound Lines and Continental Trailways buses. *By Air*—United Airlines serves Merced and Fresno and Trans World Airlines serves Fresno.

ACCOMMODATIONS: Cabins, campgrounds, group campsites, hotels, tents, and trailer sites.

ACTIVITIES: Boating, camping, fishing (license required), guided tours, hiking, horseback riding, mountain climbing, nature walks, picnicking, scenic drives, swimming, water sports, and winter sports.

SERVICES: Food service, gift shop, guide service, health service, kennel, laundry, post office, religious services, service station, ski rental, ski tow, ski trails, telegraph, telephone, transportation, picnic tables, rest rooms, and general store.

INTERPRETIVE PROGRAM: Campfire programs, museum, nature trails, roadside exhibits, self-guiding trails, trailside exhibits.

NATURAL FEATURES: Canyons, erosional features, forests, geologic formations, glaciation, glaciers, lakes, mountains, rivers, rocks and minerals, unusual birds, unusual plants, waterfalls, wilderness area, wildlife, and early pioneer features.

Camping Accommodations in the National Parks

ACADIA NATIONAL PARK, MAINE

Black Woods	Isle au Haut	Seawall

BIG BEND NATIONAL PARK, TEXAS

Chisos Mountains, Lower Basin	Rio Grande Village	Santa Elena Canyon

BRYCE CANYON NATIONAL PARK, UTAH

North	Sunset

CANYONLANDS NATIONAL PARK, UTAH

Island in the Sky	Squaw Flat

CRATER LAKE NATIONAL PARK, OREGON

Annie Springs	Lost Creek	Mazama
		Rim

EVERGLADES NATIONAL PARK, FLORIDA

Cane Patch	Flamingo	Graveyard Creek
		Long Pine Key

GLACIER NATIONAL PARK, MONTANA

Apgar	Granite Park Chalet	Logging Lake
Arrow Lake	Grinnell Glacier	Logging Lake (upper end)
Avalanche	Grinnell Lake	Lower Kintla Lake (upper end)
Belly River	Gunsight Lake	Lower Quartz Lake
Boundary	Harrison Lake	Many Glacier
Bowman Creek	Hole-in-the-Wall	Medicine Grizzly Lake (foot of)
Bowman Lake	Howe Lake	Mokowanis Lake
Bowman Lake (upper end)	Isabel Lake	Mud Creek
Crossley Lake	Kintla Lake	Old Man Lake
Cut Bank	Kootenai Lake	Ole Lake
Elizabeth Lake	Lake Ellen Wilson	Ptarmigan Lake
Fifty Mountain	Lake Francis	Quartz Creek
Fish Creek	Lake Janet	Quartz Lake
Glenns Lake (lower end)	Lake Josephine (upper end)	Red Eagle Lake
Glenns Lake (upper end)	Logging Creek	Rising Sun

River   Stoney Indiana Lake   Upper Two Medicine Lake (foot
                                                                  of)
St. Mary Lake   Trout Lake   Walton
Sperry Chalet   Two Medicine   Waterton Ranger Station
Sprague   Upper Kintla Lake (upper end) 3 Mile Camp

GRAND CANYON NATIONAL PARK, ARIZONA

Bright Angel Point   Havasu   4.0 Mile
Cape Royal   Indian Gardens   5.5 Mile (Ribbon Falls)
Cottonwood   Mather   9.4 Mile (Roaring Springs)
Desert View   2.6 Mile

GRAND TETON NATIONAL PARK, WYOMING

Colter Bay   Jenny Lake   Mountain Climbers
Gros Ventre   Lizard Point   South Landing
Jackson Lake

GREAT SMOKY MOUNTAINS NATIONAL PARK, TENNESSEE AND NORTH CAROLINA

Abrams Creek   Double Spring Gap
Bald Creek   Eagle Creek Island   Moore Spring (Gregory Bald)
Bee Cove   Elkmont   Mount Collins
Big Creek   False Gap   Mount LeConte
Big Creek (Walnut Bottoms)   Fish Camp Prong   Mount Sterling
Big Pool   Flat Creek   Pecks Corner
Birch Spring   Forney Creek (lower)   Pin Oak Gap
Bone Valley (Hazel Creek Area) Forney Creek (upper)   Pole Road (Deep Creek Area)
Bryson Place (Deep Creek)   Greenbrier   Porters Flat
Buckeye Gap   Haw Gap   Proctor (Hazel Creek Area)
Cabin Flats Horse Camp   Hazel Creek Cascades   Rabbit Creek
Cades Cove   Hiking Club Barn   Ramsey Prong (upper)
Calhoun Place (Hazel Creek)   Huggins Creek   Round Bottom
Camp Rock   Ice Water Springs   Russell Field
Cataloochee (lower)   Laurel Branch (Hazel Creek Area) Sawdust Pile
Cataloochee (upper)   Laurel Gap   Silers Bald
Chasteen Creek Horse Camp   Look Rock (Foothills Parkway) Smokemont
Chimneys   Lost Cove   Spence Field
Cosby   McGee Spring   Spruce Mountain
Cosby Knob   Maddron Bald   Tremont
Davenport Gap   Marks Cove   Tricorner Knob
Deep Creek   Mill Creek (Noland Creek Area) Turkey George Horse Camp
Derrick Knob   Mollies Ridge   Twenty Mile Creek

HALEAKALA NATIONAL PARK, HAWAII

Hosmer Grove

HAWAII VOLCANOES NATIONAL PARK, HAWAII

Kipuka Kene   Namakani Paio

HOT SPRINGS NATIONAL PARK, ARKANSAS

Gulpha Gorge

ISLE ROYALE NATIONAL PARK, MICHIGAN

Beaver Island
Belle Isle
Birch Island
Caribou Island
Chickenbone Lake
Chippewa Harbor
Daisy Farm
Duncan Bay

Duncan Narrows
Grace Island
Hatchet Lake
Lake Desor
McCargo Cove
Malone Bay
Merritt Lane

Moskey Basin
Rock Harbor 3-Mile
Siskiwit Bay
Tobin-Rock Harbor
Todd Harbor
Tookers Island
Washington Creek

KINGS CANYON NATIONAL PARK, CALIFORNIA

Cedar Grove Area:
  Camp 1
  Camp 2
  Camp 3
  Camp 4
  Temporary Trailer Village

Grant Grove Area:
  Azalea
  Crystal Springs
  Sunset
  Swale

LASSEN VOLCANIC NATIONAL PARK, CALIFORNIA

Butte Lake
Hat Creek
Horsehoe Lake
Juniper Lake

Kings Creek
Manzanita Lake
Southwest Entrance
Summit Lake

Summit Lake North
Summit Lake South
Warner Valley

MAMMOTH CAVE NATIONAL PARK, KENTUCKY

Headquarters (new)
Headquarters (old)

Houchins Ferry

Onyx Cave

MESA VERDE NATIONAL PARK, COLORADO

Morfield Canyon

MOUNT MCKINLEY NATIONAL PARK, ALASKA

Igloo
Morino
Sanctuary

Savage
Teklanika

Toklat
Wonder Lake

MOUNT RAINIER NATIONAL PARK, WASHINGTON

Cougar Rock
Ipsut Creek
Longmire
Mowich Lake

Ohanapecosh
Paradise
Sunrise
Sunshine Point

Tahoma Creek
Trail Shelters
White River

OLYMPIC NATIONAL PARK, WASHINGTON

Altaire
Deer Park
Dosewallips
Elwha
Erickson Bay
Fairholm

Graves Creek
Heart o' the Hills
Hoh
July Creek
Kalaloch
Mora

North Fork Quinault
Olympic Hot Springs
Ozette Lake
Queets
Soleduck
Staircase

PLATT NATIONAL PARK, OKLAHOMA

Central

Cold Springs

Rock Creek

ROCKY MOUNTAIN NATIONAL PARK, COLORADO

Aspenglen
Endo Valley
Glacier Basin

Long Peak
Moraine Park
Timber Creek

Trail Camps
Wild Basin

SEQUOIA NATIONAL PARK, CALIFORNIA

Dorst Creek Area:
  Camp 1
  Camp 2
  Camp 3
  Camp 4
Giant Forest Area:
  Paradise
  Sugar Pine
  Sunset Rock

Lodgepole Area:
  Log Bridge
  Main Camp
  South Tokopah

Outlying Areas:
  Atwell Mill
  Buckeye Flat
  Potwisha
  South Fork

SHENANDOAH NATIONAL PARK, VIRGINIA

Bearfence Shelter
Big Flat Shelter
Big Meadows
Big Run Shelter
Black Rock Shelter
Byrd's Nest Shelter 1
Byrd's Nest Shelter 2

Byrd's Nest Shelter 3

Byrd's Nest Shelter 4
Elkwallow Shelter
Gravel Spring Shelter
Hawksbill Shelter
Hightop Shelter
Indian Run Shelter
Lewis Mountain

Lewis Spring Shelter

Loft Mountain
Old Rag Shelter
Pass Mountain Shelter
Pinefield Shelter
Rip Rap Shelter
Sawmill Run Shelter
Shaver Hollow Shelter

South River Shelter

VIRGIN ISLANDS NATIONAL PARK, U.S. VIRGIN ISLANDS

Cinnamon Bay

WIND CAVE NATIONAL PARK, SOUTH DAKOTA

Elk Mountain

YELLOWSTONE NATIONAL PARK, IDAHO-MONTANA-WYOMING

Bridge Bay	Lewis Lake	Plover Point
Canyon	Madison Junction	Slough Creek
Eagle Bay	Mammoth	South Entrance
Fishing Bridge	Norris	Specimen Creek
Fishing Bridge Trailer Village	Old Faithful	Squaw Lake
Grant Village	Otter Creek	Tower Fall
Indian Creek	Pebble Creek	Trail Creek
Lava Creek	Pelican Creek	Wolf Point

YOSEMITE NATIONAL PARK, CALIFORNIA

Bridalveil Creek	Carl Inn	Porcupine Flat
Camp 4	Crane Flat	Smoky Jack
Camp 7	Foresta	Tamarck Flat
Camp 9	Glacier Point	Tenaya Lake
Camp 11	Hardin Lake	Tuolumne Meadows
Camp 12	Hodgdon Meadow	Wawona
Camp 14	North Crane Creek	White Wolf
Camp 15	Porcupine Creek	Yosemite Creek

ZION NATIONAL PARK, UTAH

Grotto	South

APPENDIX C

Addresses of the National Parks

Prospective national park visitors desiring advance information about camping areas, fishing and boating regulations, accommodations, etc., can write to the superintendents of the respective parks at the addresses listed below.

ACADIA NATIONAL PARK
Box 338
Bar Harbor, Maine 04609

BIG BEND NATIONAL PARK
Big Bend National Park,
Texas 79834

BRYCE CANYON NATIONAL PARK
Bryce Canyon, Utah 84717

CANYONLANDS NATIONAL PARK
Post Office Building
Moab, Utah 84532

CARLSBAD CAVERNS NATIONAL PARK
Box 1598
Carlsbad, New Mexico 88220

CRATER LAKE NATIONAL PARK
Box 672
Medford, Oregon 97501

EVERGLADES NATIONAL PARK
Box 279
Homestead, Florida 33030

GLACIER NATIONAL PARK
West Glacier, Montana 59936

GRAND CANYON NATIONAL PARK
Box 129
Grand Canyon, Arizona 86023

GRAND TETON NATIONAL PARK
Box 67
Moose, Wyoming 83012

GREAT SMOKY MOUNTAINS NATIONAL PARK
Gatlinburg, Tennessee 37738

GUADALUPE MOUNTAINS NATIONAL PARK
Box 1598
Carlsbad, New Mexico 88220

HALEAKALA NATIONAL PARK
Box 456
Kahului, Maui, Hawaii 96732

HAWAII VOLCANOES NATIONAL PARK
Hawaii Volcanoes National Park,
Hawaii 96718

HOT SPRINGS NATIONAL PARK
Box 1219
Hot Springs, Arkansas 71902

ISLE ROYALE NATIONAL PARK
87 North Ripley Street
Houghton, Michigan 49931

LASSEN VOLCANIC NATIONAL PARK
Mineral, California 96063

MAMMOTH CAVE NATIONAL PARK
Mammoth Cave, Kentucky 42259

MESA VERDE NATIONAL PARK
Mesa Verde National Park,
Colorado 81330

MOUNT MCKINLEY NATIONAL PARK
McKinley Park, Alaska 99755

MOUNT RAINIER NATIONAL PARK
Longmire, Washington 98397

OLYMPIC NATIONAL PARK
600 East Park Avenue
Port Angeles, Washington 98362

PETRIFIED FOREST NATIONAL PARK
Holbrook, Arizona 86025

PLATT NATIONAL PARK
Box 379
Sulphur, Oklahoma 73086

ROCKY MOUNTAIN NATIONAL PARK
Box 1080
Estes Park, Colorado 80517

SEQUOIA & KINGS CANYON NATIONAL PARK
Three Rivers, California 93271

SHENANDOAH NATIONAL PARK
Luray, Virginia 22835

VIRGIN ISLANDS NATIONAL PARK
Box 1707, Charlotte Amalie
St. Thomas, V.I. 00802

WIND CAVE NATIONAL PARK
Hot Springs, S.D. 57747

YELLOWSTONE NATIONAL PARK
Yellowstone National Park,
Wyoming 83020

YOSEMITE NATIONAL PARK
Box 577
Yosemite National Park,
California 95389

ZION NATIONAL PARK
Springdale, Utah 84767

APPENDIX D

Camping Accommodations in the National Monuments

ARCHES NATIONAL MONUMENT, UTAH

Devils Garden

BADLANDS NATIONAL MONUMENT, SOUTH DAKOTA

Cedar Pass   Dillon Pass   Overflow

BANDELIER NATIONAL MONUMENT, NEW MEXICO

Frijoles Mesa   Upper Crossing

BLACK CANYON OF THE GUNNISON NATIONAL MONUMENT, COLORADO

North Rim   South Rim

CANYON DE CHELLY NATIONAL MONUMENT, ARIZONA

Cottonwood

CAPITAL REEF NATIONAL MONUMENT, UTAH

Utah

CEDAR BREAKS NATIONAL MONUMENT, UTAH

Point Supreme

CHACO CANYON NATIONAL MONUMENT, NEW MEXICO

Gallo

CHANNEL ISLANDS NATIONAL MONUMENT, CALIFORNIA

Channel Islands

CHESAPEAKE AND OHIO CANAL NATIONAL MONUMENT, MARYLAND

Antietam Creek	McCoys Ferry	Shinhan
Day Apart Camps	Seneca	Sidling Hill Creek
Edwards Ferry	Shaffers Landing	Taylors Landing
Fifteen Mile Creek	Shepherdstown	

CHIRICAHUA NATIONAL MONUMENT, ARIZONA

Bonita Canyon

COLORADO NATIONAL MONUMENT, COLORADO

Saddle Horn

CRATERS OF THE MOON NATIONAL MONUMENT, IDAHO

Craters of the Moon

DEATH VALLEY NATIONAL MONUMENT, CALIFORNIA

Bennetts Well	Mahogany Flat	Saratoga Springs
Daylight Pass	Mesquite Springs	Texas Springs
Emigrant Junction	Midway Wells	Thorndike
Furnace Creek	Sand Dunes	Wild Rose Canyon

DEVILS POSTPILE NATIONAL MONUMENT, CALIFORNIA

Devils Postpile

DEVILS TOWER NATIONAL MONUMENT, WYOMING

Belle Fourche River Area

DINOSAUR NATIONAL MONUMENT, COLORADO

Anderson Hole	Harding Hole	Split Mountain Gorge
Box Elder	Island Park	Tepee Rapids
Deer Lodge	Jones Hole	Triplet Falls
Echo Park	Pot Creek	Wade and Curtis
Gates of Lodore	Rainbow Park River Camps	Warm Springs
Green River	Rippling Brook	

EL MORRO NATIONAL MONUMENT, FLORIDA

El Morro

GREAT SAND DUNES NATIONAL MONUMENT, COLORADO

Pinyon Flats

HOVENWEEP NATIONAL MONUMENT, COLORADO

Square Tower House

JOSHUA TREE NATIONAL MONUMENT, CALIFORNIA

Belle	Indian Cove	Sheep Pass
Cottonwood	Jumbo Rocks	White Tank
Hidden Valley	Ryan	

LAVA BEDS NATIONAL MONUMENT, CALIFORNIA

Indian Wells

NAVAJO NATIONAL MONUMENT, ARIZONA

Keet Seel	New	Old

ORGAN PIPE CACTUS NATIONAL MONUMENT, ARIZONA

Organ Pipe Cactus

PINNACLES NATIONAL MONUMENT, CALIFORNIA

Chalone Annex   Chalone Creek   Old Pinnacles
West Side

SAGUARO NATIONAL MONUMENT, ARIZONA

Grass Shack   Manning Camp

TIMPANOGOS CAVE NATIONAL MONUMENT, UTAH

Cave Camp

APPENDIX E

Glossary of Geologist's
and Naturalist's Terms*

AA—Hawaiian term for rough, clinkery lava. (Pronounced *ah-ah.*)

ABRASION—The wearing away of rocks by rubbing or grinding, chiefly by small grains of silt and sand carried by water or air currents and by glaciers.

AGATE—A variety of chalcedony with alternate layers of opal.

ALGAE—Simple forms of plants, most of which grow in water. Seaweeds are the most common forms found as fossils.

ALLUVIAL PLAIN—A plain formed by the deposition of materials from rivers and streams.

ALPINE GLACIER—A glacier confined to a stream valley; usually fed from a cirque. Also called valley glacier or mountain glacier.

AMPHIBIAN—A cold-blooded animal that breathes with gills in early stages of life and with lungs in later stages. Intermediate between fish and reptiles.

AMYGDALOID—A general name for volcanic rocks that contain numerous gas cavities (vesicles) filled with secondary minerals.

ANTICLINE—An arch, or upfold, of rock strata, with the flanks dipping in opposite directions from its axis.

ANTICLINORIUM—A series of anticlines and synclines so arranged structurally that together they form a general arch or anticline.

APPALACHIAN REVOLUTION—The closing event of the Paleozoic Era; the time when the Appalachian Mountains were originally formed by buckling and folding.

AQUIFER—Porous, permeable, water-bearing layer of

*From *A Guide to the National Parks*, William H. Matthews, III, Doubleday & Company, Inc., 1968.

rock, sand, or gravel capable of supplying water to wells or springs.

ARCHEOZOIC—The earliest era of geologic time, during which the first known rocks were formed; known also as the Early Precambrian.

ARÊTE—Sharp crest of a mountain ridge between two cirques or two glaciated valleys.

ARTIFACTS—Structures or implements made by man.

ASH—Fine-grained material ejected from a volcano.

BASALT—A common extrusive igneous rock, usually occurring as lava flows and typically black or dark gray in color.

BASE LEVEL—The lowest level to which land can be eroded by running water; equivalent to sea level for the continents as a whole.

BASIN—Applied to a basin-shaped feature which may be either structural, with rocks dipping inwards, or purely topographical.

BATHOLITH—A huge mass of crystalline igneous rock originating within the earth's crust and extending to great depths.

BED—The smallest division of a stratified rock series.

BED LOAD—Material in movement along a stream bottom or, if wind is the transporting agency, along the surface.

BEDDING PLANES—Surfaces along which rock layers part readily, by which one layer may be distinguished from another.

BEDROCK—The unweathered solid rock of the earth's crust.

BERGSCHRUND—The gap between glacier ice and the headwall of a cirque.

BIOCHEMICAL ROCK—A sedimentary rock composed of deposits resulting directly or indirectly from the life processes of organisms.

BLOCK MOUNTAINS—Mountains that result from faulting.

BLUE RIDGE—The easternmost range of the Appalachian Mountain System, composed largely of very ancient Archeozoic and Proterozoic rocks.

BOMB, VOLCANIC—A mass of lava ejected from a volcanic vent in a plastic condition and then shaped in flight or as it hits the ground. Larger than one and a half inches across.

BOULDER—Large, water-worn, and rounded blocks of stone, most commonly found in stream beds, on beaches, or in glaciated areas.

BRAIDED STREAM—A stream whose channel is filled with deposits that split it into many small channels.

BREAKER—A wave breaking into foam in the shallow water near the shore.

BRECCIA—A rock made up of coarse, angular fragments of pre-existing rock that has been broken and the pieces recemented together.

BUTTE—A flat-topped, steep-walled hill; usually a remnant of horizontal beds, and smaller and narrower than a mesa.

CALCAREOUS—Composed of calcium carbonate.

CALCAREOUS ALGAE—Algae that form deposits of calcium carbonate, fossils of which are found in the United States.

CALCITE—A mineral composed of calcium carbonate, $CaCO_3$.

CALDERA—A large, basin-shaped volcanic depression.

CAMBRIAN—The earliest period of the Paleozoic Era or the system of rocks formed in this period.

CARBONIFEROUS—Composed largely of carbon. Also, a former period of the Paleozoic Era, now divided into the Mississippian and Pennsylvanian periods, so called because it contained the world's greatest coal deposits.

CEMENTATION—The process whereby loose grains, such as silt, sand, or gravels, are bound together by precipitation of mineral matter between them to produce firm rock beds.

CENOZOIC—The latest of geologic time, containing the Tertiary and Quaternary periods and continuing to the present time.

CENTRAL VENT—An opening in the earth's crust, roughly circular, from which magmatic products are extruded. A volcano is an accumulation of igneous material around a central vent.

CHALCEDONY—The noncrystalline forms of quartz, such as chert, flint, and agate.

CHEMICAL WEATHERING—The weathering of rock material by chemical processes whereby the original material is transformed into new chemical combinations.

CINDER CONE—Cone formed by the explosive type of volcanic eruption; it has a narrow base and steep, symmetrical slopes of interlocking, angular cinders.

CINDER, VOLCANIC—A fragment of lava, generally less than an inch in diameter, ejected from a volcanic vent.

CIRQUE—Steep-walled basin high on a mountain, produced by glacial erosion and commonly forming the head of a valley.

CLASTIC ROCK—Those rocks composed largely of fragments derived from pre-existing rocks and transported mechanically to their place of deposition, such as shales, siltstones, sandstones, and conglomerates.

CLASTIC TEXTURE—Texture shown by sedimentary rocks formed from deposits of mineral and rock fragments. *See* Clastic Rock.

CLAY—The finest type of soil or clastic fragments; having high plasticity when wet, and consisting mainly of aluminum and silica.

COAL—A black, compact sedimentary rock, containing 60 to 100 per cent of organic material, primarily of plant origin.

COASTAL PLAIN—An exposed part of the sea floor, normally consisting of stream- or wave-deposited sediments.

COL—A pass through a mountain ridge. Formed by the enlargement of two cirques on opposite sides of the ridge until their headwalls meet and are broken down.

COLUMN—A column or post of dripstone joining the floor and roof of a cave; the result of joining of a stalactite and a stalagmite.

COLUMNAR JOINTING—A pattern of jointing that blocks out columns of rock. Characteristic of tabular basalt flows or sills.

COMPLEX MOUNTAINS—Mountains that result from a combination of faulting, folding, and volcanic action.

COMPOSITE CONE—Cone formed by intermediate type of volcanic eruption, consisting of alternate layers of cinders and lava; also called a strato-volcano.

CONCHOIDAL—A characteristic break or fracture of a mineral or rock resulting in a smooth, curved surface. Typical of glass, quartz, and obsidian.

CONCORDANT PLUTON—An intrusive igneous body with contacts parallel to the layering or foliation surfaces of the rocks into which it was intruded.

CONCRETION—A nodular or irregularly shaped structure that has grown by mineral concentration around a nucleus, such as siderite concretions or oölitic hematite.

CONGLOMERATE—Water-worn pebbles cemented together; the pebbles are usually of mixed sizes.

CONTINENTAL GLACIER—An ice sheet that obscures mountains and plains of a large section of a continent. Existing continental glaciers are on Greenland and Antarctica.

CONTACT METAMORPHISM—Alteration of rocks caused by contact with igneous intrusions.

CONTINENTAL SHELF—The relatively shallow ocean floor bordering a continental landmass.

CONTOUR LINES—Lines of a map joining points on the earth having the same elevation.

COQUINA—A coarse-grained, porous variety of clastic limestone composed mostly of fragments of shells.

CORRELATION—The process of establishing the contemporaneity of rocks or events in another area.

CRATER—A bowl-shaped depression, generally in the top of a volcanic cone.

CREEP—The slow, imperceptible movement of soil or broken rock from higher to lower levels.

CRETACEOUS—The latest period of the Mesozoic Era of geologic time.

CREVASSE—A deep crack in a glacier.

CRUST—The outer zone of the earth, composed of solid rock between twenty and thirty miles thick. Rests on the mantle, and may be covered by sediments.

CRYSTAL—The form of a mineral occurring in a geometric shape with flat or smooth faces meeting each other in definite angles.

CRYSTALLINE—Pertaining to the nature of a crystal, such as a rock composed of crystals or crystal grains; often glassy in appearance.

DECOMPOSITION—Term synonymous with chemical weathering.

DEFLATION—The removal of material from a land surface by wind action.

DEFORMATION—The result of diastrophism as shown in the tilting, bending, or breaking of layers of rock.

DELTA—A deposit of sediment built at the mouth of a stream as it enters a larger, quieter body of water, such as the sea, a lake, or sometimes a larger, more slowly flowing stream.

DEPOSITION—The laying down of material that may later become a rock or mineral deposit.

DETRITAL SEDIMENTARY ROCKS—Rocks formed from accumulations of minerals and rocks derived either from erosion of previously existing rocks or from the weathered products of these rocks.

DEVONIAN—The fourth period of the Paleozoic Era.

DIASTROPHISM—The process by which the earth's crust is deformed, producing folds and faults, rising or sinking of the lands and sea bottom, and the building of mountains.

DIFFERENTIAL WEATHERING—The process by which different sections of a rock mass weather at different rates. Caused primarily by variations in composition of the rock itself and also by differences in intensity of weathering from one section to another in the same rock.

DIKE—Wall of intrusive igneous rock cutting across the structure of other rocks.

DIORITE—A coarse-grained igneous rock with the composition of andesite (no quartz or orthoclase), composed of about 75 per cent plagioclase feldspars and the balance ferromagnesian silicates.

DIP—The slope of a bed of rock relative to the horizontal.

DISINTEGRATION—Synonymous with mechanical weathering.

DISTURBANCE—Regional mountain-building event in earth history, commonly separating two periods.

DIVIDE—The ridges or regions of high ground that separate the drainage basins of streams.

DOME—An upfolded area from which the rocks dip outward in all directions.

DRAINAGE BASIN—The area from which a given stream and its tributaries receive their water.

DRIFT—General term for glacial deposits.

DRIPSTONE—A deposit, usually of limestone, made

by dripping water, such as stalactites and stalagmites in caverns.

DRUMLIN—Oval hill composed of glacial drift, with its long axis parallel to the direction of movement of a former ice sheet.

DUNE—A mound or ridge of wind-deposited sand.

EARTHQUAKE—The shaking of the ground as a result of movements within the earth, most commonly associated with movement along faults.

END MORAINE—A ridge or belt of till marking the farthest advance of a glacier; also called a terminal moraine.

ENVIRONMENT—Everything around a plant or animal that may affect it.

EOCENE—Second oldest epoch of the Tertiary Period of the Cenozoic Era.

EOLIAN—Pertaining to the erosion and the deposits resulting from wind action and to sedimentary rocks composed of wind-transported material.

EPOCH—A subdivision of a geologic period, such as the Pleistocene Epoch of the Quaternary Period.

ERA—A major division of geologic time. All geologic time is divided into five eras: the Archeozoic, Proterozoic, Paleozoic, Mesozoic, and Cenozoic eras.

EROSION—The process whereby loosened or dissolved materials of the earth are moved from place to place by the action of water, wind, or ice.

ERRATIC—A large boulder, deposited by glacial action, whose composition is different from that of the native bedrock.

ESCARPMENT—*See* Scarp.

EXFOLIATION—The scaling or flaking off of concentric sheets from bare rock surfaces, much like the peeling of onion layers.

EXFOLIATION DOME—A large, rounded, domal feature produced in homogeneous coarse-grained igneous rocks (and sometimes in conglomerates) by the process of exfoliation.

EXTRUSIVE—As applied to igneous rocks, rocks formed from materials ejected or poured out upon the earth's surface, such as volcanic rocks.

EXTRUSIVE ROCK—A rock that has solidified from a mass of magma that poured or was blown out upon the earth's surface.

FAULT—A fracture in a rock surface, along which there is displacement of the broken surfaces.

FAULT-BLOCK MOUNTAIN—A mountain bounded by one or more faults.

FAULTING—The movement of rock layers along a break.

FAULT SCARP—A cliff formed at the surface of a fault.

FAUNA—The forms of animal life of a particular region or time period.

FIRN—Granular ice formed by the recrystallization of snow. Intermediate between snow and glacial ice; also called *névé*.

FISSURE—An open fracture in a rock surface.

FISSURE ERUPTION—Extrusion of lava from a fissure in the earth's crust.

FJORD—A drowned glacial valley.

FLOOD PLAIN—The part of a stream valley that is covered with water during flood stage.

FLORA—The forms of plant life of a particular region or time period.

FLOWSTONE—A sedimentary rock, usually of limestone, formed by flowing water, most commonly in caverns.

FOLD—A bend in rock layers, such as an anticline or syncline.

FOLDED MOUNTAINS—Mountains that result from the folding of rocks.

FOLIATION—An extremely thin layering or laminated structure in rocks or minerals, often so pronounced as to permit separation or cleavage into thin sheets.

FORMATION—Any assemblage of rocks having some character in common, whether of origin, age, or composition. Also, anything that has been naturally formed or brought into its present shape, such as dripstones in caverns.

FOSSIL—Any remains or traces of plants or animals that have been naturally preserved in deposits of a past geologic age.

FOSSILIFEROUS—As applied to rocks, any rock containing fossils.

FOSSILIFEROUS LIMESTONE—Limestone made from the skeletons of fossilized sea animals.

FRICTION—The resistance due to surface rubbing.

FROST ACTION—Process of mechanical weathering caused by repeated cycles of freezing and thawing. Expansion of water during the freezing cycle provides the energy for the process.

FROST WEDGING—Prying off of fragments of rock by expansion of freezing water in crevices.

FUMAROLES—Fissures or holes in volcanic regions, from which steam and other volcanic gases are emitted.

GEANTICLINE—Very broad upfold in the earth's crust, extending for hundreds of miles.

GEODE—A hollow stone, usually lined or filled with mineral matter, formed by deposition in a rock cavity.

GEOLOGIC COLUMN—A chronologic arrangement of rock units in columnar form with the oldest units at the bottom and the youngest at the top.

GEOLOGIC REVOLUTIONS—Periods of marked crustal movement separating one geologic era from another.

GEOLOGIC TIME—All time that has elapsed since the first known rocks were formed, and continuing until recent, or modern, time when the glaciers of the last glaciation retreated.

GEOLOGIC TIME SCALE—A chronologic sequence of units of earth time.

GEOLOGICAL CYCLE—A period in which mountains are born and rise above the sea and are again eroded.

GEOLOGIST—A person engaged in geological work, study, or investigation.

GEOLOGY—The science that deals with the origin and nature of the earth and the development of life upon it.

GEOPHYSICS—The physics of the earth.

GEOSYNCLINE—A great, elongated downfold in which great thicknesses of sediments accumulate over a long period of time.

GEYSER—A hot spring that periodically erupts steam and hot water.

GLACIAL DRIFT—Boulders, till, gravel, sand, or clay transported by a glacier or its meltwater.

GLACIATION—A major advance of ice sheets over a large part of the earth's surface.

GLACIER—A body of ice compacted from snow, that moves under its own weight and persists from season to season.

GLACIOFLUVIAL—Pertaining to streams flowing from glaciers and their deposits.

GNEISS—A metamorphic rock, usually coarse-grained, having its mineral grains aligned in bands or foliations.

GRABEN—A trough developed when parallel faults allow the blocks between them to sink, forming broad valleys flanked on each side by steep fault scarps; also called *rift valley*.

GRADIENT—The difference in elevation between the head and mouth of a stream.

GRANITE—An intrusive igneous rock composed of orthoclase feldspar and quartz; it may contain additional minerals, most commonly mica.

GRANITIZATION—The process of alteration of other rocks into granite without actual melting.

GRANODIORITE—A coarse-grained igneous rock intermediate in composition between granite and diorite.

GRAVEL—A loose deposit of rounded, water-worn pebbles, mostly ranging in size from that of a pea to a hen's egg, and often mixed with sand.

GREENSTONE or GREENSCHIST—A metamorphosed basaltic rock having a greenish-black color.

GROUND MORAINE—Till deposited from a glacier as a veneer over the landscape and forming a gently rolling surface.

HANGING VALLEY—A tributary valley that terminates high above the floor of the main valley due to the deeper erosion of the latter; commonly by glaciation.

HEADWARD EROSION—The process whereby streams lengthen their valleys at the upper end by the cutting action of the water that flows in at the head of the valley.

HISTORICAL GEOLOGY—The branch of geology that deals with the history of the earth, including a record of life on the earth as well as physical changes in the earth itself.

HORN—A spire of bedrock left where cirques have eaten into a mountain from more than two sides around a central area. Example: Matterhorn of the Swiss Alps.

HOT SPRING—A spring that brings hot water to the surface. A thermal spring. Water temperature usually 15°F or more above mean air temperature.

ICE AGE—The glacial period, or Pleistocene Epoch of the Quaternary Period.

ICECAP—A cap of ice usually over a large area. *See also* Continental Glacier.

IGNEOUS ROCKS—Rocks formed by solidification of magma.

IMPRESSION—The form or shape left on a soft surface by objects that have come in contact with it and that may have later hardened into rock. A type of fossilization consisting of the imprint of a plant or animal structure.

INTRUSIVE IGNEOUS ROCK—Molten rock that did not reach the surface of the earth but hardened in cracks and openings in other rock layers.

INVERTEBRATES—Animals without backbones.

JASPER—Granular cryptocrystalline silica usually colored red by hematite inclusions.

JOINT—A break in a rock mass where there has been no relative movement of rock on opposite sides of the break.

JOINT SYSTEM—A series of two or more sets of joints passing through a rock mass so as to separate it into blocks of more or less regular pattern.

JURASSIC—The second, or middle, period of the Mesozoic Era.

KARST TOPOGRAPHY—A type of landscape characteristic of some limestone regions, in which drainage is mostly by means of underground streams in caverns.

KETTLE—A depression remaining after the melting of large blocks of ice buried in glacial drift.

KIPUKA—An "island" of old land left within a lava flow.

LACCOLITH—Lens-shaped body of intrusive igneous rock that has domed up the overlying rocks.

LACUSTRINE—Pertaining to a lake, sediments on a lake bottom, or sedimentary rocks composed of such material.

LANDSLIDE—The downward, rather sudden movement of a large section of land that has been loosened from a hill or mountainside.

LATERAL MORAINE—A ridge of till along the edge of a valley glacier; composed primarily of material that fell to the glacier from valley walls.

LAVA—Hot liquid rock at or close to the earth's surface, and its solidified products.

LAYER—A bed or stratum of rock.

LIMESTONE—A sedimentary rock composed largely of calcium carbonate.

LITHIFICATION—The process whereby unconsoli-

dated rock-forming materials are converted into a consolidated or coherent state.

LOAD—The amount of material that a transporting agency, such as a stream, a glacier, or the wind, is actually carrying at a given time.

MAGMA—Molten rock deep in the earth's crust.

MANTLE ROCK—The layers of loose weathered rock lying over solid bedrock.

MARBLE—A metamorphosed, recrystallized limestone.

MARINE—Belonging to, or originating in, the sea.

MASS-WASTING—Erosional processes caused chiefly by gravity. Example: a landslide.

MEANDERS—Wide curves typical of well-developed streams.

MECHANICAL WEATHERING—The process by which rock is broken down into smaller and smaller fragments as the result of energy developed by physical forces. Also called *disintegration.*

MESA—A large, wide, flat-topped hill, usually a remnant of horizontal beds.

MESOZOIC—The geologic era between the Paleozoic and Cenozoic eras; the "Age of Reptiles"; contains the Triassic, Jurassic, and Cretaceous periods.

METAMORPHIC ROCKS—Rocks that have been changed from their original form by great heat and pressure.

METAMORPHISM—The process whereby rocks are changed by heat, pressure, or chemical environment into different kinds.

MINERAL—A natural, inorganic substance having distinct physical properties, and a composition expressed by a chemical formula.

MINERALOGIST—A geologist who specializes in studying minerals.

MINERALOGY—The subdivision of geology that deals with the study of minerals.

MIOCENE—Fourth-oldest epoch of the Tertiary Period of the Cenozoic Era.

MISSISSIPPIAN—The fifth period of the Paleozoic Era.

MONADNOCK—A residual hill or higher elevation left standing on a peneplain after erosion of the surrounding material.

MORAINE—A ridge or mound of boulders, gravel, sand, and clay carried on or deposited by a glacier.

MOUNTAIN GLACIER—Synonymous with alpine glacier.

MUD CRACKS—Cracks caused by the shrinkage of a

drying deposit of silt or clay under surface conditions.

NATIONAL MONUMENT—An area set aside by the President of the United States or by act of Congress because of its scientific or historical value, and administered by the National Park Service.

NATIONAL PARK—An area of greater importance, and usually of greater extent, than a national monument, set aside by act of Congress, most commonly because of its scenic and geologic interest.

NÉVÉ—Compacted granular snow partly converted into ice; also called *firn*.

NUÉE ARDENTE—Avalanche of fiery ash enveloped in compressed gas from a volcanic eruption.

OBSIDIAN—A glassy rock formed from hardened lava, found just under the foamy top layer.

OLIGOCENE—Third-oldest epoch of the Tertiary Period of the Cenozoic Era.

ONYX—A translucent variety of quartz consisting of differently colored bands, often used as a decorative stone. Also, applied to similarly appearing varieties of calcite or limestone, such as dripstones and flowstones of caverns, and used for similar purposes.

OPAL—Amorphous silica, with varying amounts of water. A mineral gel.

ORDOVICIAN—The second period of the Paleozoic Era.

ORGANISM—Anything possessing life; a plant or animal body.

OROGENY—A major disturbance or mountain-building movement in the earth's crust.

OUTCROP—An exposure of bedrock at the surface of the ground.

OUTWASH—Stratified sediments laid down by the meltwater of a glacier beyond the glacier itself.

OUTWASH PLAINS—Plains formed by the deposition of materials washed out from the edges of a glacier.

OVERHANG—The upper portion of a cliff extending beyond the lower.

OXIDATION—The chemical combination of substances with oxygen.

PAHOEHOE LAVA—Lava that has solidified with a smooth, ropy, or billowy appearance.

PALEOBOTANY—The branch of paleontology that deals with the study of fossil plants.

PALEOCENE—Oldest epoch of the Tertiary Period of the Cenozoic Era.

PALEOGEOGRAPHY—The study of ancient geography.

PALEONTOLOGY—The branch of geology that deals with the study of fossil plants and animals.

PALEONTOLOGIST—A scientist who studies fossils.

PALEOZOIC—The era of geologic time that contains the Cambrian, Ordovician, Silurian, Devonian, Mississippian, Pennsylvanian, and Permian periods.

PARASITIC CONES—Volcanic cones developed at openings some distance below the main vent.

PASS—A deep gap or passageway through a mountain range.

PEAK—The topmost point, or summit, of a mountain.

PEBBLE—A smooth, rounded stone, larger than sand and smaller than a hen's egg.

PEDIMENT—Broad, smooth erosional surface developed at the expense of a highland mass in an arid climate; underlain by beveled rock, which is covered by a veneer of gravel and rock debris.

PELE'S HAIR—Volcanic glass spun out into hairlike form.

PENEPLAIN—Extensive land surface eroded to a nearly flat plain.

PENEPLANATION—The process of erosion to base level over a vast area, which results in the production of a peneplain.

PENNSYLVANIAN—The sixth period of the Paleozoic Era.

PERIOD—A main division of a geologic era, characterized primarily by its distinctive remains of life.

PERMAFROST—Permanently frozen subsoil.

PERMEABILITY—The degree to which water can penetrate and pass through rock.

PERMIAN—The seventh and last period of the Paleozoic Era.

PETRIFACTION—A process in which the original substance of a fossil is replaced by mineral matter.

PETROLOGY—The scientific study of rocks.

PIEDMONT—The area of land at the base of a mountain. That portion of the Appalachian Region that lies alongside the eastern side of the Blue Ridge.

PIEDMONT GLACIER—A glacier formed by the coalescence of alpine glaciers and spreading over plains at the feet of the mountains from which the alpine glaciers came.

PILLAR—A column of rock in a cavern produced by

the union of a stalactite and a stalagmite. Also, any column of rock remaining after erosion of the surrounding rock.

PILLOW LAVA—A basaltic lava that develops a structure resembling a pile of pillows when it solidifies under water.

PIPE (volcanic)—The tube leading to a volcano, sometimes filled with solidified material.

PIT CRATER—A crater formed by sinking in of the surface; not primarily a vent for lava.

PLAIN—A region of horizontal rock layers that has low relief due to a comparatively low elevation.

PLASTIC DEFORMATION—The folding or flowing of solid rock under conditions of great heat and pressure.

PLATEAU—A region of horizontal rock layers that has high relief due to higher elevation.

PLATEAU BASALT—Basalt poured out from fissures in floods that tend to form great plateaus; also called flood basalt.

PLEISTOCENE—The first of the two epochs of the Quaternary Period, and that which precedes modern time, known also as the Great Ice Age.

PLIOCENE—Last epoch of the Tertiary Period of the Cenozoic Era.

PLUTONIC—Applied to rocks that have formed at great depths below the surface.

PLUTONIC ROCKS—*See* Intrusive Igneous Rock.

PORPHYRY—A mineral texture of fairly large crystals set in a mass of very fine crystals.

POTHOLE—A rounded depression in the rock of a stream bed.

PRECAMBRIAN—A collective name covering the Archeozoic and Proterozoic eras and the rocks formed during those eras.

PRECIPITATED ROCKS—Sedimentary rocks formed by the precipitation of mineral matter out of solution, such as limestone or dolomite.

PROTEROZOIC—The second of the geologic eras, also called Late Precambrian.

PUMICE—A froth of volcanic glass.

PRYOCLASTIC ROCK—Fragmental rock blown out by volcanic explosion and deposited from the air; for example, bomb, cinder, ash, tuff, and pumice.

QUARTZ—One of the main rock-forming minerals, composed of pure silica.

QUARTZITE—A hard metamorphic rock composed essentially of quartz sand cemented by silica.

QUATERNARY—The second and last period of the Cenozoic Era. It includes the Pleistocene Epoch, or Ice Age, and all the time since.

RAPIDS—Stretches in a stream where the water drops over rock ledges or accumulations of loose rock, churning itself into foam and making navigation dangerous or impossible.

RECENT—All time since the close of the Pleistocene Epoch, or Ice Age.

REGIONAL METAMORPHISM—The alteration of rocks over a very large area due to some major geological process.

REJUVENATION—Any action that tends to increase the gradient of a stream.

RELIEF—The difference in elevation between the high and low places of a land surface.

REPLACEMENT—The formation of mineral replicas of organic remains by the exchange of minerals for cell contents.

RESIDUAL BOULDERS—Large rock fragments formed in place by weathering of the solid bedrock.

REVOLUTION—A time of major mountain building, bringing an end to a geologic period or era.

RIFT—A large fracture in the earth's crust.

RIFT VALLEY—A major topographical feature produced by the dropping down of a long segment of the earth's crust between two parallel faults.

RIFT ZONES—The highly fractured belts on flanks of volcanoes along which most of the eruptions take place.

RIPPLE MARKS—Wavelike corrugations produced in unconsolidated materials by wind or water.

ROCHES MOUTONNÉES—Bedrock that has been smoothed and "plucked" by the passage of glacial ice.

ROCK—Any natural mass of mineral matter, usually consisting of a mixture of two or more minerals; it constitutes an essential part of the earth's crust.

ROCK FLOUR—Finely ground rock particles, chiefly silt size, resulting from glacial abrasion.

ROCK GLACIER—An accumulation of rocky material moving slowly down a valley in the manner of a glacier.

ROCK WASTE—Fragments of bedrock produced by weathering.

RUNOFF—The water that flows on the ground surface, tending to drain through streams toward the sea.

SANDSTONE—Sedimentary rock composed of largely cemented sand grains, usually quartz.

SCARP—A steep rise in the ground produced either by the outcrop of a resistant rock or by the line of a fault.

SCHIST—A finely layered metamorphic rock that splits easily.

SCORIA—Slaglike fragment of lava explosively ejected from a volcanic vent.

SEA CAVE—Cave formed as a result of erosion by sea waves.

SEA CLIFF—Cliff formed by marine erosion.

SEDIMENT—Solid material suspended in water, wind, or ice; such material transported from its place of origin and redeposited elsewhere.

SEDIMENTARY ROCKS—Rocks formed by the accumulation of sediment derived from the breakdown of earlier rocks, by chemical precipitation, or by organic activity.

SEISMOGRAPH—An instrument that detects and records earthquake waves.

SEISMOLOGIST—A person who studies and interprets the effects of earthquake activity.

SHALE—A sedimentary rock formed by the hardening of mud and clay, and usually tending to split into thin sheets or layers.

SHEET WASH—A type of erosion in which water strips away exposed topsoil slowly and evenly on a slope.

SHIELD VOLCANO—A volcano having the shape of a very broad, gently sloping dome.

SILICA—The chemical compound of oxygen and silicon, which are the two commonest elements in the earth's crust.

SILL—A sheet of intrusive rock lying parallel to the bedding of the rock that is intruded.

SILT—Soil particles intermediate in size between clay particles and sand grains.

SILURIAN—The third period of the Paleozoic Era.

SINK—A depression in the earth's surface formed by the collapse of the roof of an underground cavern.

SLATE—A metamorphosed clay rock with a pronounced cleavage along which it readily splits.

SLIDE-ROCK—*See* Talus.

SOIL—Layers of decomposed rock and organic materials on the surface of the land areas of the earth.

SOLFATARA—A fumarole liberating sulfur-bearing gas.

SPATTER CONES—Small cones that form in lava fields away from the main vent. Lava is spattered out of them through holes in a thin crust.

SPELEOLOGY—The scientific study of caverns and related features.

SPELEOTHEM—A secondary mineral deposit formed in caves; for example, a stalagmite or a stalactite.

SPRING—Water issuing from beneath the surface through a natural opening in sufficient quantity to make a distinct current.

STACK—An isolated column of rock left standing as waves erode a shoreline.

STALACTITE—A stony projection from the roof of a cavern, formed of minerals deposited from dripping water.

STALAGMITE—A raised deposit on the floor of a cavern, formed by minerals deposited from dripping water.

STRATA—Rock layers or beds.

STRATIFICATION—The structure produced by the deposition of sediments in beds or layers.

STRATIFIED ROCKS—Rocks which occur in parallel layers.

STRATIGRAPHY—The study of rock layers.

STRATUM (pl. Strata)—A rock layer or bed.

STRATOVOLCANO—A volcano having a cone of alternate layers of lava and solid fragments.

STRIAE—Scratches on the surface of rocks resulting from the movement of glacial ice.

STRUCTURAL GEOLOGY—The study of rocks and their relationships.

SUBMERGENCE—The flooding of land by the sea. Characteristic of most geologic periods.

SUBSIDENCE—Sinking of the earth's crust.

SYNCLINE—A fold of layers of rock that dip inward from both sides toward the axis; opposite of anticline.

SYNCLINORIUM—A broad regional syncline on which are superimposed minor folds.

SYSTEM—The rocks that accumulated during a period of geologic time.

TAIGA—A type of vegetation characteristic of subarctic climates.

TALUS—A mass of rock debris at the base of a steep mountain or cliff; also called *scree.*

TECTONICS—The phenomena associated with rock deformation and rock structures generally; the study of these phenomena.

TEMBLOR—An earthquake.

TERTIARY—The first of the two periods of the Cenozoic Era; commonly called the "Age of Mammals."

TEXTURE—The composite arrangement, shape, and size of the grains or crystal particles of a rock.

TILL—Glacial deposits that have not been stratified or sorted by water action.

TILLITE—A sedimentary rock composed of firmly consolidated till.

TOPOGRAPHIC MAP—A map showing surface features of a portion of the earth.

TOPOGRAPHY—The relief and contour of the land surface.

TRANSPORT—The carrying by water, wind, or ice from one place to another.

TRAP—Old name for a lava flow.

TRAVERTINE—A variety of limestone deposited by dripping or flowing water in caverns or by springs, as in stalactites and stalagmites.

TRIASSIC—Oldest period of the Mesozoic Era.

TRIBUTARY—A stream that flows into a larger one.

TRILOBITES—An extinct group of arthropods, possibly related to the crustaceans, with a trilobed dorsal skeleton.

TROUGH—A channel or long depression between two ridges of land.

TUNDRA—A type of climate in the zone of transition between the subarctic regions and the icecaps.

UNCONFORMITY—A break in the sequence of rock formations that separates younger groups from older ones; caused primarily by removal of some of the older rocks by erosion before those of a later sequence were laid down.

UNIFORMITARIANISM—The doctrine that the past geological record can be interpreted by reference to present-day phenomena and processes. "The present is the key to the past."

UPLIFT—The elevation of any extensive part of the earth's surface from a lower position by some geologic force.

VALLEY—A long depression on the earth's surface, usually bounded by hills or mountains, and typically traversed by a stream that receives the drainage from the adjacent heights.

VALLEY TRAIN—The deposit of rock material carried down by a stream originating from a glacier confined in a narrow valley.

VEIN—A thin and usually irregular igneous intrusion.

VENT—An opening where volcanic material reaches the surface.

VENTIFACT—A stone that has been smoothed by wind abrasion.

VERTEBRATES—Animals with backbones.

VESICULAR—Having bubble holes formed by gases.

VOLCANIC—Pertaining to volcanoes or any rocks associated with volcanic activity at or below the surface.

VOLCANIC NECK—A rock plug formed in the passageway of a volcano when magma slowly cools and solidifies there.

VOLCANISM—A general term including all types of activity due to movement of magma.

VOLCANO—The vent from which molten rock materials reach the surface, together with the accumulations of volcanic materials deposited around the vent.

WARPING—The bending of sedimentary beds of rock into broad, low domes and shallow basins.

WATERFALL—The dropping of a stream of water over a vertical or nearly vertical descent in its course.

WATER GAP—A valley that cuts across a mountain ridge, through which the stream still flows.

WATER TABLE—The upper boundary of the groundwater, below which all spaces within the rock are completely filled with water.

WAVE-BUILT TERRACE—A seaward extension of a wave-cut terrace, produced by debris from wave action.

WAVE-CUT TERRACE—A level surface of rock under the water along the shore, formed as waves cut back the shoreline.

WEATHERING—The natural disintegration and decomposition of rocks and minerals.

YOSEMITE—A glacially carved, U-shaped, steep-walled canyon.

APPENDIX F

Selected Bibliography

Many readers will want to learn more about geology in general, or about the geology of some particular national park. The following list includes selected references of many types, any one of which contains additional information on various phases of geology and the national parks. This list is by no means all-inclusive, and many other interesting and worth-while publications may be found in public, school, and college libraries. The publications are grouped together according to subject matter, each list consisting of author, date of publication, title, and publisher.

Those readers who want a more comprehensive list of earth-science references will find it helpful to consult the following publications:

MATTHEWS, WILLIAM H., III, 1964. *Selected References for Earth Science Courses* (ESCP Reference Series Pamphlet RS-2). Prentice-Hall, Inc., Englewood Cliffs, New Jersey 07632

MATTHEWS, WILLIAM H., III, 1965. *Selected Maps and Earth Science Publications for the States and Provinces of North America* (ESCP Reference Series Pamphlet RS-4). Prentice-Hall, Inc., Englewood Cliffs, New Jersey 07632

PANGBORN, MARK W., JR., 1957. *Earth for the Layman: A List of Nearly 1400 Good Books and Pamphlets of Popular Interest on Geology, Mining, Oil, Maps, and Related Subjects.* American Geological Institute, 1444 N Street, N.W., Washington, D.C. 20005

Specific Parks

In addition to the selected publications listed below, the National Park Service issues descriptive brochures and other informational material about each of the parks. These may be obtained by writing the superintendents of the respective parks at the addresses listed in Appendix C.

BRYCE CANYON NATIONAL PARK

GRATER, R. K., 1950. *Guide to Zion, Bryce Canyon, and Cedar Breaks.* Binfords & Mort, 2505 S.E. 11 Ave., Portland, Oregon 97242

GREGORY, HERBERT E., 1951. *The Geology and Geography of the Paunsaugunt Region, Utah.* Geological Survey Professional Paper 226, U.S. Government Printing Office, Washington, D.C. 20402

CANYONLANDS NATIONAL PARK

KING, P. E., 1948. *Geology of the Southern Guadalupe Mountains, Texas.* Geological Survey Professional Paper 215, U.S. Government Printing Office, Washington, D.C. 20402

NEWELL, N. D., and others, 1953. *The Permian Reef Complex of the Guadalupe Mountains Region, Texas and New Mexico.* W. H. Freeman & Co., San Francisco, California 94104

ROSE, R. H., 1965. "Upheaval Dome." *National Parks Magazine* (Vol. 39, No. 216, pp. 11–16), 1300 New Hampshire Ave., N.W., Washington, D.C. 20036

ROSWELL GEOLOGICAL SOCIETY, 1964. *Geology of the Capitan Reef Complex of the Guadalupe Mountains.* Roswell

Geological Society, Box 1171, Roswell, New Mexico 88201

SPANGLE, PAUL (editor), 1960. *Guidebook to Carlsbad Caverns National Park.* Carlsbad Caverns Natural History Association, Box 1598, Carlsbad, New Mexico 88220

Western Gateways magazine, 1964. "Canyonlands Highway Issue." KC Publications, Box 428, Flagstaff, Arizona 86001

CRATER LAKE NATIONAL PARK

BALDWIN, EWART M., 1964. *Geology of Oregon.* J. W. Edwards, Ann Arbor, Michigan 48103

CONTOR, ROGER J., 1963. *The Underworld of Oregon Caves.* Crater Lake Natural History Association, Inc., Crater Lake, Oregon 97604

MACKIN, J. HOOVER, and CARY, S. A., 1965. *Origin of Cascade Landscapes.* Information Circular No. 41, Washington Division of Mines and Geology, Olympia, Washington 98501

RUHLE, GEORGE C., 1964. *Along Crater Lake Roads.* Crater Lake Natural History Association, Inc., Crater Lake, Oregon 97604

WILLIAMS, HOWEL, 1942. *The Geology of Crater Lake National Park, Oregon.* Publication No. 540, Carnegie Institution of Washington, Washington, D.C. 20005

WILLIAMS, HOWEL, 1948. *The Ancient Volcanoes of Oregon.* University of Oregon Press, Eugene, Oregon 97403

WILLIAMS, HOWEL, 1957. *Crater Lake, the Story of its Origin.* University of California Press, Berkeley, California 94720

GLACIER NATIONAL PARK

BEATTY, M. E., 1958. *Motorist's Guide to the Going-to-the-Sun Road.* Glacier Natural History Association, West Glacier, Montana 59936

DYSON, J. L., 1960. *The Geologic Story of Glacier National Park.* Glacier Natural History Association, West Glacier, Montana 59936

DYSON, J. L., 1962. *Glaciers and Glaciation in Glacier National Park.* Glacier Natural History Association, West Glacier, Montana 59936

ROSS, C. P., 1959. *Geology of Glacier National Park and the Flat-*
head Region Northwestern Montana. Geological Survey Professional Paper 296, U.S. Government Printing Office, Washington, D.C. 20402

ROSS, C. P., and REZAK, RICHARD, 1959. *The Rocks and Fossils of Glacier National Park: The Story of Their Origin.* Geological Survey Paper 294-K, U.S. Government Printing Office, Washington, D.C. 20402

RUHLE, G. C., 1963. *Guide to Glacier National Park.* John W. Forney, Northstar Center, Minneapolis, Minnesota

GRAND CANYON NATIONAL PARK

DARTON, N. H., 1961. *Story of the Grand Canyon of Arizona—How It Was Made* (33d ed.). Fred Harvey, Grand Canyon, Arizona 86023

KRUTCH, J. W., 1962. *Grand Canyon.* The Natural History Library, Doubleday & Co., Garden City, New York 11530

MAXSON, J. H., 1961. *Grand Canyon—Origin and Scenery.* Bulletin 13, Grand Canyon Natural History Association, Box 219, Grand Canyon, Arizona 86023

MCKEE, E. D., 1965. *Ancient Landscapes of the Grand Canyon Region* (23d ed.). Grand Canyon Natural History Association, Box 219, Grand Canyon, Arizona 86023

GRAND TETON NATIONAL PARK

BONNEY, O. H., and BONNEY, L. G., 1961. *Bonney's Guide: Jackson's Hole and Grand Teton National Park.* Orrin H. Bonney and Lorraine G. Bonney, 1309 American Investors Bldg., Houston, Texas 77002

FRYXELL, F. M., 1959. *The Tetons—Interpretations of a Mountain Landscape.* Grand Teton Natural History Association, Moose, Wyoming 83012

LOVE, J. D., and REED, JOHN C., JR., 1967. *Creation of the Teton Landscape.* Grand Teton Natural History Association, Moose, Wyoming 83012

HALEAKALA NATIONAL PARK

See Hawaii Volcanoes National Park

HAWAII VOLCANOES NATIONAL PARK

MACDONALD, G. A., and HUBBARD, D. H., 1965. *Volcanoes of the National Parks in Hawaii.* Hawaii Natural History Association, Hawaii Volcanoes National Park, Hawaii 96718

STEARNS, H. T., 1966. *Geology of the State of Hawaii.* Pacific Books, Box 558, Palo Alto, California 94302

KINGS CANYON NATIONAL PARK

See Sequoia-Kings Canyon National Parks.

LASSEN VOLCANIC NATIONAL PARK

LOOMIS, B. F., 1966. *Eruptions of Lassen Peak* (3d ed.). Loomis Museum Association, Lassen Volcanic National Park, Mineral, California 96063

SCHULZ, P. E., 1959. *Geology of Lassen's Landscape.* Loomis Museum Association, Lassen Volcanic National Park, Mineral, California 96063

MESA VERDE NATIONAL PARK

BURNS, W. A., 1960. *The Natural History of the Southwest.* Franklin Watts, New York, New York 10022

WANEK, A. A., 1959. *Geology and Fuel Resources of the Mesa Verde Area, Montezuma and La Plata Counties, Colorado.* Geological Survey Bulletin 1072-M, U.S. Government Printing Office, Washington, D.C. 20402

WATSON, DON (no date). *Cliff Dwellings of the Mesa Verde.* Mesa Verde Museum Association, Box 38, Mesa Verde National Park, Colorado 81330

MOUNT McKINLEY NATIONAL PARK

BROOKS, A. H., 1911. *The Mount McKinley Region, Alaska.* Geological Survey Professional Paper 70, U.S. Government Printing Office, Washington, D.C. 20402

REED, J. C., 1961. *Geology of the Mount McKinley Quadrangle, Alaska.* Geological Survey Bulletin 1108-A, U.S. Government Printing Office, Washington, D.C. 20402

MOUNT RAINIER NATIONAL PARK

COOMBS, H. A., 1936. "The Geology of Mount Rainier National Park." Washington University Publications in Geology (Vol. 3, No. 2) Seattle, Washington 98105

CRANDELL, D. R., and FAHNESTOCK, R. K., 1965. *Rockfalls and Avalanches from Little Tahoma Peak on Mount Rainier, Washington.* Geological Survey Bulletin 1221-A, U.S. Government Printing Office, Washington, D.C. 20402

FISKE, R. S., HOPSON, C. A., and WATERS, A. C., 1963. *Geology of Mount Rainier National Park, Washington.* Geological Survey Professional Paper 444, U.S. Government Printing Office, Washington, D.C. 20402

GRATER, R. K., 1949. *Grater's Guide to Mount Rainier National Park.* Binfords & Mort, 2505 S.E. 11 Ave., Portland, Oregon 97242

STAGNER, HOWARD, 1952. *Behind the Scenery of Mount Rainier National Park.* Mount Rainier Natural History Association, Longmire, Washington 98397

OLYMPIC NATIONAL PARK

DANNER, W. R., 1955. *Geology of Olympic National Park.* University of Washington Press, Seattle, Washington 98105, and Olympic Natural History Association, Port Angeles, Washington 98362

FAGERLUND, G. O., 1954. *Olympic National Park.* Natural History Handbook No. 1, U.S. Government Printing Office, Washington, D.C. 20402

KIRK, RUTH, 1964. *Exploring the Olympic Peninsula.* University of Washington Press, Seattle, Washington 98105, and Olympic Natural History Association, Port Angeles, Washington 98362

PETRIFIED FOREST NATIONAL PARK

Arizona Highways Magazine, 1963. "Petrified Forest National Parks Issue," Arizona Highway Department, Phoenix, Arizona 85009

BRODERICK, HAROLD, 1951. *Agatized Rainbows: A Story of the Petrified Forest.* Petrified Forest Museum Association, Holbrook, Arizona 86025

ROCKY MOUNTAIN NATIONAL PARK

ALBERTS, E. C., 1954. *Rocky Mountain National Park, Colorado.* Natural History Handbook No. 3, U.S. Government Printing Office, Washington, D.C. 20402

ROCKY MOUNTAIN NATURE ASSOCIATION, 1959. *Glaciers in Rocky Mountain National Park.* Rocky Mountain Nature Association, Estes Park, Colorado 80517

WEGEMANN, C. H., 1961. *A Guide to the Geology of Rocky Mountain National Park.* U.S. Government Printing Office, Washington, D.C. 20402

ZIM, H. S., 1964. *The Rocky Mountains.* Golden Press, New York, New York 10022

SEQUOIA-KINGS CANYON NATIONAL PARKS

COOK, L. F., 1955. *The Giant Sequoias of California* (rev. ed.). U.S. Government Printing Office, Washington, D.C. 20402

FRYXELL, F. M., 1962. *François Matthes and the Marks of Time.* Sierra Club, 1050 Mills Tower, San Francisco, California 94100

MATTHES, F. E., 1956. *Sequoia National Park—A Geological Album.* University of California Press, Berkeley, California 94700

MATTHES, F. E., 1965. *Glacial Reconnaissance of Sequoia National Park.* Geological Survey Professional Paper 504-A, U.S. Government Printing Office, Washington, D.C. 20402

OBERHANSLEY, F. R., 1965. *Crystal Cave in Sequoia National Park* (rev. ed.). Sequoia Natural History Association, Three Rivers, California 93271

STORER, TRACY, and USINGER, ROBERT, 1963. *Sierra Nevada Natural History.* University of California Press, Berkeley, California 94700

WHITE, J. R., and PUSATERI, SAMUEL, 1965. *Illustrated Guide— Sequoia and Kings Canyon National Parks* (rev. ed.). Stanford University Press, Stanford, California 94305

YELLOWSTONE NATIONAL PARK

BAUER, C. M., 1962. *Yellowstone—Its Underworld. Geology and Historical Anecdotes of Our Oldest National Park.* University of New Mexico Press, Albuquerque, New Mexico 87106

CHITTENDEN, HIRAM, 1933. *Yellowstone National Park.* Stanford University Press, Stanford, California 94305. (Republished in 1964 by the University of Oklahoma Press, Norman, Oklahoma 73069.)

DOUGLASS, I. B., 1939. *Some Chemical Features of Yellowstone National Park.* (Reprinted from *Journal of Chemical Education,* Vol. 16, No. 9). Yellowstone Library and Museum Association, Yellowstone National Park, Wyoming 83020

FISCHER, W. A., 1960. *Yellowstone's Living Geology.* Yellowstone Library and Museum Association, Yellowstone National Park, Wyoming 83020

HAYNES, J. E., 1961. *Haynes' Guide: A Handbook of Yellowstone National Park.* Haynes Studios, Bozeman, Montana 59715

LINK, L. W., 1964. *Great Montana Earthquake.* L. W. Link, Cardwell, Montana 59721

MARLER, G. D., 1963. *The Story of Old Faithful Geyser.* Yellowstone Library and Museum Association, Yellowstone National Park, Wyoming 83020

MARLER, G. D., 1964. *Studies of Geysers and Hot Springs Along the Firehole River.* Yellowstone Library and Museum Association, Yellowstone National Park, Wyoming 83020

WITKIND, I. J., 1962. *The Night the Earth Shook.* U.S. Department of Agriculture, Forest Service, Misc. Publication No. 907, U.S. Government Printing Office, Washington, D.C. 20402

YOSEMITE NATIONAL PARK

BEATTY, M. E., 1943. *Brief Story of the Geology of Yosemite Valley.* Yosemite Natural History Association, Box 545, Yosemite National Park, California 95389

BROCKMAN, C. F., 1945. *Falls of Yosemite and Famous Waterfalls of the World.* Yosemite Natural History Association, Box 545, Yosemite National Park, California 95389

HUNTINGTON, H. E., 1966. *The Yosemite Story.* Doubleday & Co., Garden City, New York 11530

MATTHES, F. E., 1930. *Geologic History of the Yosemite Valley.* Geological Survey Professional Paper 160, U.S. Government Printing Office, Washington, D.C. 20402

MATTHES, F. E., 1950. *The Incomparable Valley.* University of California Press, Berkeley, California 94700

MUIR, JOHN, 1962. *The Yosemite.* The Natural History Library, Doubleday & Co., Garden City, New York 11530

ZION NATIONAL PARK

BRUHN, A. F., 1962. *Southern Utah's Land of Color*. Zion Natural History Association, Springdale, Utah 84767

GRATER, R. K., 1950. *Guide to Zion, Bryce Canyon, and Cedar Breaks*. Binfords & Mort, 2505 S.E. 11 Ave., Portland, Oregon 97242

GREGORY, H. E., 1940. *Geologic and Geographic Sketches of Zion and Bryce Canyon National Parks*. Zion Natural History Association, Springdale, Utah 84767

GREGORY, H. E., 1950. *Geology and Geography of the Zion Park Region, Utah and Arizona*. Geological Survey Professional Paper 220, U.S. Government Printing Office, Washington, D.C. 20402

General

ALBRIGHT, H. M., and TAYLOR, F. J., 1946. *Oh, Ranger!* Dodd, Mead & Co., New York, New York 10016

BOLIN, L. A., 1962. *The National Parks of the United States*. Alfred A. Knopf, New York, New York 10022

BUTCHER, DEVEREUX, 1956. *Exploring Our National Parks and Monuments* (5th ed.). Houghton Mifflin Company, Boston, Massachusetts 02107

BUTCHER, DEVEREUX, 1965. *Our National Parks in Color*. Clarkson N. Potter, New York, New York 10016

FALK, GENE, and O'HARA, MICHAEL, 1965. *National Parks Summer Jobs*. O'Hara/Falk-Research, Box 4495, Fresno, California

HEATH, MONROE, 1959. *Our National Parks at a Glance*. Pacific Coast Publishers, Campbell Ave. at Scott Dr., Menlo Park, California 94026

ISE, JOHN, 1961. *Our National Park Policy: A Critical History*. Johns Hopkins Press, Baltimore, Maryland 21218

JENSEN, PAUL, 1964. *National Parks: A Guide to the National Parks and Monuments of the United States*. Golden Press, New York, New York 10022

LOBSENZ, NORMAN, 1959. *The First Book of National Parks*. Franklin Watts, New York, New York 10022

MELBO, I. R., 1960. *Our Country's National Parks* (2 vols.). The Bobbs-Merrill Company, Indianapolis, Indiana 46206

EDITORS, NATIONAL GEOGRAPHIC SOCIETY, 1959. *America's Wonderlands—The Scenic National Parks and Monuments of the United States*. The National Geographic Society, Washington, D.C. 20036

NATIONAL PARK SERVICE, 1964. *Parks for America: A Survey of Park and Related Resources in the Fifty States, and a Preliminary Plan*. U.S. Government Printing Office, Washington, D.C. 20402

SHANKLAND, ROBERT, 1951. *Steve Mather of the National Parks*. Alfred A. Knopf, New York, New York 10022

STORY, ISABELLE F., 1957. *The National Park Story in Pictures*. U.S. Government Printing Office, Washington, D.C. 20402

EDITORS, SUNSET BOOKS AND SUNSET MAGAZINE, 1965. *National Parks of the West*. Lane Magazine and Book Co., Menlo Park, California 94025

SUTTON, ANN, and SUTTON, MYRON, 1965. *Guarding the Treasured Lands: The Story of the National Park Service*. J. B. Lippincott Company, Philadelphia, Pennsylvania 19105

THOMSON, PETER, 1961. *Wonders of Our National Parks*. Dodd, Mead & Co., New York, New York 10016

TILDEN, FREEMAN, 1961. *The National Parks: What They Mean to You and Me*. Alfred A. Knopf, New York, New York 10022

UDALL, STEWART L., 1963. *The Quiet Crisis*. Holt, Rinehart & Winston, New York, New York 10017

UDALL, STEWART L., 1966. *The National Parks of America*. Country Beautiful Foundation, 24198 Bluemound Rd., Waukesha, Wisconsin 53186

YEAGER, DORR, 1959. *National Parks in California*. Lane Magazine and Book Co., Menlo Park, California 94025

Nontechnical Geological References

AMERICAN GEOLOGICAL INSTITUTE, 1962. *A Dictionary of Geological Terms*. Dolphin Books, Doubleday & Co., Garden City, New York 11530

CHAMBERLAIN, BARBARA B., 1964. *These Fragile Outposts—A Geological Look at Cape Cod, Martha's Vineyard, and Nantucket*. The Natural History Press, Garden City, New York 11530

FARB, PETER, 1962. *Face of North America.* Harper & Row, New York, New York 10016

LEET, L. D., and LEET, F. J., 1961. *The World of Geology.* McGraw-Hill Book Co., New York, New York 10036

MATHER, K. F., 1964. *The Earth Beneath Us.* Random House, New York, New York 10022

MATTHEWS, WILLIAM H., III, 1962. *Fossils: An Introduction to Prehistoric Life.* Barnes & Noble, New York, New York 10003

MATTHEWS, WILLIAM H., III, 1967. *Geology Made Simple.* Made Simple Books, Doubleday & Co., Garden City, New York 11530

PEARL, RICHARD M., 1960. *Geology.* Barnes & Noble, New York, New York 10003

SHELTON, JOHN S., 1966. *Geology Illustrated.* W. H. Freeman & Co., San Francisco, California 94104

SHIMER, J. A., 1959. *This Sculptured Earth: The Landscape of America.* Columbia University Press, New York, New York 10027

STRAHLER, A. N., 1966. *A Geologist's View of Cape Cod.* The Natural History Press, Garden City, New York 11530

WYCKOFF, JEROME, 1960. *The Story of Geology.* Golden Press, New York, New York 10022

John Muir *Ecological Prophet*

The world of nature, which provides us with treasured joy in ideal beauty, also provides us with the necessary means for physical existence. Pollute the air, poison the seas, and waste the earth, and man is threatened not merely with ugliness but also with extinction.

Almost one hundred years ago, in a letter to the Sacramento *Record-Union* of February 5, 1876, Muir prophesied that the abuse of nature by men intent only upon their immediate interests would result in irreparable injury to both nature and man.

Muir vividly portrayed the ecological relationship of forest, climate, soil, and stream in California. But ecological unity is not confined to any one state or any one nation. Muir's plea to preserve the forests in order to save California from becoming a desert is a timely reminder that we need to preserve not only our forests, but also our air, water, and earth—in California, the United States, and throughout the world.

"GOD'S FIRST TEMPLES."

HOW SHALL WE PRESERVE OUR FORESTS?
The Question Considered by John Muir, the California Geologist
—The Views of a Practical Man and a Scientific Observer
—A Profoundly Interesting Article.

(Communicated to the *Record-Union*)

EDS. RECORD-UNION: The forests of coniferous trees growing on our mountain ranges are by far the most destructible of the natural resources of California. Our gold, and silver, and cinnabar are stored in the rocks, locked up in the safest of all banks, so that notwithstanding the world has been making a run upon them for the last twenty-five years, they still pay out steadily, and will probably continue to do so centuries hence, like rivers pouring from perennial mountain fountains. The riches of our magnificent soil beds are also comparatively safe, because even the most barbarous methods of wildcat farming cannot effect complete destruction, and however great the impoverishment produced, full restoration of fertility is always possible to the enlightened farmer. But our forest belts are being burned and cut down and wasted like a field of unprotected grain, and once destroyed can never be wholly restored even by centuries of persistent and painstaking cultivation.

The practical importance of the preservation of our forests is augmented by their relations to climate, soil and streams. Strip off the woods with their underbrush from the mountain flanks, and the whole state, the lowlands as well as the highlands, would gradually change into a desert. During rainfalls, and when the winter snow was melting, every stream would become a destructive torrent overflowing its banks, stripping off and carrying away the fertile soils, filling up the lower river channels, and overspreading the lowland fields with detritus to a vastly more destructive degree than all the washings from hydraulic mines concerning which we now hear so much. Dripping forests give rise to moist sheets and currents of air, and the sod of grasses and underbrush thus fostered, together with the roots of trees themselves, absorb and hold back rains and melting snow, yet allowing them to doze and percolate and flow gently in useful fertilizing streams. Indeed every pine needle and rootlet, as well as fallen trunks and large clasping roots, may be regarded as dams, hoarding the bounty of storm clouds, and dispensing it as blessings all through the summer, instead of allowing it to gather and rush headlong in short-lived devastating floods. Streams taking their rise in deep woods flow unfailingly as those derived from the eternal ice and snow of the Alps. So constant indeed and apparent is the relationship between forests and never-failing springs, that effect is frequently mistaken for cause, it being often asserted that fine forests will grow only along stream sides where their roots are well watered, when in fact the forests themselves produce many of the streams flowing through them.

The main forest belt of the Sierra is restricted to the western flank, and extends unbrokenly from one end of the range to the other at an elevation of from three to eight thousand feet above sea level. The great master existence of these noble woods is *Sequoia gigantea,* or Big Tree. Only two species of sequoia are known to exist in the world. Both belong to California, one being found only in the Sierra, the other (*Sequoia sempervirens*) in the Coast Ranges, although no less than five distinct fossil species have been discovered in the tertiary and cretaceous rocks of Greenland. I would like to call attention to this noble tree, with special reference to its preservation. The species extends from the well-known Calaveras groves on the north, to the head of Deer Creek on the south, near the big bend of the Kern River, a distance of about two hundred miles, at an elevation above sea level of from about five to eight thousand feet. From the Calaveras to the South Fork of Kings River it occurs only in small isolated groves, and so sparsely and irregularly distributed that two gaps occur nearly forty miles in width, the one between the Calaveras and Tuolumne groves, the other between those of the Fresno and Kings rivers. From Kings River the belt extends across the broad, rugged basins of the Kaweah and Tule rivers to its southern boundary on Deer Creek, interrupted only by deep, rocky canyons, the width of this portion of the belt being from three to ten miles.

In the northern groves few young trees or saplings are found ready to take the places of the failing old ones, and because these ancient, childless sequoias are the only ones known to botanists, the species has been generally regarded as doomed to speedy extinction, as being nothing more than an expiring remnant of an ancient flora, and that therefore there is no use trying to save it or to prolong its few dying days. This, however, is in the main a mistaken notion, for the Sierra as it now exists never had an ancient flora. All the species now growing on the range have been planted since the close of the glacial period, and the Big Tree has never formed a greater part of these post-glacial forests than it does today, however widely it may have been distributed throughout pre-glacial forests.

In tracing the belt southward, all the phenomena bearing upon its history goes to show that the dominion of *Sequoia gigantea*, as King of California trees, is not yet passing away. No tree in the woods seems more firmly established, or more safely settled in accordance with climate and soil. They fill the woods and form the principal tree, growing heartily on solid ledges, along water courses, in the deep, moist soil of meadows, and on avalanche and glacial debris, with a multitude of thrifty seedlings and saplings crowding around the aged, ready to take their places and rule the woods.

Nevertheless nature in her grandly deliberate way keeps up a rotation of forest crops. Species develop and die like individuals, animal as well as plant. Man himself will as surely become extinct as sequoia or mastodon, and be at length known only as a fossil. Changes of this kind are, however, exceedingly slow in their movements, and, as far as the lives of individuals are concerned, such changes have no appreciable effect. Sequoia seems scarcely further past prime as a species than its companion firs (*Picea amabilis* and *P. grandis*), and judging from its present condition and its ancient history, as far as I have been able to decipher it, our sequoia will live and flourish gloriously until A.D. 15,000 at least—probably for longer—that is, if it be allowed to remain in the hands of nature.

But waste and pure destruction are already taking place at a terrible rate, and unless protective measures be speedily invented and enforced, in a few years this noblest tree species in the world will present only a few hacked and scarred remnants. The great enemies of forests are fire and the ax. The destructive effects of these, as compared with those caused by the operations of nature, are instantaneous. Floods undermine and kill many a tree, storm winds bend and break, landslips and avalanches overwhelm whole groves, lightning shatters and burns, but the combined effects of all these amount only to a wholesome beauty-producing culture. Last summer I found some five sawmills located in or near the lower edge of the sequoia belt, all of which saw more or less of the Big Tree into lumber. One of these (Hyde's), situated on the North Fork of the Kaweah, cut no less than 2,000,000 feet of sequoia lumber last season. Most of the Fresno Big Trees are doomed to feed the mills recently erected near them, and a company has been formed by Chas. Converse to cut the noble forest on the South Fork of Kings River. In these milling operations waste far exceeds use. After the choice young manageable trees have been felled, the woods are cleared of limbs and refuse by burning, and in these clearing fires, made with reference to further operations, all the young seedlings and saplings are destroyed, together with many valuable fallen trees and old trees, too large to be cut, thus effectually cutting off all hopes of a renewal of the forest.

These ravages, however, of mill fires and mill axes are small as compared with those of the "sheepmen's" fires. Incredible numbers of sheep are driven to the mountain pastures every summer, and in order to make easy paths and to improve the pastures, running fires are set everywhere to burn off the old logs and underbrush. These fires are far more universal and destructive than would be guessed. They sweep through nearly the entire forest belt of the range from one extremity to the other, and in the dry weather, before the coming on of winter storms, are very destructive to all kinds of young trees, and especially to sequoia, whose loose, fibrous bark catches and burns at once. Excepting the Calaveras, I, last summer, examined every sequoia grove in the range, together with the main belt extending across the basins of Kaweah and Tule, and found everywhere the most deplorable waste from this cause. Indians burn off underbrush to facilitate deer-hunting. Campers of all kinds often permit fires to run, so also do millmen, but the fires of "sheepmen" probably form more than ninety per cent of all destructive fires that sweep the woods.

Fire, then, is the arch destroyer of our forests, and sequoia forests suffer most of all. The young trees are most easily fire-killed; the old are most easily burned, and the prostrate trunks, which *never rot* and would remain valuable until our tenth centennial, are reduced to ashes.

In European countries, especially in France, Germany, Italy, and Austria, the economics of forestry have been carefully studied under the auspices of Government, with the most beneficial results. Whether our loose-jointed Government is really able or willing to do anything in the matter remains to be seen. If our law makers were to discover and enforce any method tending to lessen even in a small degree the destruction going on, they would thus cover a multitude of legislative sins in the eyes of every tree lover. I am satisfied, however, that the question can be intelligently discussed only after a careful survey of our forests has been made, together with studies of the forces now acting upon them.

A law was constructed some years ago making the cutting down of sequoias over sixteen feet in diameter illegal. A more absurd and short-sighted piece of legislation could not be conceived. All the young trees might be cut and burned, and all the old ones might be burned but not cut.

JOHN MUIR
Sacramento *Record-Union*, February 5, 1876

INDEX

Note: All numbers in *italics* refer to pages on which captions to photographs appear.

Acadia National Park, 175, 181
Ahwahnee Hotel, 167, 168
Alpenglow, 4, 27, *38*
Ancient Lake Yosemite, 159–60
Arch Rock, 165
Arches, 164, 168
Arches National Monument, 183
Arctic Willow, 22
Aspen, 23

Badger Pass Ski Center, 170, 172
Badlands National Monument, 183
Bandelier National Monument, 183
Basket Dome, 168, 170
Belding's ground squirrel, 165
Benson Lake, 172
Big Bend National Park, 175, 181
Big Meadow, 24, 160
Big Oak Flat Road, 170
Big Tuolumne Meadows, 20
Black Canyon of the Gunnison National Monument, 183
Black oak, 165
Blue gentian, 22
Blue grouse, 165
Boating, 172
Bridalveil Creek, 159, 169, 170
Bridalveil Creek campgrounds, 167, 171
Bridalveil Fall, 14, 159, 164, 168, 169, 170
Broderick, Mount, 163–64
Bryant, William Cullen, 20
Bryanthus, 22
Bryce Canyon National Park, 175, 181
Buckthorn, 165

Calaveras Grove, 204
California mule deer, 165
California red fir, 165
California Tree (sequoia), 166
Camp Curry, 86, 167–69, 172
Camp 7, 167
Camp 14, 167
Camper trucks, 171–72

Campfire programs, 167
Campgrounds, 167, 171–72, 179
Canyon de Chelly National Monument, 183
Canyon live-oak, 165
Canyonlands National Park, 175, 181
Capital Reef National Monument, 183
Carex, 22
Carlsbad Caverns National Park, 181
Cascade Creek, 22
Cascade Fall, 14
Cassiope, 22–23
Castle Peak, 29
Cathedral Peak, 29
Cathedral Rocks, 4, 10, *34*, 44, *76*, 162, 169
Cathedral Spires, 169
Cedar Breaks National Monument, 183
Chaco Canyon National Monument, 183
Channel Islands National Monument, 183
Chapel, 66
Chesapeake and Ohio Canal National Monument, 183
Chinquapin, 169
Chipmunks, 165
Chiricahua National Monument, 183
Clark's nutcracker, 165
Cliffs, 161–62
Clouds Rest, 4, 16, *34*, 110, 112, 126
Colorado National Monument, 184
Columbia Tree (sequoia), 166
Conness, Mount, 29
Converse, Chas., 205
Cottonwood, *126*
Crane Flat, 170
Crane Flat campgrounds, 167, 171
Crater Lake National Park, 175, 181
Craters of the Moon National Monument, 184

Daisies, 22
Dana, Mount, 9, 10, 29, *136, 138*, 161

Dana Glacier, 161
Death Valley National Monument, 184
Devils Postpile National Monument, 184
Devils Tower National Monument, 184
Digger pine, 165
Dinosaur National Monument, 184
Ditton, Richard P., 168
Dodecatheons, 22
Domes, 160–64, 168
   exfoliation formation of, 160, 162–63
   glaciation formation of, 162–64
   See also specific domes
Douglas, David, 17
Douglas squirrel, 165

Eagle Peak (of Three Brothers Cliff), 159, 168
El Capitan, 4, *34, 38*, 44, *50, 52, 54, 56, 58, 60, 78*, 148, 168, 169
   formation of, 161
   glaciers and, 159
El Capitan Bridge moraine, 159
El Capitan Fall, 14, *60*
El Capitan meadow, *50, 76*
El Capitan Picnic Area, 58
El Capitan View, *52, 54, 56, 78*, 114
El Morro National Monument, 184
El Portal, 159, 167
Emerald Pool, 15, 16
Everglades National Park, 175, 181
Exfoliation, 160, 162–64, 168

Fairview Dome, 20–21, 160, 170
Firefall, 167, 169, 170, 173
Fishing, 172
Fox sparrow, 165

Gibbs, Mount, 10, 29, *136, 138*
Glacier National Park, 175–76, 181
Glacier Point, 16, 128, *150, 152*, 167–70
   campground at, 171
   formation of, 161, 162
   glaciers on, 159

trail to, 171
 view from, 19, 100, 108, 146, 148
Glacier Point Cliff, *88*
Glacier Point Lookout, 170
Glacier Point Road, 136, 163
Glaciers, 7–13, 20–22, 158–60
 arches formed by, 164
 erratics from, 160, 169, 171
 in High Sierra, 4, 160–61
 mountain meadows and, 160
 Muir on, 7–13, 20–22, 25, 26
 polish from, 160
 quarrying by, 159
 staircases from, 159
 See also specific glaciers
Glossary, 187–96
"God's First Temples" (Muir), 203–6
Golden-mantled ground squirrel, 165
Grand Canyon National Park, 176, 181
Grand Teton National Park, 158, 176, 181
Granite, 12–13
 glacial action on, 159, 160
 joints in, 159, 161–62, 168
 types of, 161
Gray fox, 165
Gray squirrel, 165
Great Sand Dunes National Monument, 184
Great Smoky Mountains National Park, 176, 181
Grizzly Club, 172
Grizzly Giant (sequoia), *120,* 166
Guadalupe Mountains National Park, 181
Gunnison National Monument, 183

Haleakala National Park, 176, 181
Half Dome, 4, 5, 15, *34, 50, 62, 64, 66, 72, 128, 130, 132, 134, 140, 150,* 152
 formation of, 162, 163
 during glacial stage, 159, 162
 height of, 112
 Mirror Lake and, 16, 110
 Muir on, 19, 128
 from Sentinel Bridge, 19–20
 views of, 4, *126,* 148, 168, 170
Hanging valleys, 159, 164, 169
Happy Isles, 68, *110,* 166–67
Happy Isles Nature Center, 167, 168
Hawaii Volcanoes National Park, 176, 181
Hemlock Spruce, 23
Hetch Hetchy Valley, 8, 20
High Country, 20–31, 136, 170–71
 glaciation in, 4, 160–61
 glacier lakes in, 21–23, 24

glacier meadows in, 23–24
 mountaineering in, 25–31
High Sierra Loop trail, 171
Hiking, 25–31, 167–68, 170–71
Hodgdon Meadow campground, 171
Hoffman, Mount, 148
Hoffman Creek, 22
Hoffman Range, 20, 22
Honeyworts, 22
Hooker (author), 19
Horseback riding, 18, 172
Hot Springs National Park, 177, 181
House trailers, 171–72
Housekeeping Camp, 172
Hovenweep National Monument, 184
Humphreys, Mount, 9

Illilouette Creek, 22, 148, 164
Illilouette Fall, 14, 15, 164
"In the Heart of the California Alps" (Muir), 24
Incense Cedar, 18, *124,* 165
Indian Canyon, 148
Indian Circle, 166
Indian War, 78
Inspiration Point self-guiding nature trail, 167–68
Inyo Range, 29
Isle Royale National Park, 177, 181

Jeffrey Pine, *146,* 165, 169
Jointing, 159, 161–62, 168
Joshua Tree National Monument, 184
Junior Ranger Program, 166–67, 172

Kalmia, 22
Kern River, 10, 29
Kibbie Lake, 172
Kiddie Camp, 172
Kings Canyon National Park, 157, 177, 182
Kings River, 9, 10

Lady Franklin Rock, 100, 102
Lake Hollow, 22
Lassen Volcanic National Park, 177, 181
Lava Beds National Monument, 184
LeConte, Joseph, 169
LeConte Memorial, 169
Leidig Meadow, 72
Lembert Dome, 160, 170
Liberty Cap, 161, 163–64, 170
Little Yosemite, 15
Lodgepole pine, 165
Lost Arrow, 74
Lower Yosemite Fall, 14, 15, 92, *94,* 164
Lyell Glacier, 161

Lyell, Mount, 9, 161, 165
Lyell group *névé* amphitheaters, 8

McClure Glacier, 161
McHenry, Donald E., 168
Maclure, Mount, 161
Mammoth Cave National Park, 177, 181
Mammoth Mountain, 29, *136*
Many Islands Lake, 172
Manzanita, 165
Mariposa Grove, *120,* 166, 169, 170
Mariposa Grove Museum, 167
Mariposa Grove Road, 166
Marmot, 165
Mather stables, 172
May Lake, 172
Merced Canyon, 159
Merced Glacier, 8, 164, 165
"Merced Group," 148
Merced Grove, 166
Merced Lake, 172
Merced River, 42, 44, *56,* 68, *110, 114, 116, 118, 126*
 basin of, 7, 20, 22
 Half Dome and, 130, 132
 Muir on, 7, 16, 20, 22, 23
 Nevada Fall and, 165
 Sentinel Bridge and, 130, 169
 Stoneman Bridge and, 84, 88
 Tenaya Creek and, 112
 Vernal Fall and, 165
 views of, 4, 34, *124,* 170
 Yosemite Valley formation and, 158
Mesa Verde National Park, 177, 181
Middle Brother (of Three Brothers Cliff), 5, *80, 82*
Middle Cascade (Yosemite Falls), 14, 15, 92, 164
Minarets, 10, 29
Mirror Lake, 16, 19, 62, 110, *112,* 128, 169
Mist Trail, 14, 92, 102, 106, 108
Mono Desert, 26, 29
Monument, the, 20
Moraines, 10–11, 15, 19, 159
Motor drives, 168–71
Mount Broderick, 161, 163–64
Mount Conness, 29
Mount Dana, 9, 10, 29, *136, 138,* 161
Mount Gibbs, 10, 29, *136, 138*
Mount Hoffman, 148
Mount Humphreys, 9
Mount Lyell, 9, 161, 165
Mount McKinley National Park, 177, 181
Mount Maclure, 161
Mount Ord, 29

Mount Ranier National Park, 177, 181
Mount Ritter, 10, 26–28
Mount Starr King, 148, *152*
Mount Tyndall, *9*
Mount Watkins, 168
Mount Whitney, *9*, 29
Mountain bluebird, 165
Mountain hemlock, 165
Mountain quail, 165
Muir, John
  on canyons, 7
  celebration of Yosemite by, 3
  on El Capitan, 50
  on erosion, 11
  on Fairview Dome view, 20–21
  on forest preservation, 203–6
  on glacial action, 20–22, 25, 26
  glacial origin theory of, 7–13
  on glacier lakes, 21–23, 24
  on glacier meadows, 23–24
  on Glacier Point view, 148
  on granite structure, 12–13
  on Half Dome, 19, 128
  on Incense Cedar, 124
  on Jeffrey Pines, 146
  on life of a lake, 23
  on Merced River, 7, 16, 20, 22, 23
  on mountaineering in the High
    Country, 25–31
  on peaklets, 10
  on pinnacles, 10
  on plant succession, 24, 205
  on rock structure, 12–13
  on sequoias, 120, 204–6
  on sheepmen, 17, 205–6
  on Sierra Nevada, 3–4, 9
  on streams, 16–17
  on Three Brothers Cliff, 78
  on trees of Yosemite, 17–19, 120, 122, 124, 146, 205–6
  on valleys, 7, 11, 13
  on waterfalls, 14–16, 60, 96
  on Yellow Pine, 122
Muir (John) Trail, 171
Museums, 166–67

Naturalist program, 166–68, 170
Nature walks, 167
Navajo National Monument, 184
Nevada Creek, 22
Nevada Fall, 14–16, 92, 108, 148, 159, 164–65, 170–71
North Dome, 5, *68, 72, 84, 86,* 88, 126, 148, 168, 170
Nunataks, 159

Old Village, 169
Olmsted Point, 140, 142, 144
Olympia National Park, 178, 182
Ord, Mount, 29
Organ Pipe Cactus National Monument, 184
Ouzels, 17, 23
Owens Valley, 29, 158

Petrified Forest National Park, 182
Photography, 172–73
Pillars, 161–62
Pinnacles, 161–62
Pinnacles National Monument, 185
Pioneer Cemetery, 168
Pioneer Yosemite History Center, 167, 170
Pioneer Yosemite Transportation
    Center, 167
Plant life, 7, 17–19, 165
  climate and, 18–19, 165
  of glacier meadows, 23–24
  moraines and, 19
  succession of, 24, 205
  See also specific plants and types of plants
Platt National Park, 178, 182
Pohono Creek, 22
Polly Dome, *142, 144*
Ponderosa pine, *122,* 165, 169
Pothole Dome, 160, *161*
Profile Cliffs, *76*

Red Mountain, 21
Redbud, 165
Ribbon Creek, 164
Ribbon Fall, 14, 162, 164, 168
Ringtail, 165
Ritter, Mount, 10, 26–28
Roches moutonnés, 164
Rocky Mountain National Park, 178, 182
Rocky Point Picnic Area, 64, 80, 82, 126
Royal Arches, 5, *84, 86,* 88, 126, 128, 148, 164, 168, 170
Rush Creek, 30

Saguaro National Monument, 185
San Joaquin River, 9, 29
Scrub jay, 165
Sedges, 22, 23
*Self-guiding Auto Tours in Yosemite
    National Park* (Ditton and
    McHenry), 168
Senior Ranger Program, 167
Sentinel Bridge, 19, 66, 90, 128, 130, 132, 134, 169
Sentinel Creek, 169

Sentinel Dome, 4, 34, *146,* 159, 162, 163, 170
Sentinel Fall, 14, 169
Sentinel Rock, 4, *34, 70, 76, 114,* 126, 162, 168, 169
Sequoia National Park, 157, 166, 171, 178, 182
Sequoias, 18, *120,* 166, 167, 204–6
Sheeting, 162–63
Shenandoah National Park, 178, 182
Sierra Club, 169
Sierra Crown, 29
Silver Fir, 17, 18
Silver Mountain, 29
Skiing, 172
South Fork (of Merced River), 22, 167
Spinoza, Baruchs, 132
Staircase Falls, 14
Starr King, Mount, 148, *152*
Steller's jay, 165
Stone Mountain, 162
Stoneman Bridge, *84,* 88
Studies in the Sierra (Muir), 9
Sugar pine, 17, 18, 165, 169
Swimming, 172

Taft Point, *76*
Tenaya (Yosemite chief), 78
Tenaya Basin, 20
Tenaya Canyon, 20, 112, 159, 160
Tenaya Creek, 16, 22, 110, 112
Tenaya Glacier, 159, 163
Tenaya Lake, *142, 144,* 160, 172
Tenaya Peak, *142*
Teton Range, 158
Thanatopsis (Bryant), 20
Thoreau, Henry David, 70
Thrasher, 165
Three Brothers Cliff, 5, *78, 80, 82,* 126, 148, 159, 162, 168
Tilden Lake, 172
Timpanogos Cave National Monument, 185
Tintern Abbey (Wordsworth), 5–6
Tioga Pass, 136, 138, 171
Tioga Road, 136, 138, 140, 160, 170–71
Tower Peak, 29
Townsend's solitaire, 165
Tunnel View, 4, *34, 36, 38,* 40, 167, 169
Tuolumne Basin, 21, 160
Tuolumne Canyon, 20, 22
Tuolumne Glacier, 20
Tuolumne Grove, 166, 170, 204
Tuolumne Meadows, *136, 138,* 160, 167, 170, 171
Tuolumne Mer de Glace, 24
Tuolumne River, 20, *136,* 138, 160

Turtleback Dome, 163, 169
Twin Lakes, 172
Two-leaved pine, 24
Tyndall, Mount, 9

Upper Yosemite Fall, 14, 15, 92, *96, 98,* 162, 164

Valley View, 4, 34, 42, 44, *46, 48,* 124, 168
Vernal Fall, 14, 15, 92, *100, 102, 104,106,* 108, 148, 159, 164–65, 170–71
Violets, 22
Virgin Islands National Park, 178, 182
Visitors Center, 166, 168, 171

Washburn Point, 100, 108, 163, 170
Washington Column, 5, *84, 86,* 88, 126, 128, 162, 168, 170
Waterfalls, 13–16, 60, 96, 164–65. *See also specific waterfalls*
Watkins, Mount, 168

Wawona, 167, 170–72
Wawona Hotel, 170
Wawona Road, 163, 167, 169, 170
Wawona tunnel, 4, 34, 163, 169
Wawona Tunnel Tree, 166
Weather pits, 160–61
Western bluebird, 165
Western tanager, 165
Western white pine, 165
White-crowned sparrow, 165
White fir, 165
White Wolf campgrounds, 167, 171, 172
Whitney, Mount, 9, 29
Wind Cave National Park, 178, 182
Winter sports, 172
Wordsworth, William, 5

Yellow Pine, 18
Yellowstone National Park, 179, 182
Yosemite (type) canyon, 7, 8
Yosemite cliff, 34
Yosemite Creek, 22, 92, 148, 159

Yosemite Falls, 14–15, 74, 78, 90, *92,* 126, 148, 164, 168–70
Yosemite Falls Trail, 171
Yosemite Glacier, 9, 159, 164, 169
Yosemite Lodge, 74, 94, 167, 168, 172
Yosemite Natural History Association, 168
Yosemite Valley, 3–4, 7, 15, 20, 23, 34, 157, 164
  discovery of, 17, 78
  entrances to, 3, 4, 34
  glacial origin of, 8, 9, 158–59
  plant and animal life in, 165
  stables at, 172
  visitor activity in, 166
Yosemite Valley Drive, 168–69
Yosemite Village, 96, 166, 168, 169
Yosemite Visitors Center, 166, 168, 171

Zig-Zag Trail, 108
Zion National Park, 179, 182